Backscattering from Multiscale Rough Surfaces with Application to Wind Scatterometry

For a complete listing of titles in the
Artech House Remote Sensing Library,
turn to the back of this book.

Backscattering from Multiscale Rough Surfaces with Application to Wind Scatterometry

Adrian K. Fung

ARTECH
HOUSE

BOSTON | LONDON
artechhouse.com

Library of Congress Cataloging-in-Publication Data
A catalog record for this book is available from the U.S. Library of Congress.

British Library Cataloguing in Publication Data
A catalogue record for this book is available from the British Library.

Cover design by John Gomes

ISBN 13: 978-1-63081-000-9

10 9 8 7 6 5 4 3 2 1

To all my family members, for their patience and support while this work was being done.

Contents

Preface

This book is written for remote sensing professionals who are interested in knowing the real source of backscattering from a multiscale rough surface. To the naked eye it is the entire illuminated area that is causing the backscattering (i.e., all scatterers on the surface are responsible for backscattering). To people developing scattering models it could be the surface slope or selected surface spectral components. The baffling problem is the size of the scatterer derived from backscattering models. For example, in the comparison of the backscattering model in Chapter 4 with the data from the FASINEX experiment over the sea surface at 14.6 GHz, the roughness size used is 0.22 cm for the surface rms height and 2.8 cm for the correlation length. Obviously, the waves within the illuminated area are much larger than what is indicated by these numbers. Naturally, one would ask, "Is this size really responsible for backscattering, or are they chosen because they are needed for the model to fit data?" Another question would be, "We are certain that all larger size waves within the illuminated area are reflecting, diffracting, or scattering the incident radar signal. Why are they not included in modeling?" The answer is only one specific surface spectral component, $\kappa = (4\pi/\lambda)\sin\theta$, can contribute along the backscattering direction coherently, where λ is the incident wavelength and θ is the incident angle. The scatterer associated with this spectral component is determined by the incident wavelength. When the wavelength is small, this scatterer is also small. Of course, other scatterers also cause scattering, but their contributions do not add up coherently along the backscattering direction. In other words, their contributions are filtered out by the incident wavelength.

In the study of radar backscattering from rough surfaces, the focus has been on single-scale rough surfaces. Computer simulations, theoretical models, and controlled laboratory experiments have been carried out to understand the real nature of surface backscattering. It is found that surface backscattering from a single-scale rough surface is dependent on the surface rms height and its correlation function (or all orders of its roughness spectrum). It seems logical to expect that for a multiscale surface, backscattering should depend on many scales of roughness. This means that for a multiscale surface we should expect to see a rather complex surface correlation function or surface spectrum. For example, the sea spectrum has been determined by oceanographers, and it is, indeed, a very complex spectrum. As a result, the computation of backscattering from multiscale rough surfaces, while possible, is not practical to do. In fact, only empirical surface backscattering models have been in operational use in relating backscattering from the sea surface to wind speeds to this date.

In this book we have found that the correlation function of a multiscale surface can be approximated by a modified exponential function due to the wavelength filtering property, thus simplifying the backscattering computation from multiscale surfaces. At a given incident frequency only an effective roughness scale is responsible for backscattering. These findings greatly simplify backscattering computations from multiscale surfaces. When backscattering data are available at a given frequency, incident angle, and several wind speeds, it is possible to relate physical model parameters in a theoretical backscattering model to wind speeds. This process allows the physical model to act as a geophysical model function for wind vector retrieval.

The idea that only an effective roughness scale is responsible for backscattering at a given frequency is the most basic to backscattering from multiscale rough surfaces. It also implies that the measured surface parameters may or may not be responsible for backscattering depending upon the incident wavelength. For example, at centimeter wavelengths meter-size roughness scales are not responsible for backscattering from a multiscale rough surface.

Acknowledgments

I am grateful to Professor David G. Long for providing the data from QuickSCAT and NSCAT and to the reviewers for pointing out shortcomings in the text. I am also deeply grateful to my daughter, Sally Fung, for making all the editorial changes for me on the final manuscript.

Chapter 1

Introduction

1.1 INTRODUCTION TO SURFACE SCATTERING

Although many surface scattering techniques and models are now available in the literature [Bass and Fuks, 1979; Ogilvy, 1991; Voronovich, 1998; Tsang et al., 2000; Saillard and Sentenac, 2001; DeSanto, 2002; Kozlov et al., 2002; Ishimaru, 2013; Pinel and Boulier, 2013] not much has been said about how to apply them to multiscale rough surfaces and what becomes of the scattering mechanisms as frequency or the incident angle changes. Generally, surface scattering models are developed for all possible viewing directions. However, due to practical reasons almost all field measurements are in the backscatter mode. One objective of this writing is to explain how the mechanisms of backscattering change with frequency and the incident angle on a multiscale surface and how to recognize single-scale versus multiscale surfaces. This information should be useful to the experimentalist in the design of experiments and to readers who want to use backscattering models more efficiently. Another objective is to show an application of the integral equation surface backscattering model [Fung, 1994, Chapter 7] to the sea surface to provide a set of relations for sensing the surface wind speed at a desired angle and frequency. At this writing only empirical relations are available for this purpose.

Serious attempts to develop surface scattering models for randomly rough surfaces were made beginning in the 1950s. The complexity of the problem calls for applying approximations in order to arrive at relatively simple expressions. Naturally, the exploring wavelength either short or long compared with the standard deviation of the surface height was assumed. These approximations led to the development of the Kirchhoff and the small perturbation models [Beckmann and Spizzichino, 1963; Rice, 1951] for short- and long-wavelength cases, respectively. Clearly, the next step is to develop a surface scattering model that can

1

bridge the gap between these two models. Many efforts were made in the subsequent decades. However, a relatively simple model in algebraic form for backscattering that contains both the Kirchhoff and the small perturbation or the Bragg models as special cases was not available until the 1990s, when [Fung et al., 1992] published a backscattering model based on solving the integral equation governing the current on a rough surface. Extending the use of this integral equation method to bistatic surface scattering requires a more accurate estimate of the phase of the scattered field. The report of this bistatic model appeared after another decade [Fung et al., 2002]. While this fairly general and simple surface scattering model has become available, not much has been said about the sources of surface backscattering and how they change with frequency and angle or how to differentiate between single-scale versus multiscale surfaces. For users to be able to use a surface scattering model effectively, this information is necessary to make a proper selection of model parameters in data interpretation and experiment design.

1.2 WAVELENGTH FILTERING

Before considering a scattering model and its physical meaning, it is worthwhile to review the differences among reflection, quasi-specular scattering, and incoherent scattering. When an incident wave encounters a dielectric discontinuity at a plane boundary, a reflected wave is generated in a specific direction based on the incident wave direction. The reflected wave amplitude is determined by the size of the discontinuity and the incident wave direction (i.e., there is a fixed phase relationship between the incident and reflected wave). If the boundary is not a plane but an undulating surface such that at a local point and over the distance of a wavelength the boundary is almost flat, then reflection can still take place at a local point on the surface boundary. However, the reflected direction may vary from point to point. In the literature this is the condition assumed by the Kirchhoff scattering model [Beckmann and Spizzichino, 1963]. This type of scattering is said to be *quasi-specular*, because the scattered signal is an integration over all reflected waves within an illuminated area. If the undulating surface boundary contains smaller roughness scales, so that within a wavelength distance there are small roughness scales large enough to alter the phase of the incident wave, then *incoherent scattering* is said to occur. Thus, incoherent scattering is caused by roughness scales smaller than a wavelength, and locally the large undulating surface is now serving as a reference plane for scattering. Unlike reflection, there is no coherency between the incident and the incoherently scattered waves.

It is clear that when the size of the surface roughness scale is large compared to the incident wavelength, most energy is reflected forward, and backscattering is proportional to the slope distribution of the surface. Thus, information about the size of the roughness scale of the surface is not available in the backscattered signal. This is why the size of the large-scale roughness cannot be retrieved from a backscattered signal under this condition. This phenomenon, that only scale size smaller than a wavelength can be retrieved in backscattering, is referred to as *wavelength filtering* (i.e., the information about the size of roughness scale larger than a wavelength has been filtered out by the incident wavelength). When there are smaller roughness scales present to cause incoherent scattering, the backscattered signal contains the information about the scale that generated it. This is why only small roughness scales can be retrieved from the incoherently scattered signal. Thus, to fully determine the roughness scales of a surface, a multifrequency system is needed.

1.2.1 Scattering Integral Interpretation of Wavelength Filtering

The *wavelength filtering* phenomenon mentioned in the previous paragraph can also be recognized mathematically from a basic form of the scattering integral for a randomly rough surface. The backscattered power per unit area or the backscattering coefficient from an isotropically rough random surface has the following form [Fung, 1994],

$$\sigma^\circ = \frac{k^2}{4\pi}|c|^2 \int \{e^{-(2k\sigma\cos\theta)^2[1-\rho(\xi)]} - e^{-(2k\sigma\cos\theta)^2}\} J_0(2k\xi\sin\theta)\xi d\xi \qquad (1.1)$$

where θ is the incident angle; σ is the standard deviation of the surface height (or the rms) height; k is the wave number; c is a coefficient independent of the integration variable; and $\rho(\xi)$ is the normalized surface correlation function also known as the correlation coefficient. For a Gaussian distributed and correlated surface with three independent roughness scales, L_1, L_2, L_3, we can describe its correlation function as

$$R(\xi) = \sigma^2\rho(\xi) = [\sigma_1^2 e^{-(\xi/L_1)^2} + \sigma_2^2 e^{-(\xi/L_2)^2} + \sigma_3^2 e^{-(\xi/L_3)^2}] = R_1 + R_2 + R_3 \quad (1.2)$$

where we assume $L_1 \geq 2L_2 \geq 4L_3$ as illustrated in Figure 1.1. The key frequency controlling factors in the integral are $2k\sigma\cos\theta$ and the oscillatory Bessel function, $J_0(2k\xi\sin\theta)$. Under low-frequency conditions, $2k\sin\theta$ is small, λ is large, and the effective wavelength $\lambda_e = \lambda/(2\sin\theta)$ associated with the integration distance is also large. The integration in (1.1) can be carried to large ξ values before sign changes in the Bessel function. The smaller scale terms in (1.2) are negligible because λ and λ_e are large compared with the rms heights of the smaller scale roughness. Thus, scattering is dominated by the large-scale roughness. On the other hand, under high-frequency conditions and away from grazing incidence, λ is small and $2k\sigma\cos\theta$ is large, so that $\rho(\xi)$ cannot deviate from unity very much before the integral vanishes. Hence, the effective range of integration is small so that the large-scale roughness has no chance to contribute under high-frequency conditions. When the incident angle is large, $\lambda_e = \lambda/(2\sin\theta)$ is small and the Bessel function will change sign over short distances. Thus, scattering is still dominated by the small-scale term in (1.2). *In summary, there is a gradual shifting in contribution from large to smaller roughness scales as frequency increases, because the effective range of integration decreases as frequency increases.* This is the mathematical version of *wavelength filtering* in backscattering from rough surfaces. In applying a surface scattering model to an unknown surface, this phenomenon is the basis for choosing a surface root-mean-squared (rms) height an order smaller than the electrical wavelength and a surface correlation length that leads to a physically meaningful surface rms slope.

In the literature on sea surface scattering in the microwave range, the chosen correlation length used in a surface backscatter modeling is in the centimeter range over a wide range of wind speeds, while the chosen surface rms height is restricted by the surface rms slope. Physically, we know that large waves many meters or more in length are present. Definitely these waves are lying within the antenna illuminated area. Why are they excluded in all backscatter models? The answer is that *wavelength filtering* has excluded them as contributing scatterers. Blindly including these large scatterers in modeling will generate error and misrepresent the real cause in scattering.

1.3 CORRELATION PROPERTIES OF MULTISCALE SURFACES

In this section we want to show that all multiscale surfaces have an exponential-like correlation function. For this reason an exponential correlation function can be a good approximation to the true correlation function of all multiscale surfaces under mid- to low-frequency conditions. This may also be the reason why the exponential correlation function is widely used in practice.

Consider an example of the multiscale correlation function R by assuming $\sigma_1 = 0.4$, $\sigma_2 = 0.25$ cm, $\sigma_3 = 0.13$ cm, $L_1 = 7$ cm, $L_2 = 3$ cm, and $L_3 = 1.5$ cm for the Gaussian correlated roughness scales as defined in (1.2). In

Figure 1.1 we show a plot of this normalized correlation function $\rho(\xi)$ along with its three components, R_1, R_2, and R_3. The tail of this correlation R is in close agreement with the Gaussian correlation function R_1, while over short lag distances it peaks up significantly above R_1 due to the presence of R_2 and R_3. As a result, it looks more like an exponential function. Clearly, this deviation from the Gaussian form is caused by the presence of the small-scale roughness. For the purpose of comparison, we show an exponential function with a correlation length, $L = 0.75L_1$, denoted as "exp" in Figure 1.1. It is lower than the surface correlation over small lag distances and higher over large lag distances. However, the general trend is similar. Thus, with a proper choice of L it is possible for the area under the two curves to be about the same. This means that whenever all three scales are contributing to scattering, the exponential function could be a good approximation to the three-scale Gaussian correlation function. This point will be examined further in Chapter 2. Over a small region near the origin, the exponential function is a poor representation of this multiscale correlation. Hence, it is not an acceptable correlation under high-frequency conditions where the shape of the correlation function near the origin is important. A possible way to deal with this problem is discussed in the next section.

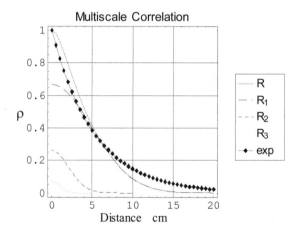

Figure 1.1 A comparison between the normalized correlation function from a multiscale Gaussian correlated surface with $\sigma_1 = 0.4$ cm, $\sigma_2 = 0.25$ cm, $\sigma_3 = 0.13$ cm, $L_1 = 7$ cm, $L_2 = 3$ cm, and $L_3 = 1.5$ cm and an exponential function with $L = 0.75L_1$.

Next, we want to consider roughness scales with non-Gaussian correlation functions of the form referred to as an *n*-power correlation function,

$$R(\xi) = \frac{\sigma_1^2}{[1 + (\xi/L_1)^2]^n} + \frac{\sigma_2^2}{[1 + (\xi/L_2)^2]^n} + \frac{\sigma_3^2}{[1 + (\xi/L_3)^2]^n} \qquad (1.3)$$

The scale sizes are assumed to be the same as in the previous paragraph. If we choose the correlation length for the exponential function selected for comparison to be $L = 0.65L_1$, we can plot all the functions similar to Figure 1.1 in Figure 1.2 assuming $n = 2$ in (1.3). Here, it shows once again that the surface correlation function R peaks up over small lag distances relative to the large-scale roughness correlation function. This is the reason why it has an exponential look and could be the reason why many natural surfaces seem to possess an exponential correlation function. From Figures 1.1 and 1.2, it is clear that the smaller roughness scales are responsible for creating the sharper peak in the surface correlation function. *Hence, regardless of the form of the correlation of the individual roughness scales, essentially all multiscale surfaces have correlation functions that look like an exponential.*

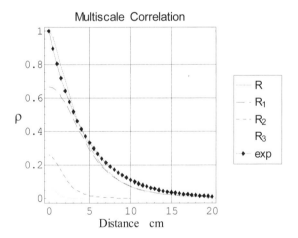

Figure 1.2 A comparison between the correlation function from a multiscale two-power-correlated surface with $\sigma_1 = 0.4$ cm, $\sigma_2 = 0.25$ cm, $\sigma_3 = 0.13$ cm, $L_1 = 7$ cm, $L_2 = 3$ cm, and $L_3 = 1.5$ cm and an exponential function with $L = 0.65L_1$.

We shall explain in Chapter 2 that under low-frequency conditions, it is possible for surface scattering to be dominated by the large-scale roughness alone. In that case the issue of approximating the correlation function of a multiscale surface by an exponential function does not exist. On the other hand, under high-frequency conditions the region of the correlation function near the origin is important. By definition a correlation function is a centro-symmetric function and should be twice differentiable at the origin in order to possess a slope distribution [Fung, 1994, p. 117]. The exponential correlation function is for surfaces that do not possess a slope distribution, while, in practice, most surfaces do have a slope distribution. For this reason, Section 1.4 examines two possible ways to modify the exponential function, so that it is differentiable at the origin similar to the Gaussian function.

1.4 MODIFIED EXPONENTIAL CORRELATION FUNCTIONS

In this section we shall consider two modified exponential correlation functions that resemble the Gaussian function near the origin and the exponential function over large lag distances. We shall call the first one an exponential-like function (expl) and the second one a modified exponential function (mexp). Both functions should possess or approach a bell-shaped curve (Gaussian-like function) around the origin and follow the exponential function over large lag distances. Allowing the correlation function to be Gaussian-like near the origin gains some control of the rate of drop-off in backscattering over large angles of incidence, because the Gaussian correlation function has a narrower spectrum than the exponential correlation function with the same correlation length. Another reason for requiring a correlation function to be Gaussian-like around the origin is that it is a differentiable function at the origin. We require this property because the slope variance of a surface is proportional to the second-order derivative of its correlation function evaluated at the origin. If the surface correlation is not twice differentiable at the origin, the surface will not possess a slope distribution.

1.4.1 The Exponential-Like Correlation Function (expl)

In the comparisons shown in Figure 1.1 and Figure 1.2 we noticed that the exponential correlation function is not differentiable at the origin because its slope is not continuous along any direction and behaves very differently from a Gaussian function in the neighborhood of the origin. One way to modify an exponential to become differentiable at the origin is to make it behave like a Gaussian function near the origin. For example, consider

$$R(\xi) = \exp\left[-\left(\frac{|\xi|}{L}\right)(1 - e^{-|\xi|/r})\right] \qquad (1.4)$$

When $\xi \ll r$, we can expand $\exp\left[-\frac{|\xi|}{r}\right]$ about $\xi = 0$ so that

$$R(\xi) \approx \exp\left[-\frac{\xi^2}{rL}\right].$$ This is a differentiable function.

Clearly, when $\xi \gg r$, this correlation function acts like the exponential function, $\exp[-\xi/L]$. An illustration showing how (1.4) changes from an expl function into a more and more Gaussian-like function as r increases from 0.2 to 16 is shown in Figure 1.3. To justify that it does approach a Gaussian function, Figure 1.3 plots a Gaussian correlation function with $L = 10$ cm in the same figure to compare with $R(\xi)$ in which $L = 5$ cm and $r = 16$ cm. Note that the agreement appears mainly from the origin to about 9 cm. It does not include the tail part of the functions. For low-frequency applications the angular shape of the correlation function near the origin has little influence on backscattering, because the incident wavelength is longer than the correlation length. For high-frequency applications backscattering at large angles of incidence is sensitive to the angular shape of the surface correlation function near the origin. A more Gaussian-like angular shape will lead to a significantly lower backscattering than an exponential correlation function over large angles of incidence. An illustration of this point is given in Chapter 3.

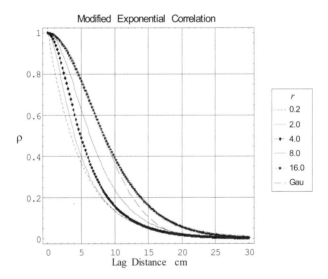

Figure 1.3 Illustration of an expl correlation function $R(\xi) = \exp[k(-(\xi/5)(1 - e^{-\xi/r}))]$ varying with r. $Gau = \exp[-(\xi/10)^2]$ is plotted in long dashes to show that $R(\xi)$ with $r = 16$ cm is in agreement with Gau up to $\xi = 9$. Generally, the function acts more like an exponential when $L \gg r$ and more like a Gaussian when the values of L and r are reversed.

The correlation function illustrated in Figure 1.3 has a clear Gaussian property near the origin when the correlation parameter r is larger than L. However, when the lag distance is large the correlation function always returns to having an exponential tail. This property is particularly important for explaining some measurements over the sea surface where over a range of small incident angles the backscattering curve is controlled by the Gaussian property and over large incident angles it has an exponential behavior. This point will be illustrated in Chapter 4.

Our objective of creating an expl function here is to obtain a correlation function that is able to fit the multiscale correlation function near the origin. In Figure 1.4 we compare the correlation function given by (1.4) with $r = 2.5$ cm and $L = 5$ cm with the multiscale correlation function shown in Figure 1.1. Clearly, very good agreement is possible over the region around the origin. The tail part remains very different as it should.

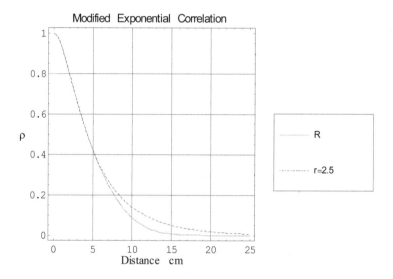

Figure 1.4 A comparison of the expl correlation function $R(\xi) = \exp[-(\xi/5)(1 - e^{-\xi/2.5})]$ with the multiscale correlation function given in Figure 1.1.

Please note that for all correlation functions with two parameters, neither parameter is the correlation length. The definition of correlation length is the lag distance where the correlation function drops to $1/e$ of its value at the origin. When we first introduce the parameter L in a single-scale exponential or Gaussian function, it does correspond to the correlation length, and we have been calling L the correlation length. When it is associated with a two-parameter correlation function, it is truly just a correlation parameter.

1.4.2 The Modified Exponential Correlation Function (mexp)

It is well known that the correlation function and its spectrum are uniquely related through the Fourier transformation. Thus, it should be possible to modify the spectrum of the exponential function instead of the exponential itself to achieve a similar result to (1.4). The advantage of having both the mexp and the expl correlation functions is that it offers computational benefits. For example, if our scattering model is in terms of the surface spectrum, we can avoid converting the correlation function into its spectrum.

For an isotropically rough, exponentially correlated surface, its spectrum is given by the Bessel transform of the exponential function $\exp[-\xi/L]$, yielding

$$W(K) = \frac{L^2}{(1 + K^2 L^2)^{1.5}} \tag{1.5}$$

Under high-frequency conditions, the expression in (1.5) often overestimates scattering at large incident angles. To reduce backscattering at large incident angles we must reduce the amplitude of $W(K)$ at large K values. We shall see that this is equivalent to forcing the exponential function to be more Gaussian-like. For example, let the modified exponential spectrum be

$$W_m(K) = \frac{L^2}{(1 + K^2 L^2)^{1.5}} \exp[-(zKL)^2] \tag{1.6}$$

When z or K is very small, the spectrum remains similar to the spectrum of an exponential correlation. For large z or K the amplitude of $W_m(K)$ is reduced. To show that this modified spectrum can behave like what we expect, we can compute the corresponding correlation function, which is the Bessel transform of $W_m(K)$. The normalized correlation function is given by

$$\rho(\xi) = \frac{1}{n_0} \int_0^\infty W_m(K) J_0(K\xi) K dK \tag{1.7}$$

where $n_0 = \left. \int_0^\infty W_m(K) J_0(K\xi) K dK \right|_{\xi=0}$

In Figure 1.5 we select $L = 5$ cm and compute $\rho(\xi)$ for several values of z. It is seen in Figure 1.5 that the computed curves begin to take on a more Gaussian form around the origin as z increases from 0.02 toward 0.2.

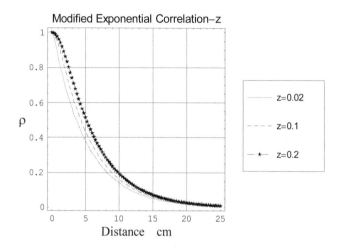

Figure 1.5 The mexp function, which is the Bessel transform of
$W_m(K) = L^2(1 + K^2L^2)^{-1.5}\exp[-(zKL)^2]$, with z chosen to be 0.02, 0.1, and 0.2. Larger values of z allow the correlation function to be more Gaussian-like in the region around the origin.

To demonstrate that the mexp function can also match the multiscale correlation function given in Figure 1.1 over a short lag distance, we show a comparison in Figure 1.6 in which the multiscale correlation function is denoted by R and the value of L is chosen to be 5 cm while z is set to 0.1. For this particular case, the agreement is up to a distance less than 5 cm, whereas with (1.4) the agreement is over 5 cm.

We have demonstrated that the mexp and the expl functions have some similar behaviors, but obviously they are not identical. One may be more suitable to use in a given situation than the other. A specific property to keep in mind is that the expl function always acts like a Gaussian function near the origin. The size of this Gaussian-like region is determined by choosing the size of r. On the other hand, the mexp function always acts like an exponential, but it can approach the Gaussian function as we increase the size of z.

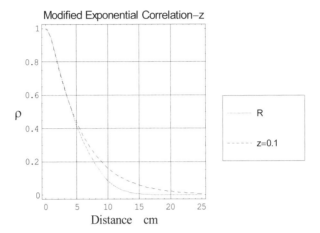

Figure 1.6 A comparison of the mexp function computed from taking the Bessel transform of $W_m(K)$ with the multiscale correlation function defined in Figure 1.1. Selected L and z in $W_m(K)$ are 5 cm and 0.1, respectively.

1.4.3 Surface Spectra for Backscattering Computation

For the purpose of computing backscattering the nth-order surface spectrum (which is the Fourier transform of the nth power of the expl correlation) is needed. It has a closed-form spectral representation given by

$$W^{(n)}(\kappa) = \sum_{m=0}^{\infty} L^2 \frac{n^m}{m!} \left(\frac{r}{nr + mL} \right)^{m+2} Gamma[m+2]$$

$$Hypergeometric2F1\left[\frac{m+2}{2}, \frac{m+3}{2}, 1, -\left(\frac{r\kappa L}{nr + mL} \right)^2 \right] \tag{1.8}$$

Although it is possible to compute $W^{(n)}(\kappa)$ given in (1.8) through the inverse Fourier transformation of (1.4), the use of (1.8) is generally more accurate than carrying out a numerical integration.

For the mexp function, the expression corresponding to (1.8) has been given in (1.6). For convenience of reference we also state it here as (1.9)

$$W^{(n)}(\kappa) = \frac{nL^2}{[n^2 + \kappa^2 L^2]^{1.5}} \exp[-(z\kappa L)^2] \qquad (1.9)$$

1.5 CONCLUDING REMARKS

In this chapter, we have discussed some general and basic properties of surface scattering from multiscale random surfaces. Ideas important to knowing how to use a backscattering model include the following:

1. Only roughness scales smaller than a wavelength contribute to backscattering from a multiscale surface. Mathematically, the effective lag distance contributing to the scattering integral decreases as the incident wavelength decreases. Roughness scales larger than a wavelength can modify the local incident angle but they are not the sources of backscattering. We shall see in Chapters 4 and 5 that this finding is critical to establish a practical backscattering model for the sea surface.

2. The correlation function of all multiscale surfaces looks like an exponential. In general, the exponential correlation function can be a good approximation to the true correlation function of a multiscale surface in some frequency ranges. However, it does not work in the high-frequency region when the portion of the correlation function near the origin is important to the scattering integral.

3. Both the mexp and the expl correlation functions are a better choice than the exponential function to serve as an approximation to the true correlation function of a multiscale surface, because such functions can be chosen to be close to an exponential or a Gaussian function near the origin.

To get into specifics, we need to choose a surface backscattering model. This is described in Chapter 2 along with a theoretical analysis of the surface scattering sources. With a scattering model we can then carry out numerical illustrations of the nature of surface scattering and identify the sources of backscattering at a given frequency and incident angle.

References

Bass, F. G., and I. M. Fuks, *Wave Scattering from Statistically Rough Surfaces*, Oxford: Pergamon Press, Ltd., 1979.

Beckmann, P., and A. Spizzichino, *The Scattering of Electromagnetic Waves from Rough Surfaces*, New York: Macmillan, 1963.

DeSanto, J. A., "Scattering by Rough Surfaces," in *Scattering: Scattering and Inverse Scattering in Pure and Applied Science*, R. Pike and P. Sabatier, eds., New York: Academic Press, 2002, pp. 15–36.

Fung, A. K., Z. Li, and K. S. Chen, "Backscattering from a Randomly Rough Dielectric Surface," *IEEE Trans. Geosci. Remote Sens.* Vol. 30, 1992, pp. 356–69.

Fung, A. K., *Microwave Scattering and Emission Models and Their Applications*, Norwood, MA: Artech House, 1994.

Fung, A. K., et al., "An Improved IEM Model for Bistatic Scattering from Rough Surface," *J. Electromagnetic Waves and Applications*, Vol. 16, No. 5, 2002, pp. 689–702.

Hsieh, C. Y., and A. K. Fung, "Application of an Extended IEM to Multiple Surface Scattering and Backscatter Enhancement," *J. Electromagnetic Waves and Applications*, Vol. 13, 1999, pp. 121–135.

Ishimaru, A., *Propagation and Scattering of Waves in Random Media*, New York: Elsevier Science, 2013.

Kozlov, A. I., L. P. Ligthart, A. I. Logvin, *Mathematical and Physical Modelling of Microwave Scattering and Polarimetric Remote Sensing*, Dordrecht: Kluwer Academic Publishers, 2002.

Ogilvy, J. A., *Theory of Wave Scattering from Random Rough Surfaces*, Bristol: Adam Hilger, 1991.

Pinel, N., and C. Boulier, *Electromagnetic Wave Scattering from Random Rough Surfaces: Asymptotic Models*, New York: John Wiley and Sons, 2013.

Rice, S. O., "Reflection of Electromagnetic Waves from Slightly Rough Surface," *Communications in Pure and Applied Mathematics*, Vol. 4, 1951, pp. 361–378.

Saillard, M., and A. Sentenac, "Rigorous Solutions for Electromagnetic Scattering from Rough Surfaces," *Waves Random Media*, 11, 2001, pp. R103–R137.

Tsang L., J. A. Kong, K. H. Ding, *Electromagnetic Waves, Theories and Applications*, New York: John Wiley and Sons, 2000.

Ulaby, F. T., R. K. Moore, and A. K. Fung, *Microwave Remote Sensing*, Chapters 11 and 12, Vol. 2, Norwood, MA: Artech House, 1982.

Ulaby, F. T., R. K. Moore, and A. K. Fung, *Microwave Remote Sensing*, Chapter 21, Vol. 3, Norwood, MA: Artech House, 1986.

Voronovich, A. G., *Wave Scattering from Rough Surfaces* (second edition), New York: Springer, 1998.

Chapter 2

Surface Backscattering Mechanisms

2.1 INTRODUCTION

In this chapter we show the mechanisms of surface scattering via an existing backscattering model that is applicable under all frequency conditions. We shall see that the sources of backscattering change continuously with the incident frequency and the incident angle in the form of an effective wavenumber, $\kappa = 2k\sin\theta$. Under low-frequency conditions, the dominant source of backscattering is the surface spectrum evaluated at $\kappa = 2k\sin\theta$. As frequency increases there is a gradual shift in dominance from the surface spectrum into higher order spectra. However, the spectral components remain those defined by $\kappa = 2k\sin\theta$. In the high-frequency limit only the surface slope distribution is important. In general, this limit cannot be reached as long as roughness scales smaller than the incident wavelength are present.

The surface backscattering model is given in Section 2.2. Then, a theoretical analysis of the model behavior over frequency is provided to illustrate the change in the sources of backscattering. This is followed by a numerical illustration of how the different orders of the surface spectra normalized by k change with frequency and angle. It is found that the approximate region of transition into the high-frequency limit can be defined in terms of the wavenumber and surface rms height product, $k\sigma$.

2.2 THE BACKSCATTER MODEL

For backscattering from a randomly rough surface, the simplified integral equation model (IEM) [Fung, 1994] is generally sufficiently accurate. Theoretically, we require the surface to be continuous and describable statistically. In practice, a surface is considered continuous if the geometric discontinuities on it are small compared with the incident wavelength or occupy a region small compared to the illuminated area.

The geometry of backscattering of an electromagnetic wave from a randomly rough surface is depicted in Figure 2.1 where the physical constants of the media are also defined. The general form of the backscattering coefficients for vertically, σ_{vv}^0 and horizontally, σ_{hh}^0, polarized scattering excluding multiple surface scattering is given by (2.1) [Fung, 1994, p. 249]:

$$\sigma_{pp}^0 = \frac{k^2}{2}\exp[-2k^2\sigma^2\cos^2\theta]\sum_{n=1}^{\infty}|I_{pp}^n|^2\frac{\sigma^{2n}W^{(n)}(2k\sin\theta,0)}{n!} \tag{2.1}$$

where

$$I_{pp}^n = (2k\cos\theta)^n f_{pp}\exp[-k^2\sigma^2\cos^2\theta]+(k\cos\theta)^n F_{pp}, \quad p = v,h$$

$$f_{vv} = \frac{2R_v}{\cos\theta}, \quad f_{hh} = \frac{-2R_h}{\cos\theta}$$

$$F_{vv} = \frac{\sin^2\theta}{\cos\theta}(1+R_v)^2\left[\left(1-\frac{1}{\varepsilon_r}\right)+\frac{\mu_r\varepsilon_r-\sin^2\theta-\varepsilon_r\cos^2\theta}{(\varepsilon_r\cos\theta)^2}\right]$$

$$F_{hh} = -\frac{\sin^2\theta}{\cos\theta}(1+R_h)^2\left[\left(1-\frac{1}{\mu_r}\right)+\frac{\mu_r\varepsilon_r-\sin^2\theta-\mu_r\cos^2\theta}{(\mu_r\cos\theta)^2}\right]$$

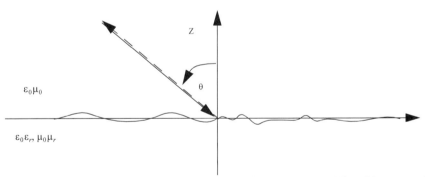

Figure 2.1 Geometry of the backscattering problem. The permittivity and permeability of the upper and lower medium are ε_0 and μ_0, and $\varepsilon_0\varepsilon_r$ and $\mu_0\mu_r$ respectively. The incident angle is θ.

In the above, k is the wavenumber; R_p is the p-polarized Fresnel reflection coefficient; and the quantity $W^{(n)}$ is the nth-order surface spectrum (or roughness spectrum) corresponding to the two-dimensional Fourier transform of the surface correlation coefficient $\rho(x, y)$ raised to its nth power, $\rho^n(x, y)$. It is defined as follows in polar form:

$$W^{(n)}(\kappa, \varphi) = \frac{1}{2\pi} \int_0^{2\pi} \int_0^{\infty} \rho^n(r, \phi) e^{-j\kappa r \cos(\varphi - \phi)} r \, dr \, d\phi \qquad (2.2)$$

Both $\rho^n(r, \phi)$ and $W^{(n)}(\kappa, \varphi)$ are quantities normalized by σ^{2n}. Hence, $\rho^n(r, \phi)$ is dimensionless and $W^{(n)}(\kappa, \varphi)$ is in centimeter squared; κ is the surface wavenumber and φ is the azimuth angle.

If the surface roughness is independent of the view direction, the correlation coefficient is isotropic depending only on r. In this case, (2.2) reduces to

$$W^{(n)}(\kappa) = \int_0^{\infty} \rho^n(r) J_0(\kappa r) r \, dr \qquad (2.3)$$

where $J_0(\kappa r)$ is the 0th order Bessel function.

In (2.1), $W^{(n)}(\kappa, \varphi)$ and $\rho^n(r, \phi)$ are related uniquely through the Fourier transform. Hence, we are free to specify either one of them. Equation (2.1) is an algebraic equation if we work directly with $W^{(n)}(\kappa, \varphi)$ instead of the correlation function. We have already learned that for all multiscale surfaces, the general shape of the correlation function is similar to an exponential function. For an exponential correlation, its nth-order spectrum defined by (2.3) has the form

$$\sigma^{2n} W^{(n)}(\kappa) = \frac{n\sigma^{2n}L^2}{(n^2 + \kappa^2 L^2)^{1.5}} \qquad (2.4)$$

We also know that near the origin of the correlation function, the exponential function is unable to fit the true correlation. Thus, for high-frequency applications we should reduce the tail end of (2.4) by adding a decay factor. For example, as explained in Section 1.4, to approximate a multiscale correlation such as the one defined in (1.2) we can set

$$\sigma^{2n} W^{(n)}(\kappa) = \frac{n\sigma^{2n}L^2}{[n^2 + \kappa^2 L^2]^{1.5}} \exp[-(z\kappa L)^2] \qquad (2.5)$$

for medium- to high-frequency applications. For most applications, $z \leq 0.2$ in the high-frequency region. In the medium-frequency region where $k\sigma \leq 0.7$, we can use (2.4) without the decay factor, $\exp[-(z\kappa L)^2]$. Hence, we expect the simple spectral expression given by (2.4), to be a useful one in many practical situations. More illustrations about the use of (2.5) will be given in Chapter 3. Under very low-frequency conditions a multiscale surface may act as a single-scale surface. In that case, no approximation is applicable (see Section 2.3.3) and the value of (2.4) is restricted to exponentially correlated surfaces, while (2.5) has a wider applicability (see Section 1.4). While the last statement is demonstrated in Section 2.3.3, it is generally academic in the microwave region, because the size of the incident wavelength is generally small compared with roughness scales appearing on natural surfaces (for example, the sea surface).

In practice, under low-frequency conditions, measurements at small incident angles could be less reliable due to possible coherent contribution, wide antenna beamwidth, and sidelobe problems. At large incident angles shadowing of unknown amount can happen. Hence, in model applications care should be exercised in dealing with incident angles in the range $0° \leq \theta \leq 10°$ and near or beyond 70 degrees. At this writing an accurate way to estimate shadowing is not available. Although shadowing methods based on geometric optics have been reported in the literature [Smith, 1967; Sancer, 1969], their applicability to surface scattering in general has been questioned [Brown, 1984].

2.2.1 A Better Estimate of Surface Reflection Coefficient

In (2.1) the Fresnel reflection coefficients, $R_v(\theta)$, $R_h(\theta)$, in f_{pp} can be generalized by replacing them with a reflection transition function [Wu et al., 2001], which allows the argument of the Fresnel reflection coefficients to change from the incident angle to the specular angle as the operating frequency changes from low to high. They are defined as follows:

$$R_{tv} = R_v(\theta) + [R_{v0} - R_v(\theta)](1 - S_t/S_{to})$$
$$R_{th} = R_h(\theta) + [R_{h0} - R_h(\theta)](1 - S_t/S_{to}) \tag{2.6}$$

where R_{v0}, R_{h0} are the Fresnel reflection coefficients evaluated at the specular angle. Under backscattering condition, the specular angle is equal to zero. Other symbols in (2.6) are defined below:

$$S_t = \left[|F_t|^2 \sum_{n=1}^{\infty} \frac{(k\sigma\cos\theta)^{2n}}{n!} W^{(n)}(2k\sin\theta) \right] \Big/$$

$$\left[\sum_{n=1}^{\infty} \frac{(k\sigma\cos\theta)^{2n}}{n!} \left| F_t + \frac{2^{n+2}R_{v0}}{e^{(k\sigma\cos\theta)^2}\cos\theta} \right|^2 W^{(n)}(2k\sin\theta) \right]$$

$$F_t = 8R_{v0}^2 \sin^2\theta \left(\frac{\cos\theta + \sqrt{\varepsilon_r - \sin^2\theta}}{\cos\theta\sqrt{\varepsilon_r - \sin^2\theta}} \right)$$

$$S_{t0} = \left| 1 + \frac{8R_{v0}}{F_t\cos\theta} \right|^{-2} \text{ is the limit of } S_t \text{ as } k\sigma \to 0$$

The functional form of this transition function indicates that the transition from $R(\theta)$ to $R(0)$ is dependent on the relative contributions of the Kirchhoff term (high-frequency term) versus the complementary term (the term needed to extend the model into the medium- and low-frequency regions) in the integral equation model. In the angular region where the Kirchhoff term is dominant, R_t is very close to $R(0)$. Conversely, when the complementary term is dominant, R_t remains close to $R(\theta)$. For very large dielectric values the magnitudes of R_{vt}, R_{ht} approach unity. Thus, the reflection coefficients with transitional properties, R_{vt}, R_{ht}, provide a change when the combination of frequency, dielectric constant, and roughness influences the relative strength of the two terms. Note that this is an *estimate* that may not correctly handle all roughness, frequency, and angular changes properly especially at large angles of incidence. We shall apply the transitional reflection coefficient only to f_{pp} because this is the Kirchhoff term and keep $R_p(\theta)$ in F_{pp}, since it is the moderate- to low-frequency term.

In this section all surface height distributions are assumed Gaussian. In general, the average scattered power away from the high-frequency limit is more sensitive to the surface spectrum than its height distribution. For this reason our use of the Gaussian distribution for surface height does not constitute a serious restriction to the model. When we change the surface spectrum and or surface parameters, the scattering model defined by (2.1) predicts a different angular trend and level. Except under very low-frequency conditions, the backscattering coefficients in (2.1) depend on $W^{(n)}$ and not just $W^{(1)}$. This is why it is more accurate than the small perturbation model.

2.3 MECHANISMS OF THE SURFACE SCATTERING MODEL

In this section we want to show the theoretical variation of scattering sources based on the model defined by (2.1) as frequency changes and then illustrate these changes numerically. In so doing we also demonstrate that this backscattering model is valid over the entire frequency band. This last statement has been independently verified by [Koudogbo et al., 2004]. Finally, we want to show that wavelength filtering is an inherent property in backscattering from multiscale surfaces.

2.3.1 Variation of Backscattering Sources with Frequency

The sources of surface scattering for the classical geometric optics, Kirchhoff, and small perturbation or Bragg scattering models are the surface slope distribution, reflection and diffraction, and surface spectrum evaluated at Bragg wavenumbers, respectively. They are valid, respectively, in the high-frequency limit, high-frequency region, and low-frequency region. The IEM in (2.1) has integrated these three models and includes them as special cases. We shall show that it converges to the Kirchhoff model in the high-frequency region. In the high- frequency limit, it reduces to the geometric optics model. Away from the high- frequency limit, the model shows that higher orders of the surface spectrum, $W^{(n)}$, are more important than the lower orders. This relative importance is reversed when the incident frequency is low, where (2.1) reduces to the Bragg model. Numerical illustrations of scattering sources are given in Section 2.3.2.

    To show that the Kirchhoff model is a special case of (2.1), we begin with the backscattering coefficient,

$$\sigma_{pp}^0 = \frac{k^2}{2}\exp[-2k^2\sigma^2\cos^2\theta]\sum_{n=1}^{\infty}|I_{pp}^n|^2\frac{\sigma^{2n}W^{(n)}(2k\sin\theta,\,0)}{n!}$$

where for ease of writing we assume that I_{pp}^n is real so that

$$(I_{pp}^n)^2 = (2k\cos\theta)^{2n}f_{pp}^2e^{-2k^2\sigma^2\cos^2\theta} + 2(2k\cos\theta)^nf_{pp}e^{-k^2\sigma^2\cos^2\theta}(k\cos\theta)^nF_{pp}$$

$$+ (k\cos\theta)^{2n}F_{pp}^2$$

For an isotropically rough surface we can write $W^{(n)}$ as

$$W^{(n)} = \int_0^\infty \rho^n(r)J_o(2kr\sin\theta)r\,dr$$

There are three terms in $(I_{pp}^n)^2$. Under high-frequency conditions $k\sigma$ is very large. We want to show that only the first term is significant. It can be written as

$$\frac{k^2}{2}f_{pp}^2 \exp[-4k^2\sigma^2\cos^2\theta] \sum_{n=1}^{\infty} \int_0^{\infty} \frac{(4k^2\sigma^2\cos^2\theta)^n}{n!} \rho^n(r) J_o(2kr\sin\theta) r dr$$

$$= \frac{k^2}{2}f_{pp}^2 \exp[-4k^2\sigma^2\cos^2\theta] \int_0^{\infty} \left\{ \sum_{n=1}^{\infty} \frac{(4k^2\sigma^2\rho(r)\cos^2\theta)^n}{n!} + 1 - 1 \right\}$$

$$J_o(2kr\sin\theta) r dr$$

Adding one to the sum produces the exponential term, $\exp[4k^2\sigma^2\rho(r)\cos^2\theta]$, yielding the standard Kirchhoff integral for noncoherent surface scattering

$$\sigma^K_{pp} = \frac{k^2}{2}f_{pp}^2 \int_0^{\infty} \{ e^{-4k^2\sigma^2\cos^2\theta[1-\rho(r)]} - e^{-4k^2\sigma^2\cos^2\theta} \} J_o(2kr\sin\theta) r dr \qquad (2.7)$$

The second and third terms in $(I_{pp}^n)^2$ are multiplied by $\exp[-3k^2\sigma^2\rho(r)\cos^2\theta]$ and $\exp[-2k^2\sigma^2\rho(r)\cos^2\theta]$, respectively. These terms are negligible compared with the first term when $k\sigma$ is sufficiently large. This means that the Kirchhoff integral is valid only when $k\sigma$ is sufficiently large. Validity of (2.7) also requires that $L > \lambda$ so that reflection occurs at every local point on the rough surface. Correlation length L determines the effective width of the correlation function or the effective width of the corresponding spectrum. It also gives an indication of the approximate size of the surface roughness. This size information, however, is lost when $k\sigma \to \infty$. In this case, $1 - \rho(r)$ must be made small enough to compensate for large $k\sigma$. The normal approach is to expand $\rho(r)$ about the origin, leading to

$$\sigma^K_{pp} \cong \frac{k^2}{2}f_{pp}^2 \int_0^{\infty} \{ e^{-4k^2\sigma^2\cos^2\theta|\rho''(0)|r^2/2} \} J_o(2kr\sin\theta) r dr = \frac{R_{pp}^2 e^{-\frac{\tan^2\theta}{2\sigma^2|\rho''(0)|}}}{2\sigma^2|\rho''(0)|\cos^4\theta} \qquad (2.8)$$

where $\sqrt{\sigma^2|\rho''(0)|}$ is the rms slope of the surface and (2.8) is the geometric optics surface backscattering model for surfaces with a Gaussian surface height distribution. As seen in (2.8) in the high-frequency limit, surface slope and its reflectivity are the only information carried in this backscatter model.

In the above we have demonstrated mathematically the condition necessary for the Kirchhoff integral to be valid and the condition for Kirchhoff integral to approach the geometric optics. Physically, the $L > \lambda$ condition, needed to arrive at the Kirchhoff integral, means that there are no roughness scales smaller than the incident wavelength, which may not hold in a practical situation. The condition for the geometric optics to occur, $k\sigma \to \infty$, means that all roughness scales on the surface are much larger than the incident wavelength. This situation can occur in a natural environment, but it rarely does because soil surfaces are not smooth surfaces. They contain grains of different sizes or have some vegetation cover. Water surfaces may have ripples. In practice, Kirchhoff model behavior is seen in backscattering over small angles of incidence where the effective wavelength is large so that the surface appears to be very smooth with only large undulations. Over large angles of incidence the backscattering behavior seems to agree better with the perturbation model although the effective wavelength is shorter. These practical observations seem to contradict mathematical expectations. Actually, there is no contradiction because the scatterer contributing to backscattering is large compared with the incident wavelength in the small incident angular region and is small compared with the incident wavelength in the large incident angular region. The key is to look at the size of the contributing scatterer relative to the incident wavelength.

Away from the high-frequency limit all orders of the surface spectra are important. As seen from (2.1) the relative levels of importance are controlled by $k\sigma$.

In the very low-frequency range as $k\sigma \to 0$ we can ignore higher order terms in $k\sigma$ yielding

$$\sigma_{pp}^0 = \frac{k^2}{2}[(2k\sigma\cos\theta)f_{pp} + (k\sigma\cos\theta)F_{pp}]^2 W^{(1)}(2k\sin\theta, 0)$$

$$= \frac{k^4}{2}(\sigma\cos\theta)^2(2f_{pp} + F_{pp})^2 W^{(1)}(2k\sin\theta, 0)$$

For vertical polarization and $\mu_r = 1$ we have

$$\sigma_{vv}^0 = \frac{k^4}{2}\sigma^2\left\{4R_v + \sin^2\theta(1 + R_v)^2\left[\left(1 - \frac{1}{\varepsilon_r}\right) + \frac{\varepsilon_r - \sin^2\theta - \varepsilon_r\cos^2\theta}{(\varepsilon_r\cos\theta)^2}\right]\right\}^2$$

$$W^{(1)}(2k\sin\theta, 0)$$

$$= \frac{k^4\sigma^2}{2}\left\{4R_v + \sin^2\theta(1 + R_v)^2\left[\left(1 - \frac{1}{\varepsilon_r}\right) + \frac{\varepsilon_r - \sin^2\theta - \varepsilon_r(1 - \sin^2\theta)}{(\varepsilon_r\cos\theta)^2}\right]\right\}^2$$

$$W^{(1)}(2k\sin\theta, 0)$$

$$= 8k^4\sigma^2\left\{R_v(\cos^2\theta + \sin^2\theta) + \frac{\sin^2\theta(1+R_v)^2}{4}\left(1 - \frac{1}{\varepsilon_r}\right)\left[1 + \frac{\sin^2\theta}{\varepsilon_r\cos^2\theta}\right]\right\}^2$$

$$W^{(1)}(2k\sin\theta, 0)$$

Next, we want to rearrange the terms in the first line below in the same form as the small perturbation or Bragg model given in [Ulaby et al., 1982] and then show that the terms in the second line sum to zero as follows.

$$\sigma_{vv}^0 = 8k^4\sigma^2\left\{R_v\cos^2\theta + \frac{\sin^2\theta(1+R_v)^2}{2}\left(1 - \frac{1}{\varepsilon_r}\right)\right.$$

$$\left. + R_v\sin^2\theta - \frac{\sin^2\theta(1+R_v)^2}{4}\left(1 - \frac{1}{\varepsilon_r}\right)\left[1 - \frac{\sin^2\theta}{\varepsilon_r\cos^2\theta}\right]\right\}^2 W^{(1)}(2k\sin\theta, 0)$$

After arranging terms in the last line we apply $R_v = (\varepsilon_r\cos\theta - \sqrt{\varepsilon_r - \sin^2\theta})/(\varepsilon_r\cos\theta + \sqrt{\varepsilon_r - \sin^2\theta})$ to obtain

$$R_v\sin^2\theta - \frac{\sin^2\theta(1+R_v)^2}{4}\left(1 - \frac{1}{\varepsilon_r} - \frac{\sin^2\theta}{\varepsilon_r\cos^2\theta} + \frac{\sin^2\theta}{\varepsilon_r^2\cos^2\theta}\right)$$

$$= \sin^2\theta\left[R_v - \frac{(1+R_v)^2}{4}\right] + \frac{\sin^2\theta(1+R_v)^2}{4\varepsilon_r}\left(1 + \frac{\sin^2\theta}{\cos^2\theta} - \frac{\sin^2\theta}{\varepsilon_r\cos^2\theta}\right)$$

$$= -\frac{(1-R_v)^2}{4}\sin^2\theta + \frac{\sin^2\theta(1+R_v)^2}{4\varepsilon_r^2\cos^2\theta}(\varepsilon_r - \sin^2\theta)$$

$$= -\frac{(1-R_v)^2}{4}\sin^2\theta + \frac{(1-R_v)^2}{4}\sin^2\theta = 0$$

Hence, for vertical polarization the backscattering coefficient under small $k\sigma$ or low-frequency conditions is

$$\sigma_{vv}^0 = 8k^4\sigma^2\left\{R_v\cos^2\theta + \frac{\sin^2\theta(1+R_v)^2}{2}\left(1 - \frac{1}{\varepsilon_r}\right)\right\}^2 W^{(1)}(2k\sin\theta, 0) \qquad (2.9)$$

Equation (2.9) is in agreement with the small perturbation or Bragg model for vertical polarization [Ulaby et al., 1982]. It indicates that scattering is now controlled by the surface dielectric constant and the surface spectrum evaluated at the surface wavenumber $2k\sin\theta$. Only these specific wavenumbers can contribute to scattering. This phenomenon is referred to as Bragg scattering. The size of the surface roughness responsible for scattering is defined by the combination of σ, L, and $\kappa = 2k\sin\theta$.

Similarly, for horizontal polarization with $k\sigma \to 0$ and $\mu_r = 1$ we have

$$\sigma_{hh}^0 = \frac{k^4}{2}(\sigma\cos\theta)^2(2f_{hh} + F_{hh})^2 W^{(1)}(2k\sin\theta, 0)$$

$$= \frac{k^4}{2}(\sigma\cos\theta)^2\left\{\frac{-4R_h}{\cos\theta} - \frac{\sin^2\theta}{\cos\theta}(1 + R_h)^2\left[\frac{\varepsilon_r - \sin^2\theta - \cos^2\theta}{\cos^2\theta}\right]\right\}^2 W^{(1)}(2k\sin\theta, 0)$$

$$= 8k^4\sigma^2\left\{-R_h - \sin^2\theta\left[\frac{1}{\cos\theta + \sqrt{\varepsilon_r - \sin^2\theta}}\right]^2[\varepsilon_r - \sin^2\theta - \cos^2\theta]\right\}^2$$

$$W^{(1)}(2k\sin\theta, 0)$$

$$= 8k^4\sigma^2\left\{-R_h + \sin^2\theta\left[\frac{1}{\cos\theta + \sqrt{\varepsilon_r - \sin^2\theta}}\right]^2[\cos^2\theta - (\varepsilon_r - \sin^2\theta)]\right\}^2$$

$$W^{(1)}(2k\sin\theta, 0)$$

$$\sigma_{hh}^0 = 8k^4\sigma^2(R_h\cos^2\theta)^2 W^{(1)}(2k\sin\theta, 0) \tag{2.10}$$

where (2.10) is the small perturbation or Bragg model for horizontal polarization [Ulaby et al., 1982]. It is the $W^{(1)}$ term in the series of terms $W^{(n)}(2k\sin\theta, 0)$ in the IEM model in (2.1). All orders of the surface spectrum $W^{(n)}(2k\sin\theta, 0)$ use Bragg spectral components. The size of roughness scale that can contribute to backscattering is restricted by the rate of convergence of the scattering integral determined mainly by $k\sigma$.

2.3.2 Numerical Illustration of Backscattering Sources

In this section we shall consider the variation of the spectral content of different orders of the surface roughness spectrum responsible for backscattering. As indicated in (2.1) the wavenumber κ in the roughness spectrum is related to the electrical wavenumber k by $\kappa = 2k\sin\theta$. Since $0° \leq \theta < 90°$, it follows that $0 \leq \kappa < 2k$. In backscattering these are the roughness spectral components responsible for scattering except in the high-frequency limit as explained in the previous section. In the low-frequency region the roughness spectrum and its spectral components $(0, 2k)$ are dominant contributors. As frequency increases, the range of the spectral components increases, and there is a gradual shift of dominance into higher order spectra for larger spectral components. As we shall see in Figures 2.2 and 2.3, the transition is dependent on $k\sigma$ and not affected by σ, L, or k individually.

In $\sigma^{2n}W^{(n)}(\kappa)$ when $n = 1$, $\sigma^2 W^{(1)}(\kappa)$ is the roughness spectrum. For n larger than unity, we have higher order spectra that are smaller in amplitude within the low-frequency region but decaying more slowly with increasing k. Hence, higher order spectra become increasingly more important at higher frequencies. In Figure 2.2 we show plots of the dimensionless spectra based on (2.5), Wn, normalized by k defined by,

$$\text{Wn} = \frac{n(kL)^2(k\sigma)^{2n}}{[n^2 + (\kappa L)^2]^{1.5}}\exp[-(z\kappa L)^2]$$

for $z = 0.028$, $\sigma = 0.4$ cm, and $L = 3$ cm in Figure 2.2(a) and $L = 7$ cm in Figure 2.2(b) with n ranging from 1 to 5. As expected, a larger value of L simply allows a faster decay of the surface spectrum with its wavenumber, κ. When the incident frequency is 9 GHz or lower, the surface spectrum is clearly the dominant contributor. As frequency increases to 11 GHz, all orders of the surface spectrum rise in level. However, higher order spectra rise faster in level than the lower order spectra and at 12 GHz the higher order spectra levels actually exceed the lower order spectra for a sufficiently large surface wavenumber κ. The transition region over which this occurs may be designated approximately by $k\sigma$. At 9 GHz, $k\sigma = 0.75$. For $k\sigma < 0.75$ the level of the surface spectrum is higher than any higher order spectrum. When $k\sigma > 0.75$ the higher order spectra begin to rise. By the time $k\sigma = 1$ at 12 GHz, the higher order spectra are higher than the lower order spectra when $\kappa > 1.4$ cm^{-1} with $L = 3$ cm or $\kappa > 0.5$ cm^{-1} with $L = 7$ cm. The starting wavenumber for transition is smaller for larger L. Otherwise, L does not influence the transition region.

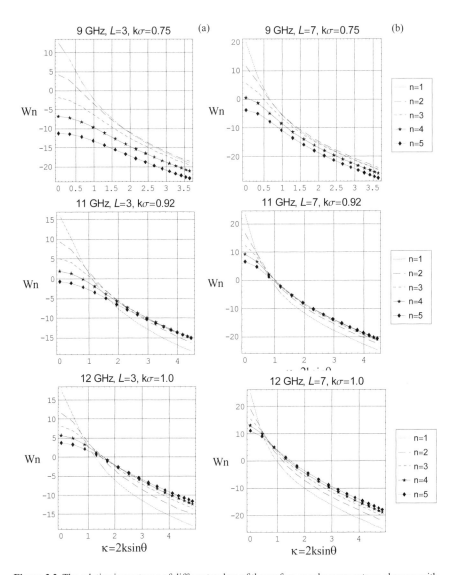

Figure 2.2 The relative importance of different orders of the surface roughness spectrum changes with $k\sigma$. For $k\sigma > 0.8$ and large values of κ it is possible for higher order spectra to be larger than the spectrum itself. Correlation length L can change the shape of the spectra. It does not influence the relative importance of different orders of the spectra. (a) $\sigma = 0.4$ cm, $L = 3$ cm, (b) $\sigma = 0.4$ cm and $L = 7$ cm.

To verify that this transition region can be indicated by $0.75 \leq k\sigma \leq 1$, we increase σ to 0.72 cm in Figure 2.3. At 5 GHz, $k\sigma = 0.75$ and all higher order spectra are lower in level than the surface spectrum similar to what we see in Figure 2.2. At 6 GHz $k\sigma = 0.9$, and we see the spectra coming together in level. At $f = 7$ GHz, $k\sigma = 1.05$ and the higher order spectrum is now higher in level than the lower order spectrum. Although both the incident frequency and the surface rms height have changed, the transition behavior of all the spectral orders still follows the changes in the value of $k\sigma$. Hence, $k\sigma$ value can decide the status of the backscattering sources and which spectral component or components are likely to be important. It also shows what is missing in both the small perturbation and the Kirchhoff surface scattering models.

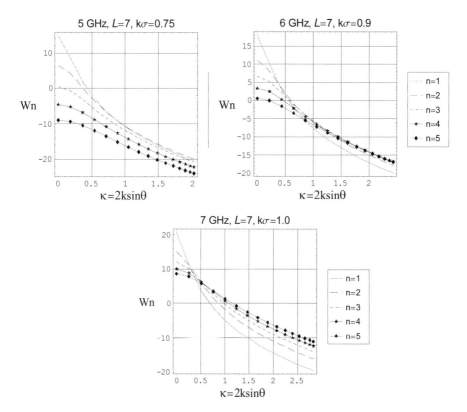

Figure 2.3 The relative importance of different orders of the surface roughness spectrum changes with $k\sigma$. A change in frequency or σ does not influence the change in the relative importance of the different orders of the spectra. In the above examples $\sigma = 0.72$ cm.

   In summary, we have shown that for single-scale roughness, the transition into the high-frequency region begins around $k\sigma = 0.75$ and starts to show saturation when $k\sigma$ exceeds 1.0. The sources of scattering are as illustrated in Figure 2.3. Backscattering is controlled by spectral components lying in the wavenumber range $(0, 2k)$. As the incident frequency increases, there is a shift in relative contributions from lower to higher order spectra. Under the low-wavenumber and low-frequency conditions the surface spectrum has the highest level (Figure 2.4).

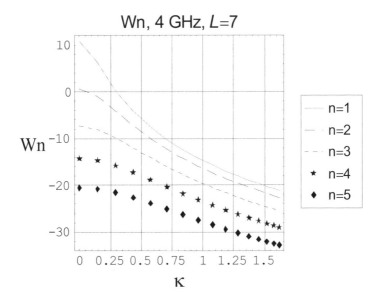

Figure 2.4 An illustration of a complete reversal of the levels of different orders of the surface spectrum from the 7 GHz case in Figure 2.3 with $\kappa \geq 1$, when at 4 GHz the surface spectrum has the highest level with $\sigma = 0.72$ cm and $L = 7$ cm.

   In the high-wavenumber ($\kappa \geq 1$) and high-frequency ($f \geq 7$ GHz) region, a reversal occurs and all higher orders of the surface spectrum are higher in level than the lower orders (Figure 2.3). The level of these higher order spectra in the high κ region affects the shape of the surface correlation near the origin. For example, if we increase z to 0.05 cm in Wn and compute the corresponding correlation function with $L = 4.9$ cm, it will show a clear difference from the exponential function as shown in Figure 2.5.

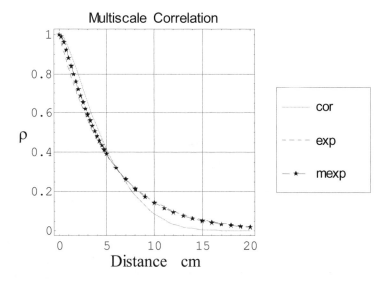

Figure 2.5 A comparison of the multiscale Gaussian correlation in Figure 1.1 denoted by, cor, with an exponential function having L = 5.25 cm and a modified exponential function, mexp, which is much more similar to the Gaussian function near the origin.

2.3.3 Numerical Illustration of Wavelength Filtering

In the previous section we have considered the effects of the different orders of the roughness spectrum $W^{(n)}$ on backscattering and the impact of $k\sigma$. Here, we want to show how backscattering based on the model in (2.1) responds to the multiscale surface defined by (1.2) and (1.3). The main purpose here is to find out which roughness scale is important under a given frequency and incident angle condition and where the correlation effect shows up. For ease of reference we rewrite the values for the parameters in the multiscale Gaussian correlation, σ_1 = 0.4 cm, σ_2 = 0.25 cm, σ_3 = 0.13 cm, L_1 = 7 cm, L_2 = 3 cm, and L_3 = 1.5 cm and choose the dielectric constant to be 16.

Backscattering coefficients based on (2.1) with the correlation function defined in (1.2) are computed at 2, 4, and 8 GHz corresponding to $k\sigma$ = 0.2, 0.41, and 0.82, respectively. Results are shown in Figure 2.6 for vertical polarization. Backscattering from the multiscale Gaussian surface is shown in solid line, while backscattering from each of the three roughness scales individually is denoted by

L, M, and S. At 2 GHz and small angles of incidence, backscattering is dominated by the large-scale roughness alone. Thus, the angular shape in backscattering before 30-degree incidence is basically the same as a surface with only the Gaussian-correlated, large-scale roughness. This means that the information about surface correlation can only be found under low-frequency conditions and small angles of incidence. This restriction to small angles can be relaxed if we reduce the incident frequency further. If so, a multiscale surface may act as a single-scale surface at a sufficiently low frequency. After 30 degrees, dominance is shifted gradually to the midsize roughness, while the small-scale roughness remains negligible. This change in dominance by different roughness scales is due to the change in the incident angle coupled with the shortening of the effective wavelength $\lambda_e = \lambda/(2\sin\theta)$. At 4 GHz the angular region dominated by the large-scale roughness becomes narrower in angular width, allowing the midsize roughness to dominate in the midangular range and the small-scale roughness to dominate at large angles. Although all three roughness scales are present at all times, shorter incident wavelength allows greater influence from smaller roughness scales. At 8 GHz it seems possible to ignore the influence of the larger roughness scales beyond 15 degrees, or we may say that the large-scale roughness is being filtered out by the shorter incident wavelength over this angular range. This shifting of dominance in backscattering by an effectively shorter wavelength is an illustration of the *wavelength filtering effect.*

For horizontal polarization, the shift in dominance toward smaller roughness scales at larger incident angles with higher frequencies, or shorter wavelengths, is similar to that of vertical polarization at 2 and 4 GHz for the large and the midsize roughness scales as shown in Figure 2.7. Unlike vertical polarization the smallest scale roughness, however, is unable to dominate in the 60–70-degree range at 4 GHz. Instead, the contribution to backscattering is about the same for both the midsize and the smallest scale roughness over 45 to 70 degrees. At 8 GHz the smallest scale is the major contributor beyond 30 degrees. However, the midsize scale continues to influence backscattering at a significant level over all angles. This is the major difference between the two polarizations for the case we are investigating. It appears that a further increase in frequency will allow the smallest scale roughness to dominate backscattering. This means that the transition in dominance of backscattering from the large to the smaller scales of roughness is slower for horizontal polarization. In most applications the surface parameters are not known. For unknown surfaces in modeling this will call for an effective roughness scale to fit the data. Note that although all the changes in dominance by different scales of roughness are gradual, the changes in dominance are much clearer in vertical polarization than horizontal polarization.

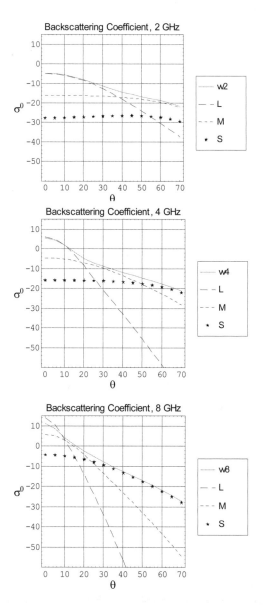

Figure 2.6 An illustration of the effects of different roughness scales on backscattering when the incident angle or frequency increases for vertical polarization. Results indicate that as frequency or the incident angle increases, backscattering will be dominated by smaller roughness scales for a multiscale rough surface.

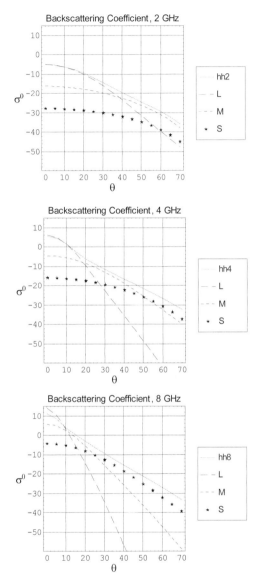

Figure 2.7 An illustration of the effects of different roughness scales on backscattering when the incident angle or frequency increases for horizontal polarization. Results indicate that as frequency or the incident angle increases, backscattering will be dominated by smaller roughness scales for a multiscale rough surface, but the change here is slower as compared to vertical polarization.

Looking at the backscattering curve by the large-scale roughness alone, we expect that it should approach the geometric optics (GO) model as frequency increases further. At 10 GHz, $k\sigma = 0.84$, the backscatter curve is in agreement with the GO over the high signal level region from about -5 dB to 15 dB as shown in Figure 2.8. Further increases in frequency should result in agreement over a wider range of the incident angle. A correct model must show such a result for single-scale rough surface.

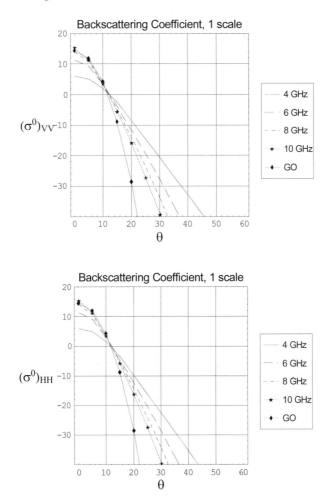

Figure 2.8 An illustration of how backscattering from a single-scale, Gaussian-correlated rough surface approaches the geometric optics model in the 0–15-degree region as frequency increases.

Next, we consider the two-scale surface including only the first two roughness scales. Recomputing backscattering over the same frequency range as in Figure 2.8 for both VV and HH polarizations shows that the shapes of the scattering curves are completely different from the corresponding GO as shown in Figure 2.9, because the additional roughness scale has caused the correlation function to differ substantially from the Gaussian shape. Physically, the additional roughness scale has altered the phase of the scattered wave. Near normal incidence scattering at 10 GHz actually peaks up instead of following a bell-shaped curve.

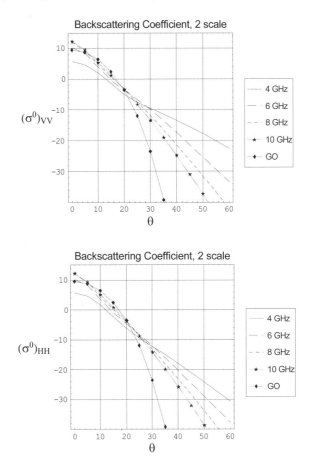

Figure 2.9 An illustration of how backscattering from a two-scale rough surface differs from the geometric optics model in the 0–25-degree region as frequency increases to 10 GHz where $k\sigma = 0.988$.

Theoretically, for a multiscale surface when the incident wavelength is about one-half or less of the smallest correlation length on the surface, backscattering must again approach the GO prediction. This is indeed the case if we increase the incident frequency further for the two-scale surface in Figure 2.9. Such a result is shown in Figure 2.10 where we see convergence toward GO prediction in the angular region 0 to 25 degrees at 22 GHz. However, while the result is consistent with modeling prediction, it is physically incorrect, because as seen in Figures 2.6 and 2.7 the large-scale roughness should not have any impact beyond 20 degrees at 8 GHz. Certainly, at 18 GHz and beyond, large-scale roughness is not responsible for scattering and should not be included.

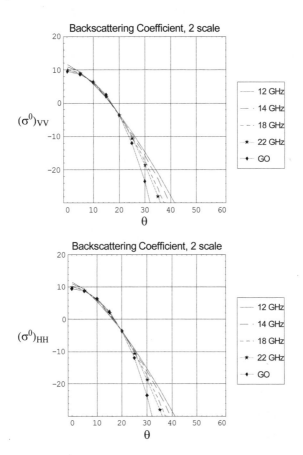

Figure 2.10 An illustration of how backscattering from a two-scale rough surface approaches the geometric optics model in the 0–25-degree region as frequency increases.

Finally, with the three-scale surface, backscattering over the frequency range 4–10 GHz should deviate substantially from the GO prediction at 10 GHz for both vertical and horizontal polarizations as shown in Figure 2.11. The small-scale roughness that rides on the large-scale roughness is controlling backscattering because phase changes on the scattered wave are controlled to the small-scale roughness. For the scattered wave to sense the presence of the large wave, the phase changes must follow the large wave, which is not the case here. Thus, the presence of small roughness scales large enough to alter the phase of the incident wave is the reason why backscattering does not approach the GO. For a multiscale surface with many small roughness scales such as the sea surface, as we increase frequency, the wavelength filtering phenomenon will exclude wave facets larger than a wavelength. As a result, the scattered wave is responding to smaller ripples riding on the large facets, so that $k\sigma$ remains less than one. *In conclusion, only in the absence of small roughness scales will backscattering approach GO and show a sharp drop over large angles of incidence when $k\sigma$ is large.*

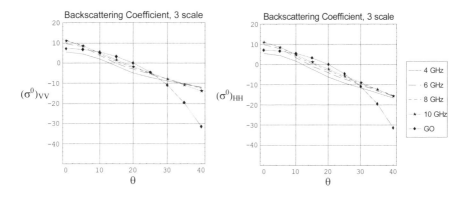

Figure 2.11 An illustration of how backscattering from the three-scale, Gaussian-correlated rough surface deviates from the geometric optics model in the 0–25-degree region as frequency increases.

To verify that the above study is not a special property of the multiscale Gaussian-correlated surface, we repeat similar calculations using the same surface parameter values with the *n*-power correlation when $n = 4$. Results for this three-scale surface are shown in Figure 2.12 for vertical polarization. The large-scale roughness is dominating over all angles at 2 GHz. Thus, at 2 GHz the scattered electromagnetic wave does not contain detectable information about the presence of the smaller roughness scales, and it is not possible to know that this is a multiscale surface. This much slower drop-off with angle relative to the Gaussian case is due to the use of the four-power correlation function. In fact, the slow drop-off with angle holds for all three scales of roughness. At 4 GHz backscattering drops off faster with the incident angle for the large-scale roughness but not the smaller scales of roughness. Thus, the midsize roughness becomes an important contributor to backscattering beyond 30 degrees, but the smallest scale remains unimportant. At 8 GHz backscattering from the large-scale roughness drops off even faster so that when the incident angle exceeds 20 degrees, contribution is dominated by the midsize roughness. Beyond 30 degrees, contribution from the large-scale roughness may be ignored, while the smallest scale roughness becomes the largest contributor after 55 degrees. Thus, the shift in dominance toward smaller roughness scales with frequency remains true, but the speed of shifting is much slower than with the multiscale Gaussian correlation. Clearly, the surface correlation function has an impact on both the angular shape of the backscattering curve and the speed of shifting toward dependence on smaller roughness scales as frequency increases. It is also evident that a multifrequency system is needed to sense different scales of roughness.

Apparently, all correlation functions decaying more slowly over large lag distances than the Gaussian will have a slower shift toward dependence on smaller roughness scales as frequency increases. This is because such a correlation function allows a larger contribution at large angles of incidence than the Gaussian function. For horizontal polarization this shifting is even slower than the corresponding vertical polarization as shown in Figure 2.13 where the smallest roughness scale cannot exceed the midsize roughness in contributing to backscattering even at 8 GHz. However, it remains similar to vertical polarization in that the midsize roughness is making a dominating contribution at 4 GHz after 40 degrees, and at 8 GHz the smallest scale is making a significant contribution to backscattering after 35 degrees. We have noticed that both the correlation function and the polarization can affect wavelength filtering, but the effect of wavelength filtering is always present.

For a four-power correlated surface with only the large-scale roughness, convergence in backscattering to the GO predictions for both vertical and horizontal polarizations is also a certainty. In Figure 2.14 we show how this happens by computing backscattering at 6, 8, 10, and 14 GHz. At 14 GHz, we can see that above -10 dB there is a good agreement with the GO predictions. Such a surface has a rms slope four times larger than the Gaussian-correlated surface with the same surface rms height and correlation length. Hence, it is a physically rougher surface.

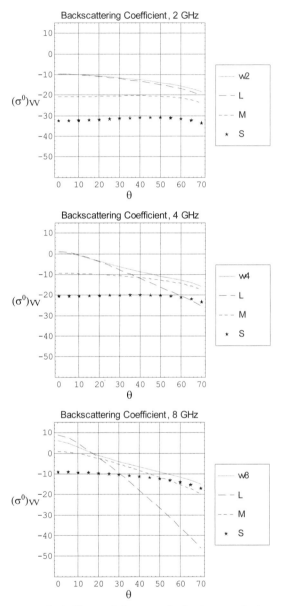

Figure 2.12 As frequency or the incident angle increases, the dominance on backscattering will be shifted toward smaller roughness scales for a multiscale rough surface. This shifting is faster with the Gaussian-correlated than the four-power correlated surface.

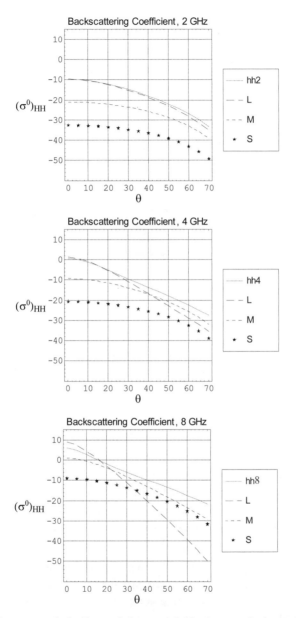

Figure 2.13 As frequency or the incident angle increases, the dominance on backscattering will be shifted toward smaller roughness scales for a multiscale rough surface. This shifting is faster with the Gaussian-correlated than the four-power correlated surface especially for horizontal polarization.

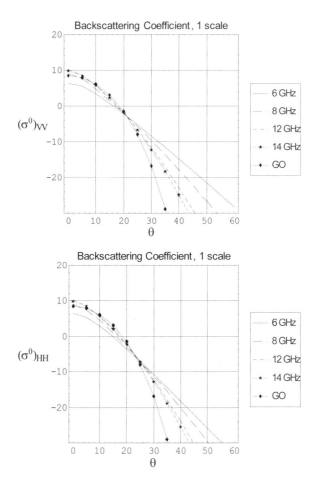

Figure 2.14 As frequency increases, backscattering from the single-scale, four-power correlated sur-face converges toward the geometric optics prediction similar to the Gaussian-correlated surface, except it happens at a higher frequency, 14 GHz, where $k\sigma = 1.17$.

As expected when the surface is made up of the large and the midsize roughness scales, the convergence shown in Figure 2.14 can no longer occur at 14 GHz. The phase of the scattered wave is now modified by the midsize roughness and the correlation function no longer has a simple four-power shape. This result is illustrated in Figure 2.15. The change in the scattering pattern from the single-scale case is very similar to the corresponding two-scale Gaussian-correlated surface.

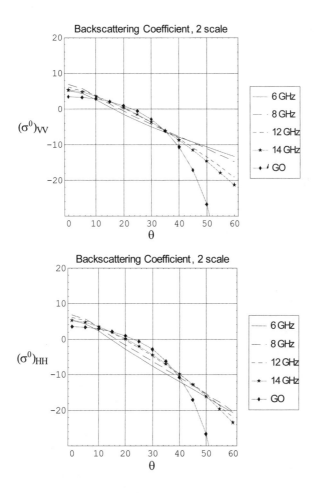

Figure 2.15 The addition of another roughness scale makes the overall correlation function closer to an exponential, thus causing a small peak to occur near nadir and the backscattering curve to drop off more slowly at large angles. This additional roughness scale prevented scattering from converging to geometric optics.

In summary, model calculations beyond $k\sigma \geq 1$ should show convergence toward the GO for single-scale surfaces as is required. For multiscale surfaces, convergence toward the GO cannot occur due to the presence of the smaller scale roughness. Furthermore, when $k\sigma > 1$, the computed result may not be applicable in practice because the wavelength filtering effect has to be accounted for. As we explained earlier, this means that both σ and L need be reduced to fit higher frequency measurements from multiscale surfaces.

2.4 APPROXIMATION OF BACKSCATTERING FROM A MULTISCALE SURFACE USING THE MODIFIED EXPONENTIAL CORRELATION FUNCTION (MEXP)

In this section we want to show how closely can we approximate the backscattering from a multiscale surface with a correlation function defined by (1.2) and then another multiscale surface defined by (1.3) by the backscattering from a surface with a modified exponential correlation function (mexp), which is the inverse Bessel transform of (2.5) repeated below as (2.11),

$$\sigma^{2n} w^{(n)}(\kappa) = \frac{n \sigma^{2n} L^2}{[n^2 + \kappa^2 L^2]^{1.5}} \exp\left[-(z \kappa L)^2\right] \tag{2.11}$$

Before we begin let us first compare (1.2) with the mexp by taking the inverse Bessel transform of (2.11) with $n = 1$, $L = 0.65 L_1$, and $z = 0.07$. A comparison between normalized (1.2) and the mexp is shown in Figure 2.16. An exponential function with $L = 0.75 L_1$ is also plotted for reference purpose. It is well known that a Gaussian function has a sharp drop-off while an exponential does not. Hence, under medium-frequency conditions over small lag distances, the mexp should be smaller than the multiscale Gaussian function in order to balance the difference between the two functions in the tail region. This is why L should be significantly less than L_1. Clearly, mexp is a better fit to the multiscale Gaussian correlation near the origin than the exponential function. It is also clear that the difference between the two functions is very large at the tail end. Hence, we do not expect mexp to work under low-frequency conditions for Gaussian correlated surfaces.

A key point to remember in this example is that we are talking about approximating backscattering from a multiscale surface. Under sufficiently low-frequency conditions, the multiscale surface may act as a single-scale surface defined by a specific correlation. If so, there is nothing to approximate. At higher frequencies when scattering is coming from more than one scale of roughness, then we can use (2.11) to approximate backscattering from such a surface. For a real sea surface at microwave frequencies, use of (2.11) to approximate backscattering is always possible, because many roughness scales are available and larger than the microwave wavelength.

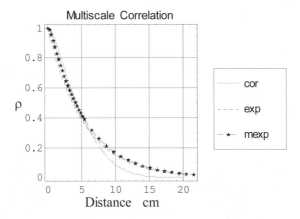

Figure 2.16 A comparison of the normalized multiscale Gaussian correlation defined by (1.2) denoted as corps with the mexp defined by the inverse Bessel transform of (2.11).

Backscattering calculations using the two correlation functions in Figure 2.16 with the same σ are shown in Figure 2.17. At 2 GHz we let $L = 0.61L_1$ and $z = 0.1$. As expected there is a clear disagreement in angular trend over a small incident angle region, where the large-scale roughness is dominating for both polarizations. This is because the correlation function mexp is exponentially based, while the multiscale correlation is a Gaussian function.

At 4 GHz we use $L = 0.65L_1$ and change z to 0.12. The agreement for both vertical and horizontal polarizations is much better, indicating that it is possible to approximate backscattering from a multiscale Gaussian surface with the mexp when contribution to backscattering is coming from more than one scale of roughness. Note that there is a small disagreement in the 10–15-degree region, which reflects the basic difference in the properties of the correlation functions. Such differences are not noticeable in practical measurements because of inherent data fluctuations in field measurements.

What we have done is to choose x in $L = xL_1$ to fit the return at normal incidence and choose z to fit the return near the 50–60-degree region. The end result is that we miss the return between 10 and 30 degrees at 2 GHz and a smaller angular region at 4 GHz. Since the correlation functions are basically different, a difference in backscattering over some angular region is unavoidable. As we shall see in the Section 2.5, better agreement in backscattering is possible when the correlation function used in the approximation shares some common properties with the multiscale correlation function being approximated.

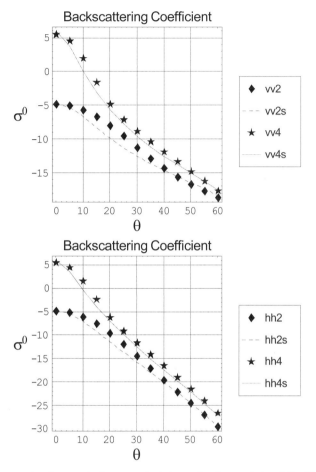

Figure 2.17 A comparison between backscatter calculations using the correlation defined by (1.2) versus using mexp at 2 and 4 GHz. As expected there is a large disagreement over angular regions where the large-scale roughness alone dominates scattering. The notation vv2 means vertically polarized backscattering at 2 GHz by the multiscale surface, and the additional "s" means simulated backscattering with the mexp.

At 6 GHz, we let $L = 0.65L_1$ and $z = 0.11$, and at 8 GHz, we let $L = 0.68L_1$ and $z = 0.106$. In Figure 2.18 there is an overall agreement between the backscattering calculations. In particular, the agreement at normal incidence and over large angles is very good. However, the approximated backscattering has more exponential influence in the mid-angle region, and the backscattering signal is lower than those computed from the multiscale Gaussian correlation.

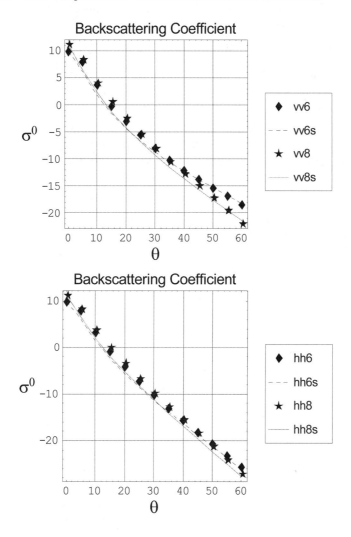

Figure 2.18 A comparison between backscatter calculations using the correlation defined by (1.2) versus using the mexp at 6 and 8 GHz. The idea that backscatter from a multiscale Gaussian-correlated surface can be estimated using the mexp seems to work. The notation vv6 means vertically polarized backscattering at 6 GHz by the multiscale surface, and the additional "s" means approximate backscattering with the mexp.

In practice, the correlation functions of natural surfaces are not known, but we know it is common for these surfaces to contain more than one scale of roughness. The mexp and expl correlation functions we introduced allow us to analyze unknown multiscale surfaces and obtain the effective roughness parameters responsible for backscattering.

Next, we consider backscattering from the surface defined by the two-power multiscale correlation function given by (1.3). The behavior of this correlation function is in between the Gaussian and the exponential functions. Hence, we believe a better agreement in backscattering is possible with the multiscale two-power correlation function than the multiscale Gaussian correlation. By selecting $L = 0.6L_1$, $z = 0.001$ at 2 GHz and $L = 0.6L_1$, $z = 0.05$ at 4 GHz, we obtain the following match for the backscattering coefficients in Figure 2.19.

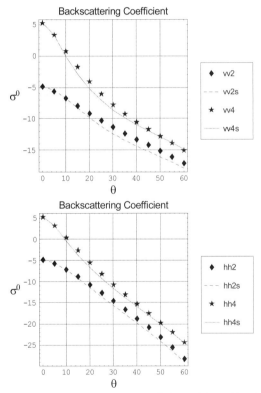

Figure 2.19 A comparison between the backscattering coefficients of the multiscale two-power correlated surface and the modified exponentially correlated surface at frequencies of 2 and 4 GHz for vertical and horizontal polarizations.

Note that the choice of a very small z at 2 GHz means that we are actually using a simple exponential function at that frequency. Even at 2 GHz the agreement between the backscattering coefficients computed from using the multiscale correlation function given by (1.3) and the mexp correlation is quite good, especially in angular trends for both vertical and horizontal polarizations. The maximum difference in level is around 1 dB, which is normally within measurement error. A point worthy of notice is that the multiscale correlation function is able to generate backscattering at a higher level than a simple exponential correlation function at large angles of incidence. Since no other single scale correlation function can produce a higher return signal than the exponential, the higher level serves as an indication that the real surface is a multiscale surface.

At 4 GHz even better agreement between the backscattering coefficients is obtained in both the overall level and angular trends for vertical and horizontal polarizations, especially over the small angle region close to normal incidence. We know that generally a higher frequency allows backscattering contributions to come from more roughness scales, which provides one reason why the agreement is better than those at 2 GHz. Another reason is because the multiscale two-power correlation function is closer in functional shape than the multiscale Gaussian function to the mexp correlation function. Further evidence that the shape of the approximating correlation function also plays a role in approximating backscattering is provided in Section 2.5.

At 6 and 8 GHz we use $L = 0.65L_1$. We set $z = 0.064$ at 6 GHz and $z = 0.066$ at 8 GHz in the modified exponential function. A larger z at 6 and 8 GHz reflects the fact that a pure exponential function is not an appropriate function to use at high frequencies. A comparison of the computed backscattering coefficients with those based on the multiscale two-power correlation is shown in Figure 2.20. The computed backscattering coefficients show a strong exponential character in the midangular region, leading to a lower estimate of the backscattering signal than those provided by the multiscale two-power correlation. However, the angular trends and signal levels at both large and small angles of incidence are in good agreement.

The analysis in this section shows that the mexp or its spectra defined in (2.11) is useful for estimating backscattering from all multiscale surfaces, regardless of the actual correlation property of the individual roughness scales. For natural surfaces such as a sea surface, waves of many sizes larger or smaller than the microwave wavelength are always present. Hence, the type of disagreement we saw at 2 GHz is not likely to occur in dealing with backscattering from natural surfaces. The mexp is therefore a useful approximation to the portion of the true correlation function responsible for backscattering from multiscale rough surfaces.

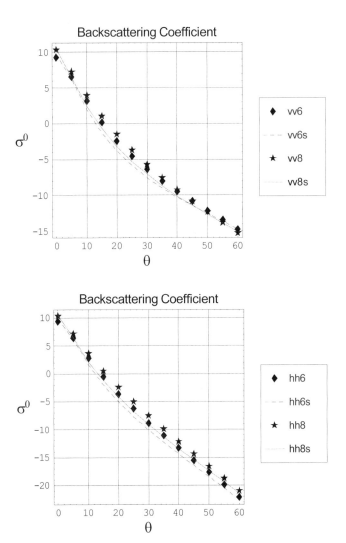

Figure 2.20 A comparison between the backscattering coefficients of the multiscale two-power correlated surface and the modified exponentially correlated surface at frequencies of 6 and 8 GHz for vertical and horizontal polarizations. The notation vv6 means vertically polarized backscattering at 6 GHz by the multiscale surface, and the additional "s" means approximate backscattering with the mexp.

2.5 APPROXIMATION OF BACKSCATTERING FROM A MULTISCALE SURFACE USING THE EXPONENTIAL-LIKE CORRELATION FUNCTION (EXPL)

We have shown in Chapter 1 that the correlation functions, expl and mexp, can take on a similar shape over some range of the lag distance depending on the choice of their correlation parameters. In this section we want to investigate whether the use of the expl correlation function can also approximate backscattering from multiscale rough surfaces defined by (1.2) and (1.3). If so, what is the difference that might appear due to this correlation function as opposed to the mexp used in Section 2.4?

We shall begin with a comparison of the backscattering coefficients computed with the multiscale Gaussian correlation function given by (1.2) and the expl. Similar to the mexp function, expl contains a correlation parameter r and a correlation length, L. At 2 GHz we choose $L = 0.49L_1$ to fit backscattering at normal incidence and $r = 6$ cm to fit the backscattering signal at large angles of incidence. The large r value is chosen to have a large Gaussian influence at 2 GHz. At 4 GHz we let $L = 0.6L_1$ and reduce r substantially to 2.7 cm. The computed results are shown in Figure 2.21. We see that very good agreement is obtained over small angles of incidence where backscattering takes on a bell-shaped curve for both vertical and horizontal polarizations. The agreement is clearly better than the one shown for the mexp correlation in Figure 2.17. Apparently, the reason why better results are obtained here is because the expl function contains more Gaussian characteristics than the mexp function, when we let r larger than L. When instead we let L be larger than r, then expl behaves more like an exponential over a large lag distance. There is a minor difference in backscattering (less than 1 dB) around 35 to 45 degrees in vertical polarization. While this minor difference is generally not detectable experimentally and is not present in horizontal polarization, it does show a slight difference in the angular trends.

At 4 GHz the overall agreement is also better than those shown in Figure 2.17 for both vertical and horizontal polarizations. By itself, except for a small angular region around 25 degrees, where it is off by 1 dB, the agreement is very good everywhere else in signal level and angular trends for both vertical and horizontal polarizations as shown in Figure 2.21. The good agreement near vertical incidence is due to the expl, which behaves like a Gaussian function near the origin and over small lag distances. The disagreement may be due to the transition region where the correlation function is turning into an exponential function over large lag distances.

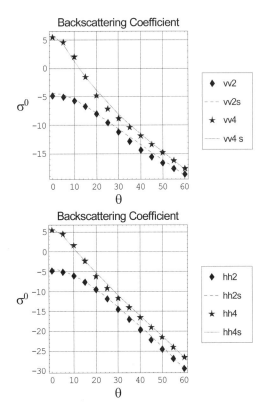

Figure 2.21 A comparison between the backscattering coefficients of the multiscale Gaussian correlated surface and a surface with an expl at frequencies of 2 and 4 GHz for vertical and horizontal polarizations. The notation vv2 means vertically polarized backscattering at 2 GHz from the multiscale
surface and the additional "s" means approximate backscattering with the expl. At 2 GHz, $L = 3.43$
cm and $r = 6$ cm. At 4 GHz, $L = 4.2$ cm and $r = 2.7$ cm.

At 6 and 8 GHz we let $L = 0.65L_1$ and set $r = 2.2$ cm at 6 GHz and
$r = 2.6$ cm at 8 GHz in the expl. The computed backscattering coefficients and
comparisons with the backscattering coefficients based on the multiscale Gaussian
correlation function are shown in Figure 2.22. The large bending in the mid-angle
region that appeared in Figure 2.18 does not show up here in Figure 2.22. Again,
this is because the expl has more Gaussian properties than the mexp. As a result, a
better overall fit is realized here at both 6 and 8 GHz and for both vertical and
horizontal polarizations. Note that for vertical polarization the backscattering

curves at 6 and 8 GHz cross each other near 23 degrees before the 8-GHz curve goes higher than the 6-GHz curve at normal incidence. Of course, it also goes lower than the 6-GHz curve at large angles, which is quite obvious because of the large separation between them. In horizontal polarization, a similar situation occurs. Here, the two backscattering curves at 6 and 8 GHz cross each other around 30 degrees, but they do not separate very far from each other at either normal incidence or large angles. The maximum difference is less than 1.5 dB. However, the approximate backscattering curves are able to track these behaviors, indicating that the expl is also a suitable correlation function to approximate backscattering from multiscale surfaces.

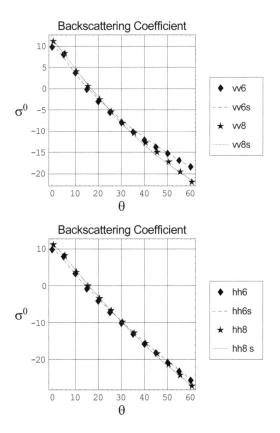

Figure 2.22 A comparison between the backscattering coefficients of the multiscale Gaussian-correlated surface and the surface with an expl at frequencies of 6 and 8 GHz. At 6 GHz, $L = 4.55$ cm and $r = 2.2$ cm, and at 8 GHz, $L = 4.55$ cm and $r = 2.6$ cm.

The reason why the expl correlation function is able to show a better agreement in backscattering than the mexp correlation function is that the multiscale correlation function being approximated is a combination of Gaussian functions. If the multiscale correlation function consisted of more exponential-type functions, the results would be different. The multiscale two-power correlation function consists of non-Gaussian functions, and these functions are differentiable at the origin. We want to show below how the expl correlation function performs in such a case at 2, 4, 6, and 8 GHz.

Next, we want to simulate backscattering from the multiscale two-power correlated surface with the expl correlation function. At 2 GHz we choose $L = 0.5L_1$ to fit the backscattering from the multiscale surface at normal incidence and set $r = 4.5$ cm to fit the backscattering at an incident angle of 60 degrees. At 4 GHz we carry out a similar procedure and obtain $L = 0.6L_1$ and $r = 1.8$ cm. The comparisons between the backscattering coefficients for vertical and horizontal polarizations are shown in Figure 2.23. At 2 GHz in Figure 2.19 there is separation between the approximating backscattering curve and the computed backscattering for vertical polarization between 20 and 60 degrees. This separation is gone in Figure 2.23 showing a much better agreement. Similar improvement in agreement also holds for horizontal polarization in Figure 2.23. At 4 GHz in Figure 2.19 there is also some disagreement in the region between 10 and 35 degrees. In Figure 2.23 the approximating curve is in excellent agreement with the computed backscattering coefficient. Hence, the matching between the backscattering coefficients at both 2 and 4 GHz is better than the corresponding comparisons shown in Figure 2.19 in terms of the overall signal level and angular trends for both vertical and horizontal polarizations. This is because the multiscale two-power correlation function has properties closer to the expl correlation function than the multiscale Gaussian correlation function. As expected, the agreement at 4 GHz is better than that at 2 GHz, because more roughness scales are involved.

At higher frequencies, 6 and 8 GHz, there is not much separation between the computed backscattering signals based on the multiscale two-power correlation function as we have seen in Figure 2.20. However, there is a definite angular trend at 6 GHz that is different from the one at 8 GHz. For vertical polarizations the two backscattering angular trends cross each other in the region near 45 to 50 degrees, and the maximum separation is generally less than 1.2 dB. For horizontal polarization there is no crossover, and the 8-GHz backscattering curve is always higher at every incident angle than the 6-GHz curve. The maximum separation is less than 1.3 dB. Despite these small differences the approximating backscattering curves are able to track the said angular trends in Figure 2.24, indicating that the approximation using the expl correlation function is valid. The agreement is again better than those shown in Figure 2.20, where the approximating curves miss the computed backscattering by about 1 dB in the mid-angular range.

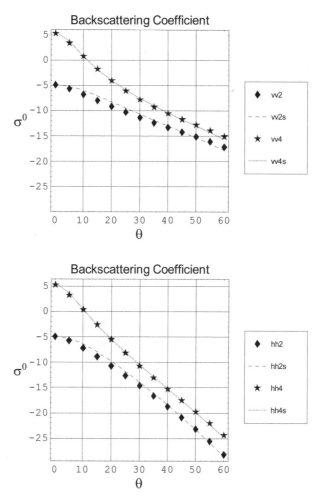

Figure 2.23 A comparison between the backscattering coefficients of the two-power correlated surface and the surface with an expl at frequencies of 2 and 4 GHz for vertical and horizontal polarizations. The notation vv2 means vertically polarized backscattering at 2 GHz from the multiscale surface and the additional "s" means approximate backscattering with the expl. At 2 GHz, $L = 3.5$ cm, $r = 4.5$ cm, and at 4 GHz, $L = 4.2$ cm and $r = 1.8$ cm.

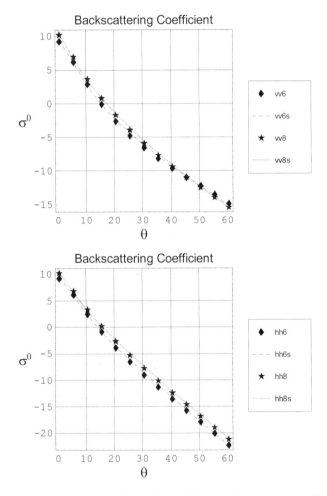

Figure 2.24 A comparison between the backscattering coefficients of the two-power correlated surface and the surface with an expl at frequencies of 6 and 8 GHz for vertical and horizontal polarizations. The notation vv6 means vertically polarized backscattering at 6 GHz from the multiscale surface and the additional "s" means approximate backscattering with the expl. At 6 GHz, $L = 4.2$ cm and $r = 1.4$ cm, and at 8 GHz, $L = 4.55$ cm and $r = 1.3$ cm.

The above studies have indicated that it is possible to simulate backscattering from a multiscale rough surface with both expl and mexp functions. The somewhat better agreements realized by the expl correlation function could be due to the fact that both correlation functions given in (1.2) and (1.3) are Gaussian-like near the origin. In Section 2.6, we shall see how the mexp correlation function performs, if it is to simulate a multiscale correlation function consisting of three functions that are in between the exponential and the Gaussian as

$$R(\xi) = \sigma^2 \rho(\xi) = [\sigma_1^2 e^{-(\xi/L_1)^{1.5}} + \sigma_2^2 e^{-(\xi/L_2)^{1.5}} + \sigma_3^2 e^{-(\xi/L_3)^{1.5}}], \xi \geq 0 \qquad (2.12)$$

2.6 APPROXIMATION OF BACKSCATTERING FROM ANOTHER MULTISCALE SURFACE

Both correlation functions, mexp and expl, are variations from a simple exponential function, but expl is differentiable at the origin and has shown better capability in approximating backscattering from the multiscale rough surfaces with correlation functions given by (1.2) and (1.3). This is because both (1.2) and (1.3) behave like a Gaussian function near the origin. When the correlation function of a multiscale surface is a combination of exponential functions defined by (2.12), we expect the mexp correlation function to do well in approximating backscattering from this type of surface similar to the expl function approximating backscattering from surfaces characterized by (1.2) or (1.3). The reason is that the multiscale correlation function in (2.12) does not have the Gaussian property, which is not possessed by the mexp correlation function.

We use the same parameter values as we did in the previous examples for multiscale surfaces. For convenience we restate them as follows: $\sigma_1 = 0.4$, $\sigma_2 = 0.25$, $\sigma_3 = 0.13$, $L_1 = 7$, $L_2 = 3$, $L_3 = 1.5$, and $\varepsilon = 16$, where all lengths are in centimeters and ε is the relative dielectric constant of the surface. The computed backscattering coefficients for vertical and horizontal polarizations at 2 and 4 GHz with the multiscale exponential correlation function given by (2.12) are shown in Figure 2.25 in symbols of diamonds for 2 GHz and stars for 4 GHz. The approximated backscattering using the mexp correlation function is denoted in solid lines for 4 GHz and in dashed lines for 2 GHz in Figure 2.25, where a very good agreement between the computed and simulated backscattering signals in trends and signal level is evident over all incident angles and for both vertical and horizontal polarizations. The agreement is clearly much better than in Figure 2.17 where we used the mexp correlation function to simulate backscattering from a multiscale Gaussian-correlated surface. This shows that for non-Gaussian-correlated surfaces, the mexp correlation can perform very well.

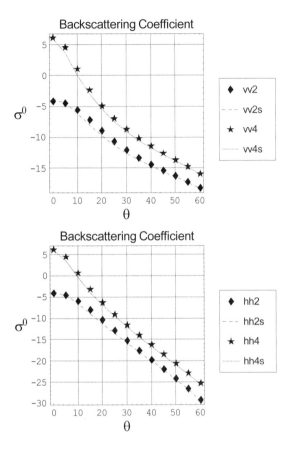

Figure 2.25 A comparison between the backscattering coefficients of the multiscale surface defined by (2.12) and the surface with an mexp correlation function at frequencies of 2 and 4 GHz. At 2 GHz, $L = 4.76$ cm and $z = 0.01$, and at 4 GHz, $L = 4.55$ cm and $z = 0.08$.

Next, we show a similar comparison at 6 and 8 GHz in Figure 2.25. Here again, the simulated backscattering coefficients are in better agreement with those computed using (2.12) than the illustrations shown in Figure 2.18. The angular trends are in excellent agreement in all four cases shown in Figure 2.25. Hence, the use of the mexp correlation function to simulate backscattering from multiscale rough surfaces is a valid approach, especially for centrosymmetric correlation functions that are not differentiable at the origin, which is the case with (2.12). In view of all the cases we have considered, a closer agreement in angular trends is an indication that the correlation function of the multiscale surface possesses similar properties as the correlation function used for simulation. This means that if we have to choose between the two correlation functions, mexp and expl, while carrying out a simulation, we need to select the one that produces the best trend agreement if both simulations are within 1 dB of the backscattering to be simulated.

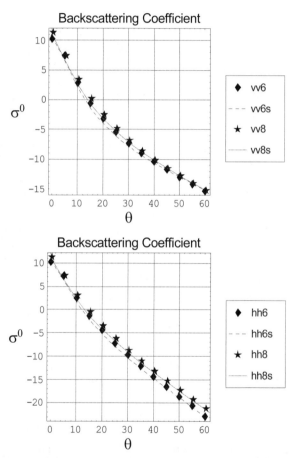

Figure 2.26 A comparison between the backscattering coefficients of the multiscale Gaussian-correlated surface and the surface with an expl at frequencies of 6 and 8 GHz for vertical and horizontal polarizations. The notation vv6 means vertically polarized backscattering at 6 GHz from the multiscale surface, and the additional "s" means approximate backscattering with the expl. At 6 GHz, L = 4.9 cm and z = 0.06 cm, and at 8 GHz, L = 4.76 cm and z = 0.06 cm.

In this section we have selected a multiscale correlation function that is not differentiable at the origin for simulation. We have seen that the correlation function, mexp, can produce good simulation results because it is also a correlation function that is not differentiable at the origin. On the other hand, the correlation function, expl, is a differentiable function at the origin. This difference in correlation property can cause disagreement somewhere, if we use it to simulate backscattering from multiscale rough surfaces with nondifferentiable correlation. When we examine backscattering signals from a surface with a differentiable correlation function, the signal level is on average the same or higher than those from a surface with a nondifferentiable correlation function. This is shown in Figures 2.17 and 2.18. In particular, at 2 and 4 GHz there is a clear disagreement in angular trend and signal level in Figure 2.17, although the disagreement is not very large. At 6 and 8 GHz the simulated backscattering with mexp is on average lower over most of the angular range as shown in Figure 2.18. When we apply the expl correlation function to approximate backscattering from the multiscale surface with the correlation function defined in (2.12), we should expect to see disagreement in level and angular trend also at 2 GHz. In this case, the approximate backscattering signal is on average higher over most of the incident angles, although the maximum signal level difference is less than 1 dB. At higher frequencies, overall agreement looks better in both signal level and angular trends than at 2 GHz. However, as expected, the approximate backscattering curve is on average higher, although the amount may not be detectable experimentally. A comparison of the backscattering signals at 2, 4, 6, and 8 GHz for vertical and horizontal polarizations is shown in Figure 2.27.

In Sections 2.4 and 2.5 we have demonstrated that the difference in the properties of correlation functions can cause disagreements in angular trends and signal level in approximating the backscattering signal from a multiscale rough surface, depending upon whether the correlation function of the multiscale surface is differentiable. If the surface correlation function is differentiable and we use mexp to approximate its backscattering, the estimation usually comes out lower. On the other hand, if we use the expl correlation function to estimate backscattering from a surface with a nondifferentiable correlation function, then the estimate comes out higher on average. In performing an approximation we consider it applicable when the difference between the approximation and what is being approximated is smaller than what can be detected experimentally. Thus, we believe that the two correlation functions, mexp and expl, are useful functions for approximating backscattering in practice and that one is more suitable than the other, depending on the property of the correlation function of the surface.

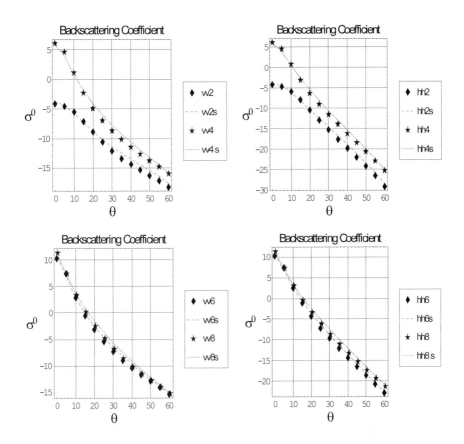

Figure 2.27 A comparison between the backscattering coefficients of the multiscale Gaussian-correlated surface and the surface with an expl at frequencies of 2, 4, 6, and 8 GHz for vertical and horizontal polarizations. The notation vv2 means vertically polarized backscattering at 2 GHz from the multiscale surface, and the additional "s" means approximate backscattering with the expl. At 2 GHz, $L = 4.55$ cm and $r = 1.3$ cm, and at 4 GHz, $L = 4.41$ cm and $r = 1.8$ cm. At 6 and 8 GHz, $L = 4.83$ cm, while $r = 1.3$ cm at 6 GHz and $r = 1.1$ cm at 8 GHz.

2.7 CONCLUDING REMARKS

The main points in this chapter may be summarized as follows:

1. The backscattering model presented in Section 2.2 contains the classical surface scattering models, the Kirchhoff and the small perturbation models, as special cases. In the high-frequency limit, it is in agreement with the GO.

2. The sources of backscattering vary continuously with frequency and the incident angle. In the high-frequency limit the surface slope distribution controls backscattering, but for multiscale surfaces the presence of small roughness scales will prevent backscattering from reaching the high-frequency limit. Hence, in practice, reaching the high-frequency limit is not a common occurrence.

3. As frequency and the incident angle increase, backscattering from a multiscale surface is dominated by smaller and smaller roughness scales, because the incident wavelength and the effective wavelength are getting shorter.

4. For a single-scale rough surface, its backscattering angular curve is controlled by its correlation function. For a multiscale surface, the effect of the correlation function of the largest scale appears in the low incident angle region, generally between 0 and 30 degrees. The width of this low-angle region decreases with an increase in frequency. Hence, it requires a multifrequency system to detect both the correlation effect and the different roughness scales.

5. The possibility of using the expl and mexp correlation functions to approximate a portion of the true correlation function of a multiscale surface in computing backscattering is demonstrated in Sections 2.4–2.6. For multiscale surfaces with correlation functions differentiable at the origin, the expl correlation function can provide a better fit than the mexp correlation. The converse is true in dealing with surfaces with correlation functions that are nondifferentiable at the origin. Thus, both of these correlation functions, expl and mexp, are needed in studying backscattering from multiscale rough surfaces.

6. The correlation parameters, z and r, in the proposed expl and mexp functions can lower the backscattering level at large angles of incidence in the mid- to high-frequency regions relative to a simple exponential correlation.

7. In dealing with an unknown multiscale surface it is better to try both correlation functions, mexp and expl, because while both can fit the measurements, one of them will provide a better trend agreement than the other.

References

Beckmann, P., and A. Spizzichino, *The Scattering of Electromagnetic Waves from Rough Surfaces,* New York: Macmillan, 1963.

Brown, G. S., "The Validity of Shadowing Corrections in Rough Surface Scattering," *Radio Science,* Vol. 19, No. 6, 1984, pp. 1461–1468.

DeRoo, R. D., and F. T. Ulaby, "Bistatic Specular Scattering from Rough Dielectric Surfaces," *IEEE Transactions on Antennas and Propagation,* Vol. 42, No. 2, February 1994, pp. 1743–1755.

Fung, A. K., *Microwave Scattering and Emission Models and Their Applications,* Norwood, MA: Artech House, 1994.

Fung, A. K., and K. S. Chen, *Microwave Scattering and Emission Models for Users,* Norwood, MA: Artech House, 2009.

Fung, A. K., and K. S. Chen, "Dependence of the Surface Backscattering Coefficients on Roughness, Frequency and Polarization States," *Int. J. Remote Sensing,* Vol. 13, No. 9, 1992 , pp. 1663–1680.

Fung, A. K., W. Y. Liu, K. S. Chen, and M. K. Tsay, "An Improved IEM Model for Bistatic Scattering from Rough Surface," *JEWA,* Vol. 16, No. 5, 2002, pp. 689–702.

Hauck, B., F. T. Ulaby, and R. D. DeRoo, "Polarimetric Bistatic Measurement Facility for Point and Distributed Targets," *IEEE Antennas and Propagation Magazine,* Vol. 40, No. 1, February 1998, pp. 31–41.

Hsieh, C. Y., et al., "A Further Study of the IEM Surface Scattering Model," *IEEE Trans. Geosci. Remote Sensing,* Vol. 35, No. 4, July 1997, pp. 901–909.

Hsieh, C. Y., and A. K. Fung, "Application of an Extended IEM to Multiple Surface Scattering and Backscatter Enhancement," *J. Electromagnetic Waves and Applications,* Vol. 13, 1999, pp. 121–135.

Joint Research Center, European Microwave Signature Laboratory (EMSL) website, http://www-emsl.jrc.it.

Koudogbo, F., P. F. Combes, and H. J. Mametsa, "Numerical and Experimental Validations of IEM for Bistatic Scattering from Natural and Man-made Rough Surfaces," *Progress in Electromagnetic Research,* PIER 46, 2004, pp. 203–244.

Nance, C. N., "Scattering and Image Analysis of Conducting Rough Surfaces," Ph.D. dissertation, University of Texas at Arlington, Arlington, TX. 1992

Nashashibi, A. Y. and F. T. Ulaby, "MMW Polarimetric Radar Bistatic Scattering from a Random Surface," *IEEE Transactions on Geoscience and Remote Sensing,* Vol. 45, No. 6, June 2007, pp. 1743–1755.

Oh, Y., K. Sarabandi, and F. T. Ulaby, "An Empirical Model and an Inversion Technique for Radar Scattering from Bare Soil Surfaces," *IEEE Transactions on Geoscience and Remote Sensing,* Vol. 30, No. 2, March 1992, pp. 370–381.

Onstott, R. G., "Polarimetric Radar Measurements of Artificial Sea Ice During CRRELEX 88," *ERIM Tech. Report 196100-23-T,* April 1990.

Qin, L., J. Shi, and K. S. Chen, "A Generalized Power Law Spectrum and Its Applications to the Backscattering of Soil Surfaces Based on the Integral Equation Model," *IEEE Transactions on Geoscience and Remote Sensing,* Vol. 40, No. 2, 2002, pp. 271–280.

Rice, S. O.,"Reflection of Electromagnetic Waves from Slightly Rough Surfaces," *Communications in Pure and Applied Mathematics,* Vol. 4, 1951, pp. 361–378.

Sancer, M. I., "Shadow-corrected Electromagnetic Scattering from a Randomly Rough Surface," *IEEE Trans. Ant. Prop.,* Vol. 17, 1969, pp. 577–589.

Smith, B. G., "Geometrical Shadowing of a Random Rough Surface," *IEEE Transactions on Antenna and Propagation*, Vol. AP-15, 1967, pp. 668–671.

Ulaby, F. T., Moore, R. K., and A. K. Fung, *Microwave Remote Sensing*, Chapter 11 and 12, Vol. 2, Norwood, MA: Artech House, 1982.

Ulaby, F. T., Moore, R. K., and A. K. Fung, *Microwave Remote Sensing*, Chapter 21, Vol. 3, Norwood, MA: Artech House, 1986.

Wu, T. D., et al., "A Transition Model for the Reflection Coefficient in Surface Scattering," *IEEE Trans. Geosci. Remote Sensing*, Vol. 39, No. 9, September 2001, pp. 2040-2050.

Chapter 3

Surface Backscattering Trends and Comparisons with Measurements

3.1 INTRODUCTION

Knowing the surface backscattering mechanisms given in Chapter 2 for multiscale surfaces we are now ready to illustrate parameter effects on surface backscattering. Chapter 2 showed that backscattering from a multiscale rough surface can be approximated using the expl or mexp modified correlation functions. Each of these correlation functions contains the surface rms height σ, the surface correlation length L, and a correlation parameter that influences the shape of the correlation function near the origin. Hence, instead of dealing with many surface scales we can use these modified exponential correlation functions to carry out our study. As a reminder note that while we keep the name of L as the correlation length, it has become a correlation parameter now, because the actual correlation length is determined by both r (or z) and L.

We shall begin with theoretical studies of the parameter effects on backscattering and then compare the surface backscattering model given by (2.1) with measurements from unknown surfaces and surfaces with reported ground truth. In principle, our model prediction must agree with measurements when all surface parameters are known. We shall see that this is indeed the case over the frequency range where the reported surface parameters are *responsible* for backscattering. Usually, this falls into the case when $k\sigma < 1$. For multiscale surfaces, some large-scale roughness may not be responsible for backscattering due to wavelength filtering. If so, the reported scale roughness is no longer applicable and a smaller, unknown roughness scale must be chosen to explain the measurement. This chapter provides examples of these filtered cases.

3.2 PARAMETER EFFECTS ON BACKSCATTERING WITH EXPL

This section illustrates how the dielectric constant, correlation parameter, r, surface roughness parameters, σ and L, and frequency changes affect surface backscattering using the expl correlation function. In general, a larger dielectric constant will raise the level of backscattering and cause a wider separation between vertical and horizontal polarizations, especially over large angles of incidence. A larger value of L decreases the surface rms slope. Hence, it will raise backscattering at and near normal incidence and cause a faster drop-off of backscattering away from normal incidence. When $k\sigma > 0.6$, a larger value of σ increases the rms slope, which decreases backscattering near normal incidence and increases it at large angles of incidence. A larger value of r allows the expl function to be more Gaussian-like over a larger lag distance and could lower backscattering at large incident angles as illustrated in Chapter 2. We begin by considering the frequency trend of the surface backscattering model and show how other model parameters affect its trend and angular shape. Similar illustrations will then be repeated for other model parameters if appropriate. Due to the nonlinear dependence of backscattering on various model parameters, different combinations of these parameters may produce unexpected results.

All our illustrations are restricted to the incident angle range, $0°$ to $60°$, so that the shadowing effect by surface roughness is reduced or can be ignored. We do so because at this time shadowing can only be estimated by a geometric optics method, which is generally not applicable in the microwave range. For applications in angular regions where shadowing is known to be present, we can only select an arbitrary amount of shadowing to realize a good fit.

3.2.1 Frequency Dependence

When we consider frequency dependence in backscattering, we also like to know whether frequency trends or angular shapes are affected by changes in other model parameters such as the correlation parameter, roughness parameters, and the dielectric constant. We shall begin with a set of surface parameters, $\sigma = 0.4$ cm and $L = 7$ cm, and set the correlation parameter to $r = 0.1$ and the dielectric constant to 6. With respect to each model parameter we shall examine frequency dependence from two different directions:

1. How do two different parameter values affect backscattering as frequency changes?

2. What are the backscattering trends versus frequency along different incident angles for two different values of this parameter?

3.2.1.1 Effect of Correlation Parameter on Frequency Dependence

To see how the correlation parameter affects backscattering as frequency changes, we shall show frequency changes with a small and a large correlation parameter, $r = 0.1$ and $r = 1.4$ cm. In Figure 3.1 we have computed vertical and horizontal backscattering coefficients with these two values of r at three different frequencies. In particular, we use the same plot range for all three figures so that the changes in level and angular trends among the three backscattering plots become obvious.

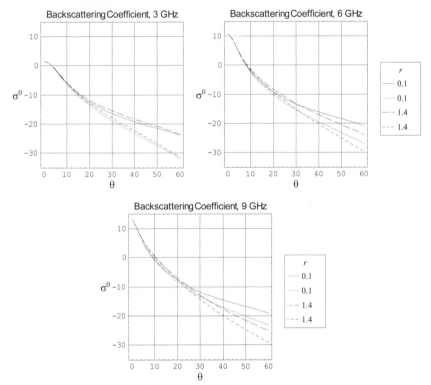

Figure 3.1 A comparison of vertical and horizontal backscattering coefficients from two expl-correlated surfaces with different correlation parameters, $r = 0.1$ cm and $r = 1.4$ cm, as frequency changes from 3 to 9 GHz. Other common surface parameters are $\sigma = 0.4$ cm, $L = 7$ cm, and $\varepsilon = 6$. For each pair of solid or dashed curves, the upper curve is vertical polarization.

At 3 GHz (or $k\sigma = 0.25$) the incident wavelength is 10 cm, which is longer than the surface correlation length. When $r = 1.4$ cm it implies that over a lag distance of 20% of the correlation length, the correlation function (expl) has a Gaussian behavior. When $r = 0.1$ cm, expl behaves mostly as an exponential function. Such a difference in the surface correlation functions has little impact on backscattering in the low-frequency range. For example, at 3 GHz, the incident wavelength is long, and the major contribution to backscattering comes from a lag distance larger than the correlation length. The much slower decay of the Gaussian-like correlation near the origin provides a slightly larger backscattering level, leading to an overall higher return than the more exponential-like correlation at 3 GHz over angles of incidence larger than 15 degrees.

At 6 GHz (or $k\sigma = 0.5$) the wavelength is reduced to 5 cm. Hence, both $k\sigma$ and kL are a factor of two larger. These larger $k\sigma$ and kL values cause a significant rise in backscattering relative to the 3-GHz signal over small angles of incidence and a smaller but significant rise over larger angles for the $r = 0.1$ cm case. For $r = 1.4$ cm, the vertically polarized backscattering actually decreases slightly, while the horizontally polarized backscattering goes up about 2 dB at 60 degrees. Beyond 30 degrees, we see a clear difference in backscattering produced by the difference in the correlation functions, because unlike at 3 GHz, the backscattering from the more exponential-like correlation is now higher. In comparison with the 3-GHz case, this higher frequency also causes a narrowing of the spacing between the two polarized scattering coefficients.

At 9 GHz (or $k\sigma = 0.75$) backscattering at normal incidence continues to rise with frequency for both the $r = 0.1$ cm and the $r = 1.4$ cm correlations. Simultaneously, the increase in the horizontally polarized backscattering curve with the more Gaussian-like correlation is negligible beyond 40 degrees. With the spacing between the two polarized scattering coefficients continuing to narrow with frequency, the end result is that the vertically polarized backscattering for the $r = 1.4$ cm case actually declines by about 1 dB at 60 degrees, causing a clear separation between the backscattering curves due to the two different correlation parameters. At all three frequencies, the difference in backscattering caused by the difference in the correlation parameters is negligible over small incident angles because the effective wavelength is long in that region.

Overall there are three main points indicated in Figure 3.1. The first one is that at normal incidence the signal level is controlled by $k\sigma$ and continues to increase with frequency when $k\sigma \leq 0.75$. The second point is that as frequency increases the $r = 1.4$ cm correlation function will lead to a lower backscattering relative to the $r = 0.1$ cm (more exponential-like) correlation over large angles of incidence. The third point is that the spacing between vertically and horizontally polarized backscattering will narrow as frequency increases.

To compare frequency trends along a given incident angle in backscattering for two different correlation parameters, we show vertically polarized backscattering as a function of frequency with $r = 0.1$ cm in Figure 3.2(a) and a similar calculation with the same model parameters except letting $r = 1.4$ cm in Figure 3.2(b). Clearly, the two parts have very different frequency behaviors, but over the first five degrees or so in the incident angle, the backscattering coefficients remain fairly close to one another with the exception of the 25-GHz case. At 25 GHz (or $k\sigma \approx 2.1$) backscattering is close to the GO condition so that the returns are controlled by the surface rms slope instead of the roughness parameters, σ and L. The surface with $r = 0.1$ cm has a larger rms slope. Its return at normal incidence is about 2.8 dB as opposed to 6.6 dB for the surface with $r = 1.4$ cm. Such a change does not occur suddenly. At 16 GHz the $r = 1.4$ cm curve is also about 1 dB higher than the $r = 0.1$ cm curve at normal incidence. At lower frequencies the returns are controlled mostly by the surface rms height σ and the correlation length L. That is why their returns are nearly the same at or close to normal incidence, but they would vary greatly at large angles of incidence due to the difference in the correlation parameter. By the same token, backscattering curves at lower frequencies in Figures 3.2(a, b) are similar over a wider range of the incident angle than the higher frequency curves.

In Figure 3.2, we see a gradual change from a bell-shaped curve to a more exponential looking curve over the small angular region as frequency increases peaking at around 8 to 12 GHz and then falling back at 16 and 25 GHz toward a more bell-shaped curve again. Beyond 15 degrees in Figure 3.2(a) and within approximately 5 to 25 degrees in Figure 3.2(b), signal level increases monotonically with frequency but shows some signs of saturation in Figure 3.2(a, b). This increasing trend with frequency remains true in Figure 3.2(a) over higher angles also. However, for Figure 3.2(b) and beyond 35 degrees the signal level increase is only from 2 to 4 GHz. Then it begins to decrease with frequency and the incident angle. This decrease for vertical polarization is like having backscattering at frequencies higher than 4 GHz folded back down. It is caused by the correlation function having a Gaussian-like behavior near the origin and backscattering from the $r = 1.4$ cm surface lower relative to the $r = 0.1$ cm surface as frequency increases as shown in Figure 3.1. The difference in the correlation properties between the two surfaces actually produces quite a drastic difference in the angular trend, frequency trend, and signal level over large angles of incidence. At 60 degrees the signal level in Figure 3.2(b) is always lower than Figure 3.2(a) when frequency is at 8 GHz or higher. At 4 GHz, the signal levels are about the same, while at 2 GHz Figure 3.2(b) is higher than Figure 3.2(a). Thus, choosing a large r such as $r = 1.4$ cm to generate a lower backscattering signal over large angles of incidence only holds at mid- to high-frequencies. It does not work at low frequencies, where the frequency trend has reversed direction.

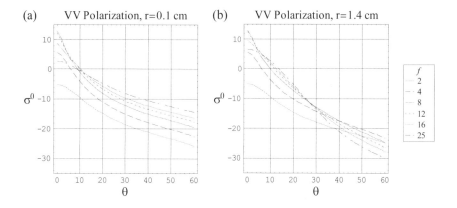

Figure 3.2 An illustration of the frequency variation of vertically polarized backscattering coefficients from two surfaces along various incident angles with common parameters, $\sigma = 0.4$ cm, $L = 7$ cm, $\varepsilon = 6$ and the expl correlation: (a) $r = 0.1$ cm and (b) $r = 1.4$ cm. Over the first five degrees backscattering coefficients in both parts have the same frequency trend, although their rates of change are different.

For horizontally polarized backscattering with the same set of surface parameters, the frequency trends are similar to vertical polarization near normal incidence as shown in Figure 3.3. However, when the incident angle is greater than 20 degrees, the frequency behaviors are quite different. In Figure 3.3(a), the signal level continues to rise with frequency showing no sign of saturation with the $r = 0.1$ cm (more exponential-like) correlation parameter, while in Figure 3.3(b) the signal level begins to saturate after reaching 8 GHz between 10 and 35 degrees for the more Gaussian-like correlation. When the incident angle is greater than 35 degrees, the signal level difference in 8, 12, and 16 GHz is negligible. A further increase in frequency to 25 GHz causes the backscattering signal to reverse direction and drops to a lower level than the previous three frequencies. These complicated variations with the incident angle are due entirely to the shape of the correlation function with $r = 1.4$ cm and the sensing with horizontal polarization.

Comparing vertical and horizontal polarization, we see that they are quite similar over the first 20 degrees. Actually, the two polarizations begin to separate after about 10 degrees, and horizontal polarization begins to get lower than vertical polarization as the incident angle increases, as shown in Figure 3.1. However, as frequency increases beyond 9 GHz ($k\sigma \approx 0.75$), the spacing between the two polarizations will eventually approach zero. For this situation to occur the vertical polarization has to drop as shown in Figure 3.2(b) over large angles of incidence, and horizontal polarization has to increase or drop depending on angle to meet with the vertical polarization as seen in Figure 3.3(b). The frequency behavior seems so strange because angular curves for backscattering are dependent on both frequency and the shape of the correlation function. Only for the exponential correlation or one very close to it can the backscattering angular curves have simple clear angular trends as shown in Figures 3.2(a) and 3.3(a).

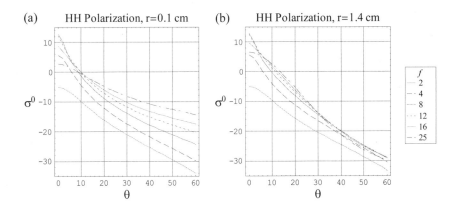

Figure 3.3 An illustration of frequency variation of horizontally polarized backscattering coefficients from two surfaces along various incident angles with common parameters $\sigma = 0.4$ cm, $L = 7$ cm, $\varepsilon = 6$ and the expl correlation: (a) $r = 0.1$ cm and (b) $r = 1.4$ cm. Only the first five degrees backscattering coefficients in both parts have the same frequency trend, although their rates of change are different.

Although the presentation in Figures 3.2 and 3.3 provides a direct view of how backscattering changes with frequency, its form in Figures 3.2(b) and 3.3(b) is too complex to give readers a clear picture of frequency properties. Hence, we want to consider another form of presentation in terms of the spacing between vertically and horizontally polarized backscattering coefficients. Results are shown in Figure

3.4 for both correlation parameters in the frequency range 2–16 GHz. Here, we see a clear narrowing in the spacing between vertically and horizontally polarized backscattering coefficients with frequency and the two polarized backscattering coefficients approaching each other at 16 GHz for both $r = 0.1$ and $r = 1.4$ cm surfaces. At 16 GHz both curves in Figure 3.4(a, b) show an exponential shape indicating that the close agreement is not a result of reaching the GO condition, which should lead to a bell-shaped curve. Furthermore, the signal levels at normal incidence in Figure 3.4(a, b) are within 1 dB of each other as opposed to several decibels, which would be the case if backscattering were determined by the surface rms slopes. Hence, the agreement should be the result of the property of the surface correlations and not the surface rms slopes. Except for the low-frequency curves (2 GHz), which have a lot of similarity, the angular shapes of backscattering curves at higher frequencies in Figure 3.4 are very different. This difference in angular shapes is due to the difference in the correlation functions. However, the change in spacing with frequency from the two surfaces is quite similar.

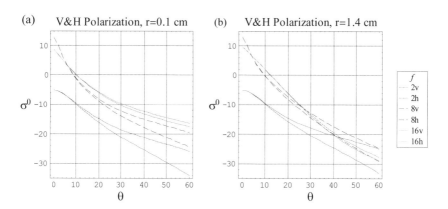

Figure 3.4 An illustration of changes in level and angular shapes of vertically and horizontally polarized backscattering coefficients with frequency for two surfaces with common parameters $\sigma = 0.4$ cm, $L = 7$ cm, $\varepsilon = 6$ and the expl correlation: (a) $r = 0.1$ cm and (b) $r = 1.4$ cm. For each polarization pair the upper curve is vertical polarization.

To show that the GO condition does occur at a higher frequency, Figure 3.5 shows a comparison similar to Figure 3.4 but for a set of higher frequencies. The signal level at normal incidence for 25 GHz is clearly higher in Figure 3.5(b) than Figure 3.5(a), while the signal levels at other frequencies are nearly the same. At lower frequencies the signal levels are controlled mainly by the surface rms height σ and the correlation length L, which are the same for both surfaces and in the two correlation functions. This is why the signal levels at lower frequencies in both parts, (a) and (b), are about the same at normal incidence. As we approach the geometric optics condition, the signal begins to depend more and more on the surface rms slope, which is different for the two surfaces. The rms slope in Figure 3.5(a) is larger because its correlation parameter is smaller than the one in Figure 3.5(b). Hence, at 25 GHz and normal incidence, its signal level is lower at about 2.8 dB, while the corresponding signal level in Figure 3.5(b) is about 6.6 dB. Looking at Figures 3.4 and 3.5, we see that the convergence toward GO begins to show up at about 12 GHz, where the maximum separation between the two polarizations is less than 2.5 dB. At 16 GHz the signal level has already been influenced by the surface rms slope causing the signal level at normal incidence in Figure 3.5(b) to be about 1 dB higher than in Figure 3.5(a). At 25 GHz it should be pretty close to the GO condition. One key finding here is that when we see an agreement between vertically and horizontally polarized backscattering coefficients in a set of experimental data, it does not necessarily imply that the GO condition has been reached. Upon examining the value of $k\sigma$, we find that it is equal to about 1 at 12 GHz and 2 at 24 GHz. The guideline is when $k\sigma \approx 1$, vertically and horizontally polarized backscattering coefficients are getting close to each other. When $k\sigma \approx 2$, we are close to the GO condition.

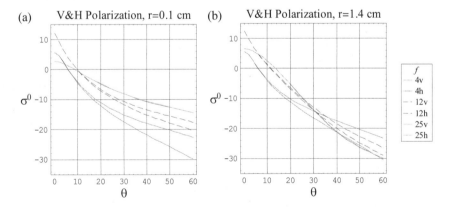

Figure 3.5 Variation of pairs of polarized backscattering coefficients with frequency for two surfaces with common parameters σ = 0.4 cm, L = 7 cm, ε = 6, and the expl correlation: (a) r = 0.1 cm and (b) r = 1.4 cm. For each polarization pair the upper curve is vertical polarization.

3.2.1.2 Effect of Surface rms Height on Frequency Dependence

This section illustrates first how the surface rms height parameter affects backscattering as frequency changes similar to Section 3.2.1.1. Then it compares backscattering trends with frequency for two different values of the surface rms height along different incident angles.

Figure 3.6 shows vertical and horizontal backscattering coefficients with σ = 0.4 cm and σ = 0.6 cm as frequency changes. Other model parameters are defined in Figure 3.6 along with polarization designation. For each pair of solid or dashed lines, the upper line is vertical polarization.

At 3 GHz the incident wavelength is 10 cm, which is longer than the surface correlation length of 7 cm. This means that we are near or in the low-frequency range. Backscattering should behave similar to what is predicted by the perturbation model, where scattering strength is proportional to the surface rms height. Thus, backscattering from the surface with a larger rms height is always higher in level for both vertical and horizontal polarizations at every incident angle than the surface with a smaller rms height (i.e., it seems that the backscattering coefficient curves with σ = 0.6 cm are obtained by shifting upward the corresponding backscattering coefficient curves with σ = 0.4 cm). More specifically, the amount of shifting is smaller at normal incidence and increases with the incident angle. For example, at 60 degrees the backscattering curves for horizontal polarization are about 4 dB apart, while at normal incidence they are 2 dB apart.

At 6 GHz the wavelength is reduced to 5 cm. Hence, both $k\sigma$ and kL are a factor of two larger. These larger $k\sigma$ and kL values cause a significant rise in backscattering relative to the 3-GHz signal at normal incidence and over small incident angles. It is clear that the backscattering curve with σ = 0.4 cm or $k\sigma$ = 0.5 rises faster at normal incidence because it is now higher than the curve with σ = 0.6 cm. On the other hand, at 60 degrees there is no significant difference in the amount of rise between the two backscattering curves for vertical polarization, because they remain parallel to each other, and each rises about 3 dB. For horizontal polarization the backscattering curves with σ = 0.4 cm and σ = 0.6 cm rise about 5 and 6 dB, respectively, at 60 degrees, which is 2 to 3 dB more than vertical polarization, giving rise to a smaller spacing between the two polarizations for the surface with a larger rms height. This property of narrowing the spacing due to a larger rms height is similar to an increase in frequency. Graphically we see that there is an overall rise in backscattering from the two surfaces over all incident angles. This rise tapers off as the incident angle increases.

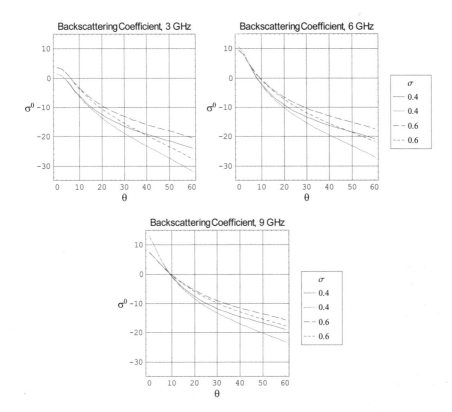

Figure 3.6 A comparison of vertical and horizontal backscattering coefficients from two expl-correlated surfaces with different surface rms heights, σ = 0.4 cm and σ = 0.6 cm, as frequency changes from 3 to 9 GHz. Other common surface parameters are r = 0.1 cm, L = 7 cm, and ε = 6. For each pair of solid or dashed curves, the upper curve is vertical polarization.

At 9 GHz and at normal incidence, backscattering continues to rise with frequency mainly for the backscattering curves with σ = 0.4 cm, while the backscattering curves with σ = 0.6 cm or $k\sigma$ = 1.13 have reversed direction and declined. However, over large angles of incidence, it is the horizontally polarized backscattering with σ = 0.6 cm that rises faster than both the vertically and horizontally polarized backscattering curves with σ = 0.4 cm, causing a separation between the two sets of polarized curves in the angular range 10–60 degrees. Recall at 3 GHz and 60 degrees, the vertically polarized backscattering from the σ = 0.4 cm surface is about 4 dB higher than the horizontally polarized backscattering from the $\sigma = 0.6$ cm surface. When comparing the spacing between polarizations at 3 GHz with 9 GHz, we find that for the $\sigma = 0.4$ cm surface the spacing has been reduced from near 8 dB to 4 dB at 9 GHz, while for the $\sigma = 0.6$ cm surface, it is from 8 dB to 2 dB.

The above description reconfirms that a convenient reference number for the change of backscattering with frequency at normal incidence is the value of $k\sigma$. In our study of surface correlation parameter in Figure 3.2, we have found that when $k\sigma < 0.75$, signal will continue to rise with frequency and when $k\sigma > 0.75$, it will reverse direction and decline. Here, at $\sigma = 0.6$ cm and 9 GHz, $k\sigma = 1.13$. Thus, the corresponding backscattering signal at normal incidence should decline relative to its value at 6 GHz.

Figure 3.6 provides a direct side-by-side comparison for the two pairs of polarized backscattering curves with different surface rms heights. It does not provide a direct backscattering trend with frequency along every incident angle direction. In order to see how different rms heights influence the frequency behavior in backscattering along different incident angles, we need to compute backscattering for many more frequencies and show the results for each polarization and choice of surface rms height separately. The new result for vertical polarization with $\sigma = 0.6$ cm is plotted in Figure 3.7(b) while Figure 3.2(a) with $\sigma = 0.4$ cm is shown as Figure 3.7(a) to provide a direct comparison of the frequency trends in the backscattering coefficients over different incident angles.

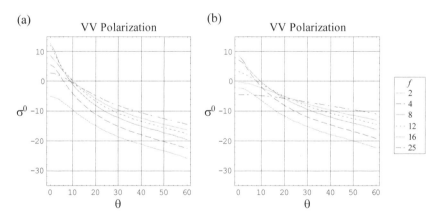

Figure 3.7 An illustration of frequency variation of vertically polarized backscattering coefficients from two surfaces along various incident angles with common parameters $r = 0.1$ cm, $L = 7$ cm, $\varepsilon = 6$, and the expl correlation: (a) $\sigma = 0.4$ cm and (b) $\sigma = 0.6$ cm.

Several general observations can be made from Figure 3.7:

1. At near normal incidence with σ = 0.4 cm, the backscattering signal peaks between 8 and 12 GHz, whereas with σ = 0.6 cm, the backscattering signal peaks between 4 and 8 GHz.

2. Beyond 25 degrees, the backscattered signal increases with frequency for both σ values.

3. Major differences in frequency trends of the backscattering signal appear within the first 25 degrees only.

The larger rms height and slope cause a large drop in signal level at normal incidence especially for frequencies above 8 GHz; for example, the 12-GHz curve drops from about 13 dB to 4 dB and the 16 GHz from about 9 to 0 dB. These changes lead to smoother curves with much smaller peaks at normal incidence as shown in Figure 3.7(b). Furthermore, the rise in level near normal incidence stops at 8 GHz beyond which the signal level begins to drop, whereas in Figure 3.7(a) the signal level remains high at 12 GHz. The drop in level at normal incidence due to the large rms slope is so large that the signal levels represented by the 12-, 16-, and 25-GHz curves fall below the 4-GHz curve. In Figure 3.7(a) only the signal level of the 25-GHz curve falls below the 4-GHz curve. At 2 and 4 GHz, $k\sigma < 0.75$. When σ increases from 0.4 to 0.6 cm, backscattering continues to increase over all incident angles including the normal and small incident angle region. The major change in the frequency trends due to a larger rms slope occurs within the first 30 degrees. Beyond 30 degrees, the signal level in Figure 3.7(b) rises with frequency quite similar to those shown in Figure 3.7(a), although the rates may be different. One interesting point is that despite the large difference in the shapes of the angular curves in Figure 3.7(a, b), over the angular range 40 to 60 degrees the decibel difference between the 2- and 25-GHz curves is almost the same. As a result, the rate of change of the backscattering signal with frequency is also about the same in Figure 3.7(a, b). In comparison with a change in the correlation function, a larger surface height causes a large change in the frequency trend mainly in the small incident angle region, while the correlation function change considered earlier causes large changes in frequency trends mainly over large angles of incidence.

A comparison between horizontal polarizations similar to Figure 3.7 is shown in Figure 3.8. Over small angles of incidence, vertically and horizontally polarized backscattering coefficients are about the same in level and angular trends. Hence, what we said about vertical polarization in signal level and frequency trends in this angular region also applies to horizontal polarization (i.e., a major difference in frequency trends occurs within the incident angle region, 0 to 30 degrees). Beyond 30 degrees, the frequency trends are the same in Figure 3.8(a, b), but the rates of change are generally different. However, between 40 to 60 degrees both the frequency trends in backscattering and the rates of change with frequency in Figure 3.8(a, b) are very close, because the total change in decibels from 2 to 25 GHz in this angular region is almost the same.

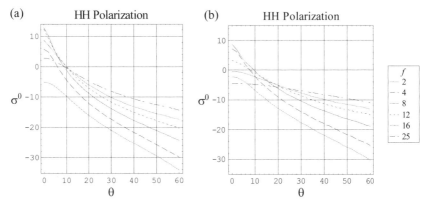

Figure 3.8 An illustration of frequency variation of horizontally polarized backscattering coefficients from two surfaces along various incident angles with common parameters $r = 0.1$ cm, $L = 7$ cm, $\varepsilon = 6$, and the expl correlation: (a) $\sigma = 0.4$ cm and (b) $\sigma = 0.6$ cm. Significant differences in frequency trends occur within the first 30 degrees, where the increase in backscattering with frequency at normal incidence stops and reverses direction after 8 GHz.

Upon comparing the corresponding parts of Figure 3.7 with Figure 3.8, we have noticed that at 16 and 25 GHz, the curves at each frequency are almost the same (i.e., there is no insignificant difference due to polarization). Plots to better demonstrate this fact are shown in Figure 3.9. However, the angular shapes of the curves for the same surface at 16 GHz are different from those at 25 GHz, indicating that at 16 GHz, backscattering is still dominated by roughness parameters, σ and L, although it may also be affected by the surface rms slope. It is clear in Figure 3.9 that the angular shape of the backscattering curve at 8 GHz is exponential and concave. It is taking on a more Gaussian look as frequency increases. At 25 GHz its angular shape has become convex in Figure 3.9(b), which indicates that backscattering is dominated by the surface slope distribution. Of the three types of graphical illustrations we have shown, Figure 3.9 provides the best illustration in terms of level and angular shape changes in backscattering with frequency for both vertical and horizontal polarizations.

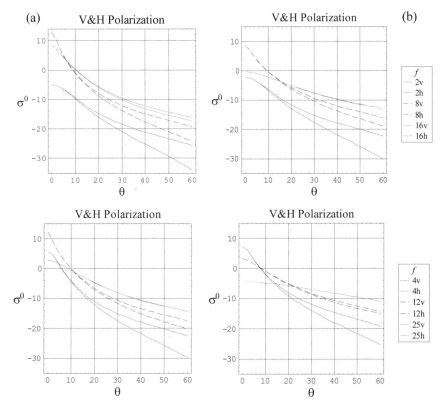

Figure 3.9 An illustration of changes in level and angular shapes of vertically and horizontally polarized backscattering coefficients with frequency for two surfaces with common parameters $r = 0.1$ cm, $L = 7$ cm, $\varepsilon = 6$, and the expl correlation. In part (a) $\sigma = 0.4$ cm and in part (b), $\sigma = 0.6$ cm. The difference in the surface rms height has caused a significant change in the angular shapes of the curves. The surface with a larger rms surface height in part (b) also leads to a narrower spacing between the two polarizations.

The plots in Figure 3.9 also allow us to examine another effect of the surface rms height on frequency dependence. We already know that both a larger surface rms height and a higher frequency can cause the spacing between polarizations to narrow. However, we have not shown a comparison between narrowing of spacing due to both frequency and a larger surface rms height. This particular comparison is now given in Figure 3.9; Figure 3.9(a) shows narrowing due to frequency and a smaller surface rms height, and Figure 3.9(b) shows narrowing due to frequency and a larger surface rms height. We see that the spacing between the two polarization curves at the same frequency is generally wider in Figure 3.9(a) than the corresponding curves in Figure 3.9(b). In particular, at 8 GHz and 60 degrees, the spacing is over 4 dB in Figure 3.9(a) and over 2 dB in Figure 3.9(b). Similarly, when we examine the 12-GHz curves, we find the spacing between polarizations in Figure 3.9(a) to be over 2 dB between 50 and 60 degrees, while in Figure 3.9(b) it is 0.5 dB or less.

The large difference in the angular shapes of the backscattering curves between the two parts of Figure 3.9 also suggests how to choose frequency and surface rms height, when the angular shapes of a set of backscatter measurements are given. A sharp drop-off near normal incidence is usually due to a small rms height or a small slope with a medium or a large correlation length relative to the operating wavelength. Significant backscattering at large angles of incidence requires a large rms slope and a medium correlation length.

3.2.1.3 Effect of Correlation Length on Frequency Dependence

Of the two surface roughness parameters, σ and L, σ appears in an exponent and through the surface spectrum in the surface backscattering model (2.1), while L appears only through the surface spectrum. To illustrate how the backscattering coefficients with $L = 3$ and 7 cm vary as frequency changes, we select common surface scattering parameters, $\sigma = 0.4$ cm, $r = 0.1$ cm, and $\varepsilon = 6$ and let frequency change from 3 to 9 GHz. Results are shown in Figure 3.10.

An obvious frequency trend in Figure 3.10 is that the spacing between the two polarizations narrows as frequency increases, and this trend is independent of the size of the correlation length. The backscattering curves with $L = 3$ cm are lower near normal incidence and higher over large angles of incidence than the $L = 7$ cm curve, because it has a larger rms slope than the surface with $L = 7$ cm. This relative position is maintained as frequency changes from 3 to 9 GHz, although the amount of separation between the two sets of curves varies with angle and frequency. The most obvious change with frequency is the location where the two sets cross. This location continues to move upward from about -10 dB to close to 0 dB and from around 15 degrees to 10 degrees as frequency increases. This means that the angular region, where the backscattering from the $L = 3$ cm surface is greater than that from the $L = 7$ cm surface, increases with frequency. Simultaneously, backscattering from the two surfaces appears to rise with frequency over the large angular region (50 to 60 degrees) at the same rate, so that the spacing between each polarization remains almost constant. Interestingly, at normal incidence the spacing between the backscattering coefficients from the two surfaces also appears unchanged with frequency. The only angular region where backscattering coefficients from the two surfaces do change with frequency is where the two sets of backscattering coefficients cross each other. To see how a difference in correlation length may affect the frequency trend in backscattering, we replot polarized backscattering coefficients versus angle with frequency instead of the correlation length as the parameter in Figure 3.11, where in Figure 3.11(a) we use $L = 7$ cm and in Figure 3.11(b) we have $L = 3$ cm. The general appearance of the figures seems very different in level and angular trends, especially in the small incident angle region (0 to 30 degrees) for both polarizations. We shall see that there are similarities in their rates of change with frequency.

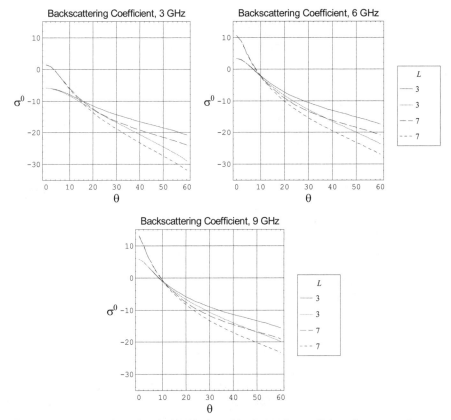

Figure 3.10 A comparison of vertical and horizontal backscattering coefficients from two expl-correlated surfaces with different correlation lengths, $L = 3$ cm and $L = 7$ cm, as frequency changes from 3 to 9 GHz. Other common surface parameters are $\sigma = 0.4$ $r = 0.1$ cm, and $\varepsilon = 6$. For each pair of solid or dashed curves, the upper curve is vertical polarization.

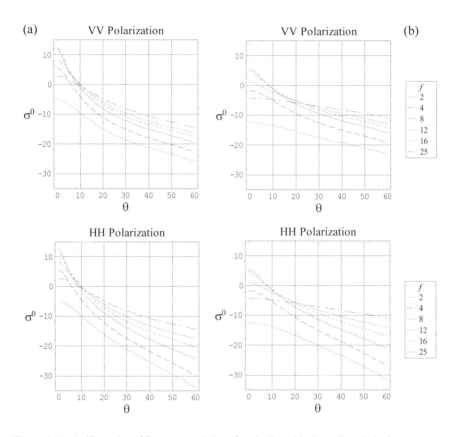

Figure 3.11 An illustration of frequency variation of vertically and horizontally polarized backscattering coefficients from two surfaces along various incident angles with common parameters $r = 0.1$ cm, $\sigma = 0.4$ cm, cm, $\varepsilon = 6$, and the expl correlation: (a) $L = 7$ cm and (b) $L = 3$ cm.

In Figure 3.11 we see that near normal incidence backscattering increases with frequency until 8 to 12 GHz and then falls back down at higher frequencies, and this is true in both Figure 3.11(a, b) and for both vertical and horizontal polarizations. For an angular width of about 5 degrees near the vertical, the frequency trends of backscattering in both parts are the same, although the rates of change of backscattering with frequency are different. Also, beyond 30 degrees backscattering is increasing monotonically with frequency in both parts also. This illustration shows that frequency trends of backscattering are different, when the correlation length is different, only in the region approximately from 5 to 30 degrees.

3.2.1.4 Effect of Dielectric Constant on Frequency Dependence

The dielectric constant is the model parameter that appears through the reflection and field coefficients independent of the surface correlation function and roughness parameters. It affects mainly the level of backscattering and its angular shape. We shall see how two different values of the dielectric constant affect frequency dependence by plotting the angular behaviors of the backscattering coefficients as frequency changes in Figure 3.12.

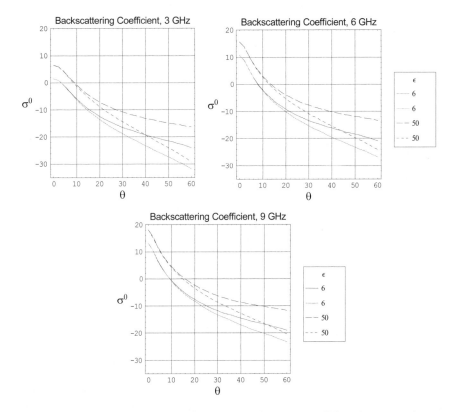

Figure 3.12 A comparison of vertical and horizontal backscattering coefficients from two expl-correlated surfaces with different dielectric constants, $\varepsilon = 6$ and $\varepsilon = 50$, as frequency changes from 3 to 9 GHz. Other common surface parameters are $r = 0.1$ cm, $L = 7$ cm, and $\sigma = 0.4$ cm. For each pair of solid or dashed curves, the upper curve is vertical polarization.

In Figure 3.12 the large dielectric constant causes close to a 5-dB rise at normal incidence for both vertical and horizontal polarizations at 3 GHz. However, for horizontal polarization the rise is getting smaller over larger angles ending at about 2 dB relative to the low dielectric case at 60 degrees. On the other hand, for vertical polarization the amount of rise is increasing with the incident angle, leading to a level more than 7 dB higher than the low dielectric case. This difference in how vertical and horizontal polarization change causes the separation between the two polarizations to widen to about 13 dB at 60 degrees as opposed to 6 dB for the low dielectric case. As frequency increases to 6 GHz, we expect signal levels for both polarizations to rise due to a larger $k\sigma$ and kL and the spacing between the polarizations to decrease. At 9 GHz the separation between vertical and horizontal polarization for $\varepsilon = 50$ is still over 8 dB as opposed to 4 dB for the $\varepsilon = 6$ case. Thus, a large dielectric constant tends to enhance the separation between the two polarizations mainly through raising the level of vertical polarization, although horizontally polarized backscattering also contributes to a wider separation. On the other hand, the reduction in the spacing between polarizations with frequency is due mainly to the faster increase in the level of horizontally polarized backscattering than the vertically polarized backscattering.

Now, let us view the same problem from another direction by using frequency instead of the dielectric constant as the parameter; we plot the backscattering coefficients versus angle in Figure 3.13(b). Figure 3.13(a) is a replot of Figure 3.2(a), where $\varepsilon = 6$, to provide a direct comparison with Figure 3.13(b), where $\varepsilon = 50$. All model parameters are indicated in Figure 3.13. Near normal incidence, backscattering increases with the frequency until frequency reaches 8 GHz. Then it decreases as frequency increases. At 10 degrees, it increases with frequency until frequency reaches 16 GHz. Then it reverses direction. Beyond about 15 degrees, backscattering continues to increase with frequency to 25 GHz. This trend in frequency and angle exists in both Figure 3.13(a) and Figure 3.13(b).

Intuitively, we know that the level of the backscattering curve will be raised when we increase the dielectric constant. As shown in Figure 3.12 the vertically polarized backscattering coefficient is raised much more than horizontal polarization over large incident angles relative to the backscattering coefficients with $\varepsilon = 6$. In Figure 3.13(a) the general appearance of the backscattering coefficients at different frequencies with a small dielectric constant ($\varepsilon = 6$) looks very similar to the one with a large dielectric constant in Figure 3.13(b) ($\varepsilon = 50$). A closer look reveals that the curves in Figure 3.13(b) are approximately 5 dB higher near normal incidence and 6 dB higher near 60 degrees than those in Figure 3.13(a). Therefore, the response over large incident angles is flatter in Figure 3.13(b) than Figure 3.13(a). Despite the differences in level we just mentioned, the relative spacing between the backscattering curves in Figure 3.13(b) is similar to those in Figure 3.13(a). It seems that at a given incident angle all curves are shifted by the same amount. Thus, both the frequency trends and their rates of change with frequency seem to be the same. In reality, the frequency trends are the same but the rates of change with frequency are different. In particular, the total increase of the backscattering signal in decibels from 2 to 25 GHz is smaller for the surface with a larger dielectric constant at 60 degrees.

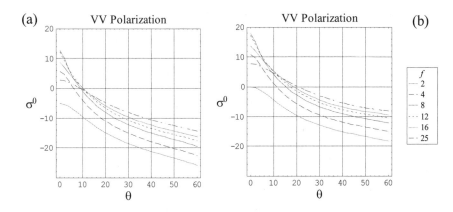

Figure 3.13 An illustration of frequency variation of vertically polarized backscattering coefficients from two surfaces along various incident angles with common parameters $r = 0.1$ cm, $L = 7$ cm, $\sigma = 0.4$, and the expl correlation: (a) $\varepsilon = 6$ and (b) $\varepsilon = 50$.

For the horizontal polarization shown in Figure 3.14 the signal level in Figure 3.14(b) is also about 5 dB higher near normal incidence than the one at the same frequency in Figure 3.14(a). Over small angles of incidence its frequency behavior is also similar to that of vertical polarization. However, unlike vertical polarization, the rise in level is mostly between 2 to 3 dB relative to the corresponding curve in Figure 3.14(a) at 60 degrees for all frequencies shown except at 25 GHz. Upon examining the 25-GHz curve in both Figure 3.13(a) and Figure 3.14(a), we find that the two polarization curves are basically the same in angular shape, indicating that these backscattering curves could be responding to the surface rms slope. If so, the backscattering curve with the larger dielectric constant in Figure 3.14(b) at 25 GHz should be approximately 5 dB higher at every incident angle than the one in Figure 3.14(a). This expectation is generally true to within 1 dB. At other frequencies, we cannot find a similar size increase in level, because while a large dielectric constant can increase the level of backscattering near normal incidence, horizontal polarization also drops off faster with the incident angle. The amount of drop-off is increasing with the incident angle and decreasing with frequency [see Figure 3.14(b)]. These backscattering curves are highly nonlinear and so are the amounts of drop-off in horizontal polarization with frequency and angle. At 20 degrees in Figure 3.14(a, b) when frequency increases from 2 to 25 GHz, the signal level changes by approximately 12 dB. At 60 degrees, the same change in frequency causes a change of about 21.5 dB in Figure 3.14(b), which is also about 2 dB more than the corresponding change in Figure 3.14(a). Hence, for horizontal polarization the rate of change with frequency is clearly larger when the surface dielectric constant is larger.

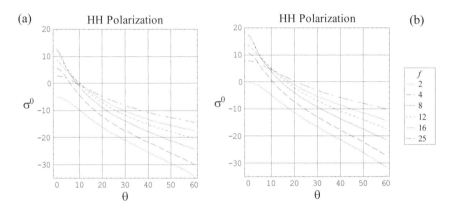

Figure 3.14 An illustration of frequency variation of horizontally polarized backscattering coefficients from two surfaces along various incident angles with common parameters $r = 0.1$ cm, $\sigma = 0.4$ cm, $L = 7$ cm, and the expl correlation: (a) $\varepsilon = 6$ and (b) $\varepsilon = 50$.

The above description indicates that the separation between the two polarizations will be much larger for surfaces with larger dielectric constants. A better view of this spacing and its variation with frequency is shown in Figure 3.15, where Figure 3.15(a) is for $\varepsilon = 6$ and Figure 3.15(b) is for $\varepsilon = 50$. All the spacings between the two polarizations in Figure 3.15(b) are wider than the corresponding one in Figure 3.15(a). For the small dielectric constant case, vertical and horizontal polarizations are not separable at 16 and 25 GHz, but for the larger dielectric constant case backscattering coefficients are clearly separate at both frequencies. It follows that the spacing between the polarizations is controlled by the combined effects of dielectric constant, frequency, and surface rms height.

When we compare the signal level and angular shape between curves of the same frequency in Figure 3.15(a, b), we see that they are different, especially in vertical polarization and its signal level. For example, at 2, 4, 8, and 12 GHz, the signal level rises about 5 dB at normal incidence and rises over 7 dB at 60 degrees in Figure 3.15(b) relative to Figure 3.15(a). For horizontal polarization the trend is different. It has a 5-dB rise at normal incidence but only a 1–3-dB rise at 60 degrees in Figure 3.15(b) relative to Figure 3.15(a). These changes affect both the shapes of the angular curves and the rate with which backscattering signals change with frequency. In model applications angular shapes are important because they can serve as a guide to model parameter selection.

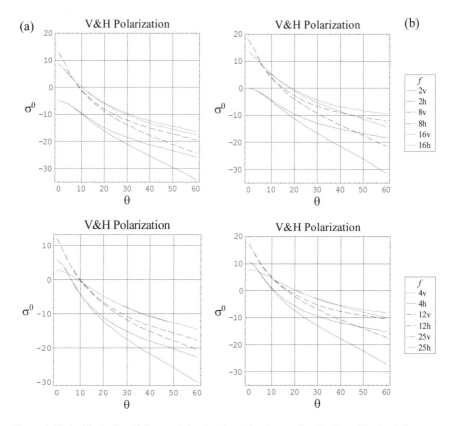

Figure 3.15 An illustration of changes in level and angular shapes of vertically and horizontally polarized backscattering coefficients with frequency for two surfaces with common parameters $\sigma = 0.4$ cm, $L = 7$ cm, $r = 0.1$, and the expl correlation: (a) $\varepsilon = 6$ and (b) $\varepsilon = 50$. For each polarization pair the upper curve is vertical polarization.

3.2.2 Surface Height Dependence

This section illustrates how backscattering varies with the surface rms height and how other model parameters may affect this variation. As in Section 3.2.1, we shall consider this variation from two different directions and display our results in three different ways as needed to get a better view of all of its properties.

Our study in Chapter 2 indicated that the product, wavenumber times surface rms height $k\sigma$, is an important parameter that affects backscattering characteristics. Here, we shall see that backscattering peaks near normal incidence when $k\sigma$ is between 0.4 and 0.6, as we change σ. Clearly, $k\sigma$ falling into this range can be the result of changing either the frequency or the surface rms height. When we discussed frequency dependence in Section 3.2.1, we saw that the backscattering signal at normal incidence reversed direction after $k\sigma > 0.75$ as we changed k. The reason why the reference numbers are different here is that when we change frequency both $k\sigma$ and kL change, while if we change σ only $k\sigma$ changes. The backscattering model given in (2.1) is a continuous function that will not change abruptly with any model parameter. Hence, all the reference numbers we provide in this book are not to be taken as exact locations of change but rather as indicators of where possible changes may occur.

3.2.2.1 Effect of Frequency on Surface Height Dependence

As surface rms height varies we want to see how backscattering changes under two different frequency conditions. To do so we select $f = 3$ and 9 GHz, $r = 0.1$ cm, $L = 7$ cm, $\varepsilon = 6$, as σ varies from 0.3 to 0.9 cm. Results are shown in Figure 3.16.

The low-frequency curves for both vertical and horizontal polarizations in Figure 3.16 are raised as the surface rms height increases from 0.3 cm to 0.9 cm. This range of surface rms heights corresponds to $k\sigma$, ranging from 0.19 to 0.57 at 3 GHz. Over this range of $k\sigma$, backscattering is supposed to increase. At 9 GHz and a surface rms height equal to 0.3 cm, $k\sigma = 0.57$. Here, the higher level of backscattering is caused by the surface being sensed by a shorter wavelength, giving rise to a large $kL = 13$, which is responsible for the high level of backscattering at normal incidence. When the surface rms height is increased to 0.6 cm, $k\sigma = 1.13$, causing backscattering to decrease and the spacing between the two polarizations to narrow. At $\sigma = 0.9$ cm, $k\sigma \approx 1.7$, bringing in the effect of surface rms slope and a clear change from an exponential-looking angular curve to a more Gaussian-looking curve. There is also a further narrowing of the spacing between the two polarizations. Overall, a low frequency has a small effect on the angular trend of backscattering versus the surface rms height, whereas a high frequency can cause a significant narrowing of the spacing between polarizations and alter the angular shape completely as the surface height changes. On the other hand, changes in signal level due to variations in rms height are significant for both frequencies.

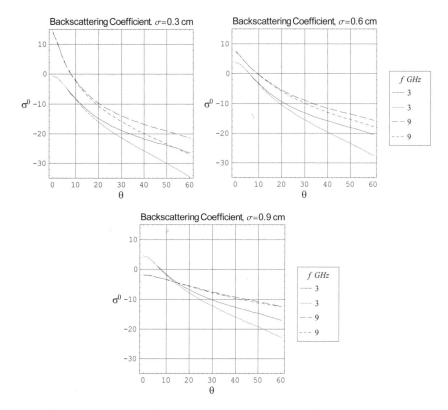

Figure 3.16 A comparison of vertical and horizontal backscattering coefficients from an expl-correlated surface operating at two different frequencies, 3 and 9 GHz, as surface rms height changes from 0.3 to 0.9 cm. Other common surface parameters are $r = 0.1$ cm, $L = 7$ cm, and $\varepsilon = 6$. For each pair of solid or dashed curves, the upper curve is vertical polarization.

To see the backscattering trends with surface rms height along different incident angles, we recompute the two frequency cases in Figure 3.16 by varying σ from 0.2 to 1.2 cm in steps of 0.2 cm corresponding to $k\sigma$ varying from 0.125 through 0.754 at 3 GHz and 0.376 through 2.26 at 9 GHz. The computed backscattering curves for VV and HH polarizations are shown in Figure 3.17.

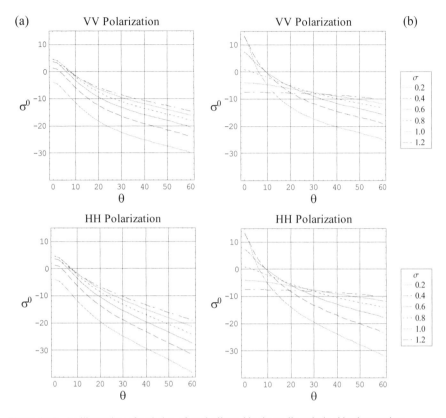

Figure 3.17 An illustration of variation of vertically and horizontally polarized backscattering coefficients with surface rms height along various incident angles. The common model parameters are $r = 0.1$ cm, $L = 7$ cm, and $\varepsilon = 6$ with expl correlation: (a) $f = 3$ GHz and (b) $f = 9$ GHz. Beyond 40 degrees of incidence, backscattering rises as σ increases. Complex trends of backscattering versus surface height exist mainly for 9 GHz from normal to 40 degrees.

At normal incidence and 3 GHz, signal rises as σ increases from 0.2 to 1.0 cm, where $k\sigma = 0.63$. Then the backscattering signal drops at $\sigma = 1.2$ cm or $k\sigma = 0.75$. When the angle of incidence increases beyond about 15 degrees, the rise in backscattering with σ is monotonic, showing some sign of saturation beyond $\sigma = 0.8$ cm. This is the case for both polarizations in Figure 3.17(a). At 9 GHz backscattering signal drops with the surface height at normal incidence. Between approximately 5 to 38 degrees we see that as the incident angle θ

increases, backscattering begins to increase, with σ up to σ = 0.4 cm between 5 and 10 degrees, up to 0.6 cm between 10 and 17 degrees, up to 0.8 cm between 17 and 27 degrees, and finally up to 1.0 cm between 27 and 38 degrees before falling back down. Beyond 38 degrees the backscattering trend with surface rms height is the same as at 3 GHz except the rates of change of backscattering with the surface height are different. This description holds approximately for both polarizations. In general, the rates of change for horizontal polarization are larger than those for vertical polarization, and the trends of backscattering versus the surface rms height are very different at the two different frequencies.

A better view of the change in angular shapes and the spacing between the two polarizations in backscattering with the surface rms height is shown in Figure 3.18, where we denote the same surface with the same type of line for both polarizations with the understanding that the upper line is for vertical polarization and the lower one is for horizontal polarization. Clearly, there is much less change in the angular shapes in backscattering with the surface rms height at 3 GHz than 9 GHz. An obvious trend is the large drop in signal level at normal incidence, with σ at 9 GHz leading to drastic changes in the angular trends. Also, there is a clear narrowing of the spacing between polarizations at both 3 and 9 GHz, as the surface rms height increases. This particular trend is similar to the increase in frequency that we saw in Section 3.2.1.

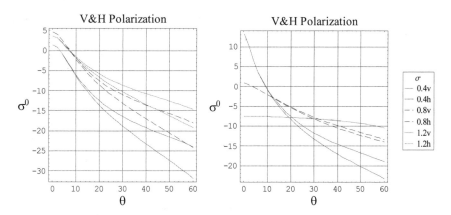

Figure 3.18 An illustration of changes in level and angular shapes of vertically and horizontally polarized backscattering coefficients with the surface rms height with model parameters, $r = 0.1$ cm, $L = 7$ cm, $\varepsilon = 6$, and the expl correlation: (a) $f = 3$ GHz and (b) $f = 9$ GHz.

We have seen that backscattering peaks at normal incidence when $k\sigma$ is around 0.6. Thus, it should be possible to order the curves at normal incidence by choosing an appropriate frequency. Our choice of 3 and 9 GHz comes very close to achieving an ascending and a descending backscattering signal with σ at normal incidence. Surely, we can lower the incident frequency to 2 GHz to get a better view of an ascending backscattering signal. Similarly, we can increase the frequency to 12 GHz to get a larger separation between backscattering signals at different surface heights. The backscattering characteristics computed at these two frequencies represent the low- and high-frequency properties of the surfaces under consideration. A better way to characterize high- and low-frequency conditions is in terms of the $k\sigma$ value. At 2 GHz, the $k\sigma$ value falls in the range $0.08 \leq k\sigma \leq 0.5$ because the surfaces considered here have $0.2 \leq \sigma \leq 1.2$ cm. At 12 GHz the $k\sigma$ value falls in the range $0.5 \leq k\sigma \leq 3$. In order to see differences in angular trends and variations with σ for both polarizations, we show backscattering curves for both polarizations at 2 GHz in Figure 3.19(a) and at 12 GHz in Figure 3.19(b). For clarity in our illustration only three values of σ are chosen, 0.2, 0.6, and 1.0 cm. At 2 GHz these values correspond to $k\sigma = 0.08$, 0.25, and 0.41, while at 12 GHz, they correspond to $k\sigma = 0.5$, 1.5, and 2.5. Under low-frequency conditions, there is not much change in the angular shapes of the backscattering curves for both polarizations. A larger value of σ simply raises the angular curve of a given polarization almost equally at every angle. However, in the high-frequency region, drastic changes in the angular shape occur as σ increases, and the separation between the polarizations becomes negligible when $k\sigma$ exceeds 1.5.

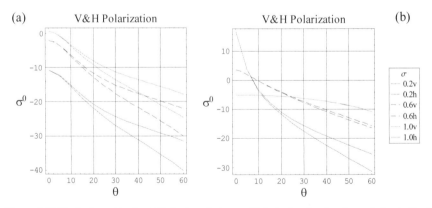

Figure 3.19 Vertically and horizontally backscattering coefficients showing the change in level of and in the spacing between the two polarizations as the surface rms height increases. The common parameters are $L = 7$ cm, $\varepsilon = 6$, and $r = 0.5$ cm: (a) $f = 2$ GHz and (b) $f = 12$ GHz.

3.2.2.2 Effect of Correlation Parameter on Surface Height Dependence

We have seen that the correlation parameter r has a very strong influence on frequency dependence, because different frequencies are sensitive to different parts of the correlation function. We have also noted that in the low-frequency region the differences in correlation properties are minimized due to integration over long wavelength. Hence, in order to see correlation effects we need to operate at a high frequency. To see how different correlation parameters react to changes in the surface rms height, we choose $f = 9$ GHz, $L = 7$ cm, $\varepsilon = 6$, $r = 0.5$, and 1.4 cm and let σ vary from 0.3 to 0.9 cm. The computed backscattering coefficients are shown in Figure 3.20.

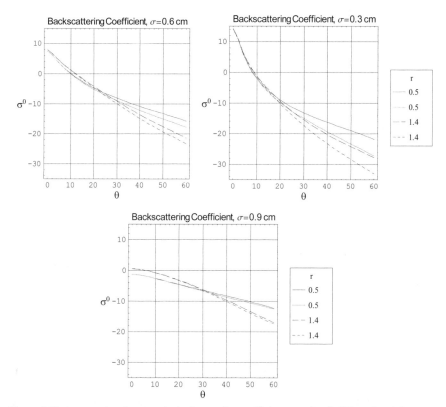

Figure 3.20 A comparison between the backscattering coefficients at $f = 9$ GHz as the surface rms height changes from 0.3 cm to 0.9 cm for a surface with $\varepsilon = 6$ and $L = 7$ cm. For each pair of solid or dashed curves, the upper curve is vertical polarization.

In Figure 3.20 as σ increases from 0.3 to 0.6 cm, $k\sigma$ increases from 0.56 to 1.13. The large $k\sigma$ causes a large drop at normal incidence and a significant narrowing of the spacing between the two polarizations. The angular shapes of the backscattering curves also change from a pure exponential to a more Gaussian shape. These changes happen to both surfaces with $r = 0.5$ and 1.4 cm. The backscattering curve from the $r = 0.5$ cm surface is slower in moving from an exponential shape toward a more Gaussian shape than the $r = 1.4$ cm surface. A further increase of σ to 0.9 cm brings $k\sigma$ to 1.69, which is close to the geometric optics region. Here, the angular shapes of the curves have turned convex and more Gaussian-like. All these changes happen to both types of surfaces. Hence, by displaying backscattering with both polarizations from the two surfaces together as shown in Figure 3.20, it seems that the two surfaces are affected by changes in σ in a similar way. Differences in correlation properties are reflected in the shapes of the angular curves.

In order to see whether backscattering trends versus the surface rms height would remain the same for surfaces with different correlation parameters, we now show backscattering plots with σ instead of r as the parameter in Figure 3.21.

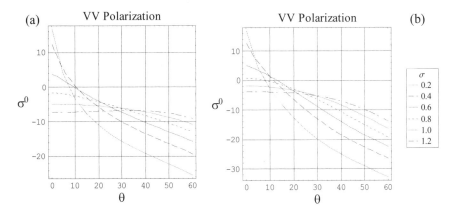

Figure 3.21 Vertically polarized backscattering coefficients computed with common parameters, $L = 7$ cm, $\varepsilon = 6$, and $f = 12$ GHz for various values of the surface rms height: (a) $r = 0.5$ cm and (b) $r = 1.4$ cm.

Figure 3.21(a) shows the backscattering trends versus surface rms height from the surface with $r = 0.5$ cm, and Figure 3.21(b) shows the surface with $r = 1.4$ cm. The backscattering trends versus the surface rms height are the same between 0 to 5 degrees and from 40 to 60 degrees, although their rates of change are not.

Outside these two stated ranges, we can find backscattering trends with the surface rms height in Figure 3.21(a) that are different from those in Figure 3.21(b). For example, along 31 degrees in Figure 3.21(a), backscattering increases with the surface rms height until $\sigma = 1$ cm and then falls back down at $\sigma = 1.2$ cm, whereas in Figure 3.21(b) backscattering continues increasing to $\sigma = 1.2$ cm. Also, at 19 degrees in Figure 3.21(a) backscattering increases with surface rms height until $\sigma = 0.6$ cm before falling back down at larger values of σ, whereas in Figure 3.21(b) the increase in backscattering with surface rms height is until $\sigma = 0.8$ cm. These findings are observable in the display in Figure 3.21 but not in Figure 3.20. Even though the presentation in Figure 3.20 shows the backscattering curves from the two surfaces side-by-side, it is not easy to identify differences in backscattering trends with surface rms height in the plot.

For the horizontal polarization shown in Figure 3.22(a, b), the choice of model parameters is the same as in Figure 3.21. The larger r in Figure 3.22(b) can cause 5-8-dB more drop-off in the backscattering coefficients over large angles of incidence. In general, the comments we made about vertical polarization are applicable also to horizontal polarization. In particular, the backscattering signal versus the surface rms height trends within the 5-40-degree region can be different between Figure 3.22(a) and Figure 3.22(b).

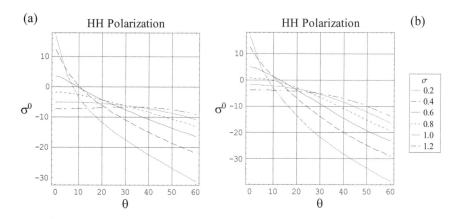

Figure 3.22 Horizontally polarized backscattering coefficients computed with common parameters, $L = 7$ cm, $\varepsilon = 6$, and $f = 12$ GHz for various values of the surface rms height: (a) $r = 0.5$ cm and (b) $r = 1.4$ cm.

Another interesting result is that despite the difference in the shape and the level of the backscattering curves in Figures 3.21(a, b) and 3.22(a, b), the way the spacing between the two polarizations changes with the surface rms height is the same for the two correlation parameters $r = 0.5$ and 1.4. An illustration of this property is shown in Figures 3.23 and 3.24, where calculations are performed at 12 GHz. The difference in the angular shapes of the curves does not affect the rate of change in the spacing with the surface rms height. The difference in the backscattering coefficients of the two polarizations becomes insignificant when $\sigma = 0.6$ cm or larger.

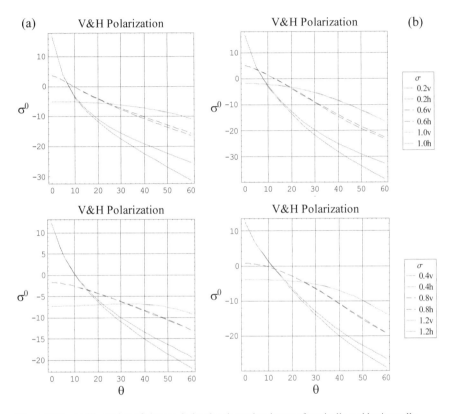

Figure 3.23 An illustration of changes in level and angular shapes of vertically and horizontally polarized backscattering coefficients with the surface rms height with model parameters, $f = 12$ GHz, $L = 7$ cm, $\varepsilon = 6$, and the expl correlation: (a) $r = 0.5$ cm and (b) $r = 1.4$ cm. For each polarization pair the upper curve is vertical polarization. Results indicate that the change in spacing between the two polarizations with the surface rms height is independent of the difference in the correlation function.

3.2.2.3 Effect of Dielectric Constant on Surface Height Dependence

In the backscattering model shown in (2.1) the dielectric constant appears through the surface reflection coefficients and field coefficients, F_{vv}, F_{hh}, which are nonlinear functions of the incident angle and are different for different polarizations. With a larger dielectric constant we expect an overall rise in signal level, but since the change is nonlinear and polarization-dependent, the rise for vertical polarization is different from horizontal polarization and the amount can vary with angle. To compare how backscattering from surfaces with different dielectric constants changes, as surface rms height changes, we choose $r = 0.5$ cm, $L = 5$ cm, and $f = 5$ GHz and let σ vary from 0.3 through 0.9. The dielectric constants are taken to be 6 and 50. Results are shown in Figure 3.24.

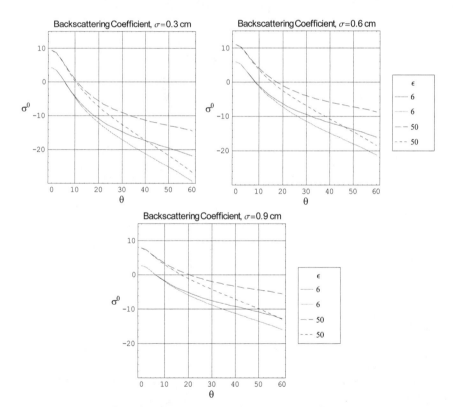

Figure 3.24 A comparison of vertical and horizontal backscattering coefficients from two expl-correlated surfaces with dielectric constants, $\varepsilon = 6$ and $\varepsilon = 50$, as surface rms height changes from 0.3 to 0.9 cm. Other common surface parameters are $r = 0.5$ cm, $L = 5$ cm, and $f = 5$ GHz.

In Figure 3.24 near normal incidence we see a rise in the backscattering coefficients of the two surfaces, when the surface rms height increases from 0.3 to 0.6 cm. This change is consistent with our previous study that when $k\sigma$ is less than 0.7, backscattering signal should be rising as $k\sigma$ increases. When σ reaches 0.9 cm, $k\sigma$ is larger than 0.7 and hence backscattering signal should be lower relative to its value at $\sigma = 0.6$ cm. The point to note here is that the backscattering coefficients from the two surfaces with different dielectric constants are moving together as the surface rms height changes in both the upward and downward directions. At large incident angles we see a general increase in signal level for both surfaces and polarizations as the surface rms height increases. At 60 degrees as surface rms height σ increases from 0.3 to 0.9 cm, horizontally polarized backscattering for both surfaces increases over 13 dB, while vertically polarized backscattering has increased about 9 dB. Thus, a difference in dielectric values has no impact on the amount of change in backscattering due to variations in the surface rms height. This implies that the backscattering trends with the surface rms height are the same for each polarization independent of the surface dielectric constant. However, the signal levels and angular shapes of the backscattering curves are different when the surface dielectric constants are different.

To verify the above idea we show variations of vertically and horizontally polarized backscattering with surface rms height along different incident angles in Figure 3.25 with model parameters, $r = 0.5$ cm, $L = 5$ cm, and $f = 5$ GHz. Comparing Figure 3.25(a) with Figure 3.25(b) in vertical polarization, we see that at normal incidence backscattering from the surface with $\varepsilon = 50$ is about 5 dB higher than the corresponding one in Figure 3.25(a) [i.e., every curve is raised by 5 dB in Figure 3.25(b) relative to Figure 3.25(a) at normal incidence]. At 60 degrees the same situation occurs except this time the amount of rise for every curve is over 7 dB. While backscattering along different incident angles may increase by a different amount when we increase the surface dielectric constant, the amount along a given incident angle and polarization is the same for all surfaces with different surface rms heights (i.e., the variation in backscattering due to changes in the surface rms height along a given incident angle is only shifted but not changed). Comparing changes in backscattering at 60 degrees in horizontal polarization, we find that the increase in signal level due to having a larger dielectric constant is only about 2 dB. At normal incidence, a similar comparison shows that the change is about 5 dB, which is the same for both polarizations. Hence, a larger dielectric constant causes a larger spacing between the polarizations at large angles of incidence. The amount of increase in backscattering for horizontal polarization is again the same along any incident direction. Thus, we can say that the backscattering trends with surface rms height are not affected by a change in the surface dielectric constant, although the angular curves with different dielectric constants can be very different.

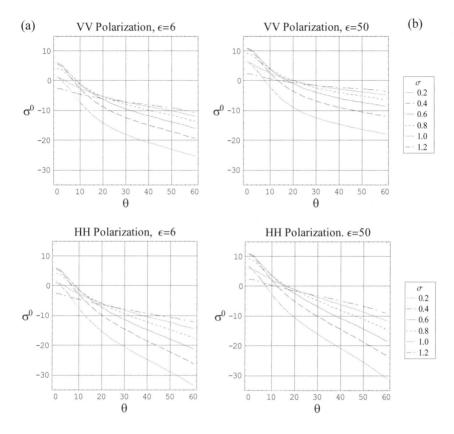

Figure 3.25 An illustration of surface rms height variation of vertically and horizontally polarized backscattering coefficients from two surfaces along various incident angles with common parameters $L = 5$ cm, $r = 0.5$, $f = 5$ GHz, and the expl correlation: (a) $\varepsilon = 6$ and (b) $\varepsilon = 50$.

The most significant difference caused by a large change in the dielectric constant is in the size of the spacing between the backscattering coefficients of the two polarizations. Generally, the spacing increases with the dielectric constant leading to a different trend with the surface rms height. This difference in both the spacing between the two polarizations and the trends of the spacing versus the surface rms height is shown in Figure 3.26. The coming together of the two polarizations shown in Figure 3.26(a) at σ = 1.2 cm is clearly missing in Figure 3.26(b).

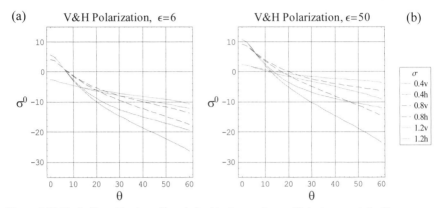

Figure 3.26 Vertically and horizontally polarized backscattering coefficients computed with common parameters, L = 5 cm, r = 0.5 , f = 5 GHz for various values of the surface rms height. In part (a) ε = 6 and in part (b) ε = 50 .

3.2.2.4 Effect of L on Surface Height Dependence

Like r the parameter L is a quantity that changes the shape of the surface correlation. It can affect the trend established by the surface rms height over a portion of the incident angle, after $k\sigma$ exceeds 0.6. This is because after $k\sigma$ exceeds 0.6, backscattering begins to decrease with the rms height over small angles of incidence. The actual range of the small angles over which the said change will take place is dependent on the value of L . Usually, the smaller the L , the wider is this range. The reason is that when L is smaller, the surface rms slope will become larger, forcing a larger amount of drop near normal incidence and a larger rise in signal level over large incident angles. In Figure 3.27 we show the cases for vertical polarization with L equal to 7, 5, and 3 cm, while all other model parameters are kept at r = 0.5 cm, f = 5 GHz, and ε = 6 . When L = 7 cm, there is a wide angular region over which the backscattering level is increasing monotonically with the surface rms height. This region is from about 25 to 60 degrees. Within the 0–25-degree region, the backscattering signal level decreases after the surface rms height exceeds 0.6, 0.8, or 1.0 cm, depending on the incident angle. When the surface correlation length is changed to L = 5 cm, the angular width over which the backscattering level is increasing monotonically with σ is reduced to approximately 35 to 60 degrees. Accordingly, the angular region over which the backscattering level will change from increasing to decreasing with the surface rms height is broadened from 0 to 35 degrees also. Similarly, further reduction of the correlation length to $L = 3$ cm will change the two angular regions to approximately 0–45 and 45–60 degrees. Overall, the backscattering curves are less peaked and flatter as L is shortened. When $L = 7$ cm, the peak at normal incidence is about 9 dB. It drops to about 1.5 dB when $L = 3$ cm for the case $\sigma = 0.6$ cm. Hence, the change is quite significant. Over the regions where the backscattering signal is decreasing with the surface rms height, the rate of change of backscattering with the surface rms height is clearly dependent on the surface correlation length.

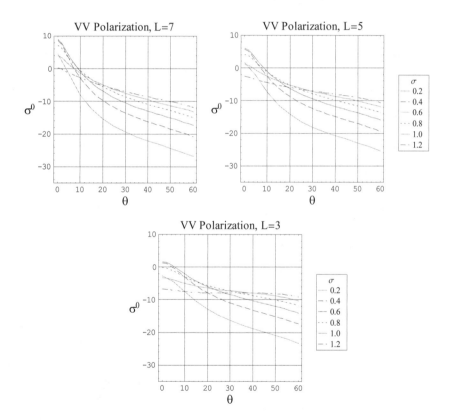

Figure 3.27 Vertically polarized backscattering coefficients computed with common parameters, $\varepsilon = 6$, $r = 0.5$ cm, and $f = 5$ GHz for various values of the surface rms height: (a) $L = 7$ cm, (b) $L = 5$ cm, and (c) $L = 3$ cm.

The corresponding cases for horizontal polarization on the effects of correlation length are shown in Figure 3.28. The angular region in which backscattering curves have reversed from their upward direction for the $L = 7$ cm case is 0 to 20 degrees, a bit smaller than for vertical polarization. When $L = 5$ cm, the angular width is broadened to approximately 25 degrees, which is 10 degrees smaller than for vertical polarization. A further decrease of the correlation length to $L = 3$ cm leads to an angular width of 35 degrees, a width that is 5 degrees smaller than for vertical polarization. In summary, the correlation length does affect dependence of backscattering on the surface rms height but only over a limited angular region, especially for horizontal polarization.

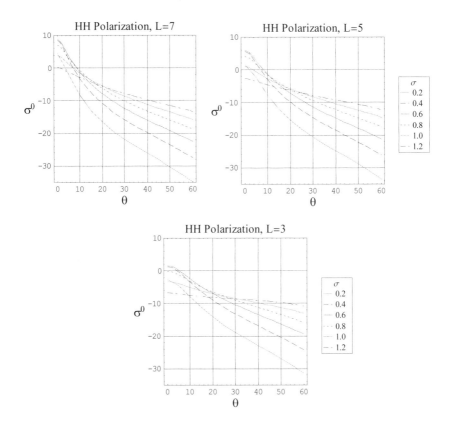

Figure 3.28 Horizontally polarized backscattering coefficients computed with common parameters, $\varepsilon = 6$, $r = 0.5$ cm, and $f = 5$ GHz for various values of the surface rms height: (a) $L = 7$ cm, (b) $L = 5$ cm, and (c) $L = 3$ cm.

Next, we want to examine the influence of the correlation length on the angular shape and spacing between polarizations and its trend with the surface rms height. A better view of angular shapes, spacing between polarizations, and their trend with the surface rms height is shown in Figure 3.29, where Figure 3.29(a) is for $L = 7$ cm and Figure 3.29(b) is for $L = 3$ cm. Other model parameters are the same as in Figure 3.28. Visually, there is a significant change in the angular shape of the backscattering curves between the two sets, $L = 3$ cm and $L = 7$ cm. These differences generate different backscattering trends with σ. For example, at 5, 10, 20, and 30 degrees the backscattering trends with the surface rms height in Figure 3.29(a) are different from the corresponding trends in Figure 3.29(b).

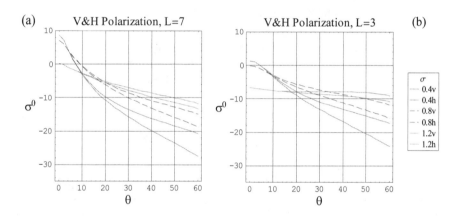

Figure 3.29 An illustration of changes in level and angular shapes of vertically and horizontally polarized backscattering coefficients with the surface rms height with model parameters, $r = 0.5$ cm, $f = 5$ GHz, $L = 7$ cm, $\varepsilon = 6$, and the expl correlation: (a) $L = 7$ cm and (b) $L = 3$ cm. For each polarization pair the upper curve is vertical polarization.

3.2.3 Correlation Parameter Dependence

The correlation parameter r controls the shape of the surface correlation function. A larger r allows the function to include more Gaussian property. Whether this property is affecting backscattering significantly or not depends on its relative size to the surface correlation length L and to the incident wavelength. The surface height parameter σ can influence the magnitude but not the shape of the correlation function. We shall begin our study with frequency effects.

3.2.3.1 Effect of Frequency on Correlation Parameter Dependence

To see frequency effects on correlation parameter variations we select two frequencies, 3 and 9 GHz, and let r vary from 0.1 through 1.4 cm. Other model parameters are $\sigma = 0.4$ cm, $L = 7$ cm, and $\varepsilon = 6$. Computed backscattering results are shown in Figure 3.30. At 3 GHz the angular shape of the backscattering curves for both vertical and horizontal polarizations does not seem to change with the correlation parameter. This is because the incident wavelength is 10 cm, which is long compared to r, and it is also larger than the correlation length L. At 9 GHz we see a different angular curve that is more exponential looking when $r = 0.1$ cm than the curves at 3 GHz.

When r increases to 0.8, vertically and horizontally polarized backscattering at 9 GHz and 60 degrees drops about 2 dB, maintaining about the same spacing in polarization difference. At 3 GHz there is no significant change in backscattering for either polarization. A further increase of r to 1.4 allows the 9 GHz pair of backscattering curves to drop below the vertically polarized backscattering curve at 3 GHz when the incident angle is larger than 45 degrees. Again, there is no appreciable change in the backscattering curves at 3 GHz, even when $r = 1.4$. Only the 9-GHz curves move down farther by another 4 dB at 60 degrees. While the description is what actually happened, the more meaningful description is that as the correlation parameter increases, the low- and high-frequency pairs of backscattering curves tend to merge together over the large incident angle region.

Next, we want to examine the correlation parameter trends in backscattering by choosing $\sigma = 0.4$ cm, $L = 7$ cm, and $\varepsilon = 6$ and compute backscattering for $r = 0.1, 0.5, 1.0, 1.5, 2$, and 2.5 cm at 20 GHz. The trends of how the backscattering curves are varying with r are shown in Figure 3.31. As we shown in Figure 3.30, a low incident frequency cannot detect the small changes in the surface correlation (i.e., small changes in r). This is why we have chosen to illustrate backscattering variations with r at 20 GHz.

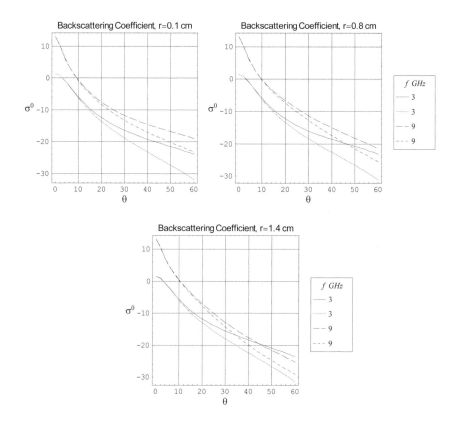

Figure 3.30 A comparison of vertical and horizontal backscattering coefficients from an expl-correlated surface operating at two different frequencies, 3 and 9 GHz, as the surface correlation parameter changes from 0.1 to 1.4 cm. Other common surface parameters are $\sigma = 0.4$ cm, $L = 7$ cm, and $\varepsilon = 6$. For each pair of solid or dashed curves, the upper curve is vertical polarization. Results indicate that as the correlation parameter increases, the backscattering coefficients due to a low and a high frequency tend to merge at large angles of incidence.

When the frequency resolution is high (20 GHz), we see a distinct trend of backscattering coefficients increasing with r within the first 10 degrees and then decreasing with r in the angular region 30 to 60 degrees. In the meantime, the shape of the angular curves is changing from an exponential look to a more Gaussian look as r increases. A significant part of the angular trend is the drop-off over large angles of incidence with r. In practical applications, a centro-symmetric exponential correlation function may cause an overestimate of backscattering at large incident angles due to its nondifferentiable property at the origin. With this exponential-like correlation such a problem is resolved. This drop-off at large angles also changes with frequency, because a lower frequency has less resolution capability and will end up with a smaller drop-off in the backscattering curves.

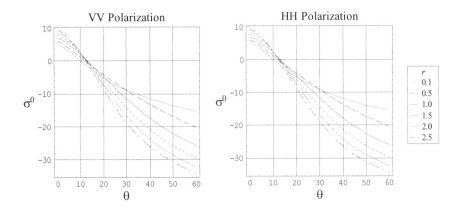

Figure 3.31 Vertically and horizontally polarized backscattering coefficients computed with common parameters, $\varepsilon = 6$, $\sigma = 0.4$ cm, $L = 7$ cm, and $f = 20$ GHz. Backscattering is increasing with r over the angular region, 0 to 10 degrees, and decreasing with r over the 30- to 60-degree region.

In Figure 3.32 we show the backscattering properties of the same case at 10 GHz (i.e., with half the resolution). It is seen that there is a substantial decrease in the separation between the backscattering curves so that we can no longer differentiate the curves in the region where backscattering is increasing with r over the small angular region for both vertical and horizontal polarizations. Furthermore, $r = 0.1$ cm and $r = 0.5$ cm curves are crossing each other.

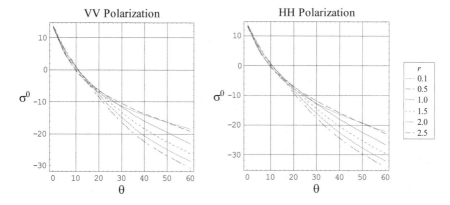

Figure 3.32 Vertically and horizontally polarized backscattering coefficients computed with common parameters, $\varepsilon = 6$, $\sigma = 0.4$ cm, $L = 7$ cm, and $f = 10$ GHz. Backscattering is increasing with r from $r = 0.1$ cm to $r = 0.5$ cm and is decreasing after r exceeds 0.5 cm.

After lowering frequency from 20 to 10 GHz, we see in Figure 3.32 that the angular region over which backscattering coefficients decrease with r has narrowed to 50 to 60 degrees. In particular, the $r = 0.1$ cm curve is lower than the $r = 0.5$ cm curve in the angular region, 20 to 50 degrees. Hence, within this region there is a trend reversal, because the maximum amount of backscattering over 20 to 50 degrees is associated with the curve $r = 0.5$ cm. Over small angles of incidence the maximum amount of backscattering should still be represented by the $r = 2.5$ cm curve, although the separation between curves is too small to see on the graph.

A further decrease in frequency to 5 GHz shows that there is the tendency for all the different r curves to coalesce into just one type of angular shape especially for horizontal polarization. This is because the long wavelength has an integration capability that tends to eliminate smaller differences in the correlation functions. Such a result is shown in Figure 3.33. The spread between the horizontally polarized backscattering curves at 50 degrees in Figure 3.31 is about 17 dB at 20 GHz. Here, it is down to about 5 dB at 5 GHz. Also, the $r = 0.1$ cm curve has dropped further to a level about the same or below the $r = 1.0$ cm curve, while the $r = 0.5$ cm curve shows the highest signal level amount the group of curves displayed.

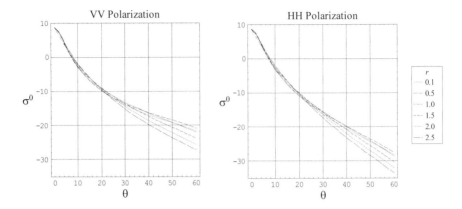

Figure 3.33 Vertically and horizontally polarized backscattering coefficients computed with common parameters, $\varepsilon = 6$, $\sigma = 0.4$ cm, $L = 7$ cm, and $f = 5$ GHz. Backscattering is increasing with r from $r = 0.1$ cm to $r = 0.5$ cm and is decreasing after r exceeds 0.5 cm.

Figures 3.31–3.33 indicate that at low enough frequency vertically polarized backscattering coefficients based on different correlation parameter values will take on just one angular shape, and the same is true of horizontally polarized backscattering coefficients. This fact is demonstrated in Figure 3.34(a), where we compute backscattering coefficients with the same model parameters as in Figure 3.33 at 1 GHz. Clearly, at a sufficiently low frequency (1 GHz) there is no resolution capability to differentiate between different surface correlation features. This is why we end up with two curves in Figure 3.34(a) instead of 12. On the other hand, at high enough frequencies there is no correlation among the scatterers. Polarization difference will disappear because backscattering is now proportional to the surface slope distribution. Each surface correlation parameter defines a surface and a corresponding slope distribution so that for each correlation parameter value r, there is a corresponding backscattering curve. Thus, under high-frequency conditions the number of backscattering curves we have is the same as the number of surfaces. This result is illustrated in Figure 3.34(b), where we show backscattering coefficients for three surfaces with $r = 0.5$, 1.5, and 2.5 cm. In summary, low enough frequencies give us a clear polarization difference but fine correlation features are not detected, while high enough frequency will provide only the slope distribution of the surface and lose all the polarization features.

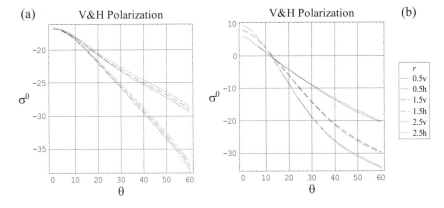

Figure 3.34 Vertically and horizontally polarized backscattering coefficients computed with common parameters, $\varepsilon = 6$, $\sigma = 0.4$ cm, and $L = 7$ cm: (a) $f = 1$ GHz. The upper curves are vertical polarization and lower ones are horizontal polarization; (b) $f = 20$ GHz. The three sets of curves correspond to the three correlation parameters.

3.2.3.2 Effect of rms Height on Correlation Parameter Dependence

We have seen in the previous section that frequency influences the backscattering dependence on correlation parameters mainly over large angles of incidence. Unless the frequency is sufficiently high, all backscattering curves are close together over small angles of incidence, for example, at 10 GHz in Figure 3.32. On the other hand, when we increase the surface rms height from 0.4 to 0.8 cm, backscattering coefficients begin to show a clear increase with the surface correlation parameter over a range of small angles of incidence at 10 GHz, while over large angles of incidence the backscattering signal level continues to decrease with the correlation parameter similar to the case in Figure 3.31 (i.e., a large rms surface height helps to improve the resolution to differentiate the effects of different correlation parameters). This new result is shown in Figure 3.35. At $r = 0.2$ cm, the correlation function is mostly exponential in shape. Near normal incidence, the area under the correlation function is smaller than the corresponding Gaussian function with the same correlation length. This is the reason why backscattering is low near normal incidence at $r = 0.2$. As r increases the correlation function is becoming more Gaussian-like, allowing the backscattering signal to increase over small incident angles. Over larger incident angles backscattering is depending more and more on the tail part of the surface correlation function. The exponential-type correlation function is slower to drop off at large lag distance relative to the Gaussian type. This is why backscattering is higher over large incident angles with the exponential-type correlation function. When $r = 2.5$ cm, the correlation function is more Gaussian-like. Hence, backscattering is higher near normal incident angles and much lower over large incident angles. At $\sigma = 0.8$ cm, the backscattering coefficients for vertical and horizontal polarizations are quite similar. This is because at this rms surface height, $k\sigma = 1.67$, we are very close to the required geometric optics condition, where backscattering is controlled by the surface rms slope instead of σ and L independently.

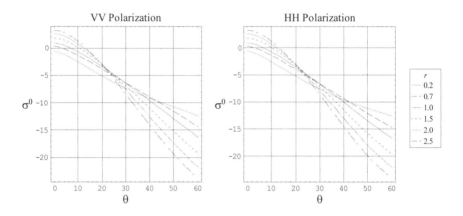

Figure 3.35 Vertically and horizontally polarized backscattering coefficients computed with common parameters, $\varepsilon = 6$, $\sigma = 0.8$ cm, $L = 7$ cm, and $f = 10$ GHz. Backscattering is increasing with r from $r = 0.2$ cm to $r = 2.5$ cm within the first 20 degrees and is decreasing at large angles of incidence, as the correlation function is changing from a more exponential-like function to a more Gaussian-like function over small lag distances.

We have seen that vertical and horizontal backscattering coefficients come close to each other in Figure 3.34(b) similar to Figure 3.35, but with differently shaped angular curves. For comparison we replot Figure 3.34(b) as Figure 3.36(a) and the corresponding results from Figure 3.35 as Figure 3.36(b). Results indicate that while both a high frequency and a large surface rms height can cause vertical and horizontal backscattering coefficients to come together, a higher frequency means a larger $k\sigma$ and kL, while a larger σ will produce a larger $k\sigma$ and a larger rms slope. It follows that the angular drop-off of the backscattering curves over the first 30 degrees for the $r = 2.5$ cm curve is very large (close to 30 dB) at 20 GHz in Figure 3.36(a), whereas in Figure 3.36(b) the $r = 2.5$ cm curve drops less than 15 dB over the same angular range. Also, the signal level at 60 degrees for this curve is down to -34 dB in Figure 3.36(a) and is above -25 dB in Figure 3.36(b). Similarly, the $r = 0.5$ cm curve has a 26-dB drop over the 0 to 60 degree range in Figure 3.36(a), while the $r = 0.5$ cm curve in Figure 3.36(b) drops only 15 dB over the same angular range.

What we mentioned in the above paragraph is about the sharp difference in the angular shapes of the backscattering curves at a high frequency versus a large rms surface height in Figure 3.36. When it comes to the trends of backscattering versus the correlation parameter along an incident angle, the results are the same in the two parts of Figure 3.36 over 0 to 12 degrees, where backscattering is increasing with the correlation parameter, and over 25 to 60 degrees, where backscattering is decreasing with the correlation parameter. Between 12 and 25 degrees the backscattering trends are different in the two parts because in Figure 3.36(a) the backscattering trend has reversed from increasing to decreasing with the correlation parameter, while in Figure 3.36(b) the backscattering trend is still increasing with the correlation parameter.

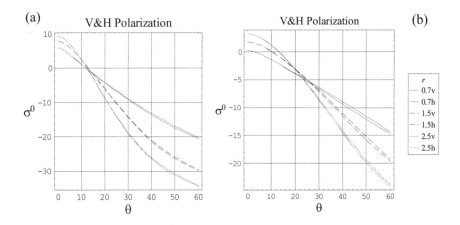

Figure 3.36 Vertically and horizontally polarized backscattering coefficients computed with common parameters, $\varepsilon = 6$ cm, and $L = 7$ cm: (a) $f = 20$ GHz, $\sigma = 0.4$; (b) $f = 10$ GHz, $\sigma = 0.8$.

3.2.3.3 Effect of L on Correlation Parameter Dependence

Both L and r are parameters affecting the shape of the surface correlation function. How each of them affects the backscattering coefficient is dependent on both the incident wavelength and their relative size. To determine the impact of the correlation length L, we shall compute backscattering coefficients for $L = 4$ and 12 cm, while other model parameters are kept the same at $\sigma = 0.4$ cm, $\varepsilon = 6$, and $f = 10$ GHz. When L is equal to 4 cm, the overall angular variation in backscattering is within a 40-dB range. However, we expect to see some increase in backscattering as the correlation parameter increases from 0.2 to 2.5 cm over small angles of incidence. This is because the r values considered here are appreciable compared with $L = 4$ cm. Simultaneously, the backscattering coefficient decreases significantly with the correlation parameter over large angles of incidence. When we increase L to 12 cm, the overall angular variation in backscattering is expanded to almost a 60-dB range. The increase in backscattering over small angles of incidence with r is no longer visible, because the values of r are now small compared to 12 cm. In the meantime, the decrease in the backscattering coefficient over large angles of incidence remains similar to the case when L is equal to 4 cm. However, the total spacing at a given angle, say 60 degrees, between the $r = 0.2$ cm and the $r = 2.5$ cm curves is about 2 dB wider for vertical polarization and 3 dB wider for horizontal polarization. Hence, the rate of change in the backscattering coefficient with variations in the correlation parameter is different when L changes. As shown in Figure 3.37 the significant change in the backscattering trends, when L changes, is in the angular region where backscattering switches from increasing to decreasing with the correlation parameter. This switching is near 22 degrees when $L = 4$ cm in Figure 3.37(a) and near 15 degrees when $L = 12$ cm in Figure 3.37(b). These locations are the same for both vertical and horizontal polarizations. Thus, in the angular region between 15 and 22 degrees the backscattering trends with the correlation parameters are in opposite directions for $L = 4$ cm as compared to the $L = 12$ cm case.

In summary, when the correlation length L becomes large compared to r, the influence of r over small angles of incidence (within 20 degrees of normal) is lost. However, the cause of a larger r to lower the backscattering signal over large angles of incidence remains, because the backscattering over this angular region is dependent on the behavior of the correlation function near the origin, which is controlled by r. The correlation length L is the cause of having a large peak near normal incidence as shown in Figure 3.37(b).

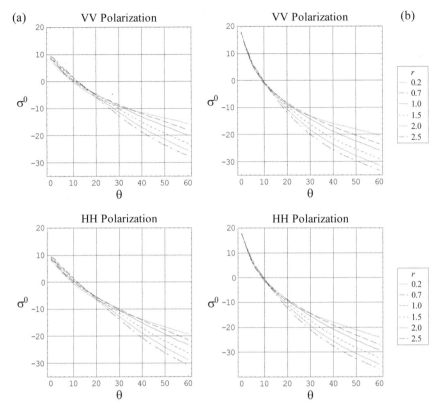

Figure 3.37 Vertically and horizontally polarized backscattering coefficients computed with common parameters, $\varepsilon = 6$, $\sigma = 0.4$ cm, $f = 10$ GHz: (a) $L = 4$ cm, and (b) $L = 12$ cm. Results indicate there are significant changes in the signal level and angular trends when L changes and a much less noticeable change in the rate of change in backscattering with the correlation parameter.

Another view that can show the angular shape and level better for both vertical and horizontal polarizations but would limit the r values to three is shown in Figure 3.38. For the three r values chosen in Figure 3.38(a), the angle where backscattering switches from increasing to decreasing with r is near 17 degrees in Figure 3.38(a), while in Figure 3.38(b) it is near 12 degrees. Here, as in Figure 3.37, Figure 3.38(a) is for $L = 4$ cm and Figure 3.38(b) is for $L = 12$ cm. We can see that within the 12–17-degree region backscattering trends for the two polarizations in Figure 3.38(a) are the opposite of those in Figure 3.38(b). These angles where switching takes place are different from those we stated for Figure

3.38 because the correlation parameters selected in the figures are different. More precisely, these angular locations vary with r and we have stated approximate locations, because the crossover points for different r curves actually spread over a narrow range of angles.

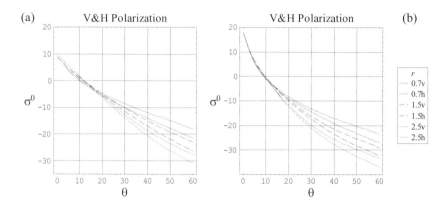

Figure 3.38 An illustration of changes in level and angular shapes of vertically and horizontally polarized backscattering coefficients with the correlation parameter. The common model parameters are $f = 10$ GHz, $\varepsilon = 6$, and $\sigma = 0.4$ cm along with the expl correlation: (a) $L = 4$ cm and (b) $L = 12$ cm. For each polarization pair the upper curve is vertical polarization.

3.2.3.4 Effect of Dielectric Constant on Correlation Parameter Dependence

Recall that the effect of the dielectric constant appears mainly through the reflection coefficients and the field coefficients, F_{vv}, F_{hh}. Generally, a larger dielectric constant will cause the vertically polarized backscattering coefficient to rise more over large angles of incidence than the small angles region. For horizontal polarization the amount of rise is reversed: it rises more over small angles than large angles. These changes will alter the angular shape of the backscattering coefficients versus the incident angle but may not affect the general backscattering trends versus the correlation parameter. For example, in Figure 3.39 the rise at normal incidence is about 4 to 5 dB due to the use of a dielectric constant of 50 as compared to 6. At 60 degrees there is a rise of about 7 dB for vertical polarization and a rise of about only 3 dB for horizontal polarization. It is seen that despite the signal-level differences, the backscattering curves for both vertical and horizontal polarizations have similar appearances. This means that the backscattering trends with the correlation parameter are mostly similar.

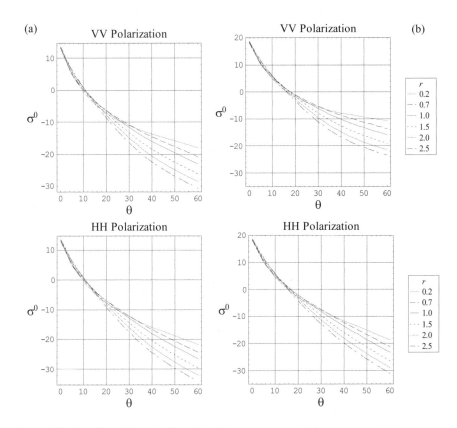

Figure 3.39 Vertically and horizontally polarized backscattering coefficients computed with common parameters, $L = 7$ cm, $\sigma = 0.4$ cm, and $f = 10$ GHz: (a) $\varepsilon = 6$, and (b) $\varepsilon = 50$. Results indicate that there are significant changes in the signal level and angular trends when ε changes, but otherwise the backscattering curves versus the correlation parameter remain similar.

With the above choices of model parameters we did not see a significant difference in the backscattering trends with the correlation parameter for either vertical or horizontal polarizations. Within the first 20 degrees there is not enough spread between the backscattering curves to see the backscattering trends. We know that under a larger surface rms height or a higher frequency, there will be more spread to see the trends along different angular directions in the small incident angle region. What affects backscattering trends with the correlation parameter are the locations where backscattering switches from an increasing to a decreasing trend depending on the correlation parameter value. If these locations are concentrated in a small angular region, the backscattering trends with the correlation parameter will remain relatively simple. On the other hand, should these locations spread out over a significant angular region, then the backscattering trends with the correlation parameter will become fairly complex over this angular region for the two surfaces. Thus, we should investigate such a case before we complete our study of the dielectric effect. In Figure 3.40 we show a case similar to the one in Figure 3.39 but with the surface rms height increased to 0.8 cm. This change is made so that backscattering from each surface is separable from other surfaces over most of the incident angles.

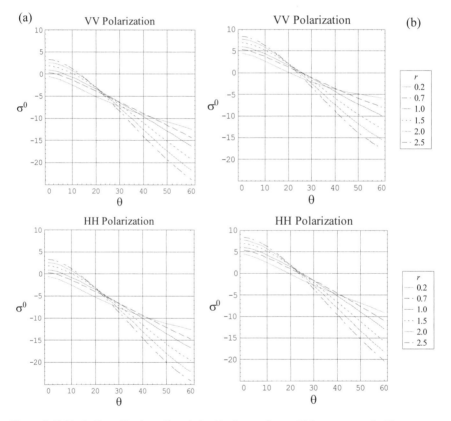

Figure 3.40 Vertically and horizontally polarized backscattering coefficients computed with common parameters, $L = 7$ cm, $\sigma = 0.8$ cm, and $f = 10$ GHz: (a) $\varepsilon = 6$, and (b) $\varepsilon = 50$.

In Figure 3.40, the backscattering curve from each surface is crossing backscattering curves from other surfaces at different incident angles. In Figure 3.40(a) we have $\varepsilon = 6$ and in Figure 3.40(b) $\varepsilon = 50$. The high in signal level in Figure 3.40(a) is about 3.5 dB, while in Figure 3.40(b) it is about 5 dB higher at normal incidence. At 60 degrees for vertical polarization the signal level for every surface is about 6.5 dB higher in Figure 3.40(b) than the corresponding one in Figure 3.40(a). For horizontal polarization the signal level for every surface is about 3 dB higher at 60 degrees in Figure 3.40(b) than the corresponding one in Figure 3.40(a). Thus, the angular shapes of all backscattering curves in Figure 3.40(b) are different from those in Figure 3.40(a) regardless of polarization. We see a clear increasing trend of backscattering with r between 0 and 15 degrees and a decreasing trend between 45 and 60 degrees for both polarizations. Although the backscattering trends with r between 15 and 45 degrees can be much more complex, they are the same along every incident angle. Only the rate of change of backscattering with r along a given incident angle is different. Results indicate that there can be significant changes in the signal level and angular shapes of the backscattering curves when ε changes, yet the backscattering trends versus the correlation parameter and the rates of change of the backscattering signal remain unchanged.

3.2.4 Correlation Length Dependence

When L is much larger than r, it is the quantity that controls the shape of the correlation function and therefore the backscattering characteristics of the associated surface except in the high-frequency limit. It is intuitively clear that as the correlation length L increases, the backscattering coefficient will increase in level at normal incidence and will drop off more with the incident angle. Hence, we expect the backscattering coefficient to be increasing with L near normal incidence and decreasing with L over large incident angles for both vertical and horizontal polarizations. For illustration, we shall select $f = 5$ GHz, $\sigma = 0.4$ cm, $r = 0.5$ cm, and $\varepsilon = 6$ with L varying from 2 through 15. Computed backscattering coefficients are shown in Figure 3.41. Within 5 degrees of normal incidence, backscattering is increasing monotonically with L, while beyond 20 degrees, the signal level is decreasing monotonically with L. Between 5 and 20 degrees, the backscattering trends with the correlation length are more complex but they are the same for both polarizations along each incident angle. This is true for both polarizations. Next, we want to examine whether the trends or angular shapes we have observed are affected by a change in frequency.

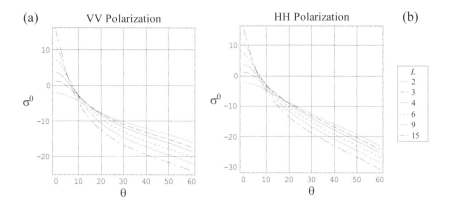

Figure 3.41 Vertically and horizontally polarized backscattering coefficients computed with common parameters, $\varepsilon = 6$ cm, $\sigma = 0.4$ cm, $f = 5$ GHz, and $r = 0.5$ cm: (a) vertical polarization, and (b) horizontal polarization.

3.2.4.1 Effect of Frequency on Correlation Length Dependence

To see how other parameters may affect the backscattering trends with the surface correlation length, we shall begin with considering backscattering at a low and a high frequency, 2 and 10 GHz. Other model parameters will remain the same as in Figure 3.41. Results are shown in Figure 3.42.

In Figure 3.42 the signal level at normal incidence for both high and low frequencies increases with the correlation length. The signal level also decreases at large angles of incidence with the correlation length. These properties are the same as in Figure 3.41. However, at 10 GHz the spacing between polarizations at 60 degrees remains essentially unchanged with the correlation length. It is about 3.6 dB at $L = 3$ cm and is close to 3.58 dB when $L = 9$ cm. Similarly, at 2 GHz the spacing at $L = 3$ cm is about 8.4 dB at 60 degrees, and it decreases to about 8.3 dB at $L = 9$ cm. Another property is that the spacing between the two frequency sets of polarized backscattering coefficients at 60 degrees is decreasing with the correlation length. We can see that at normal incidence the separation between the two sets of backscattering curves at the two frequencies is the same as L changes from 3 to 9 cm, but at 60 degrees the sets are getting closer to each other as L increases.

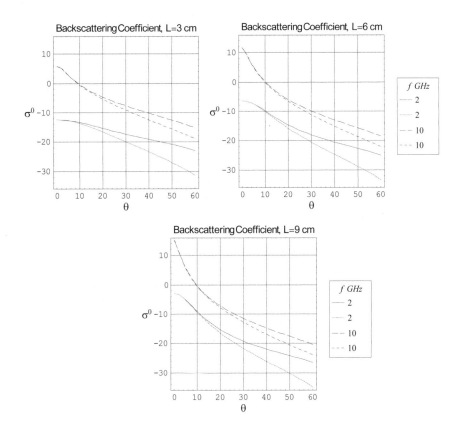

Figure 3.42 A comparison of vertical and horizontal backscattering coefficients from an expl-correlated surface operating at two different frequencies, 2 and 10 GHz, as the surface correlation length changes from 3 to 9 cm. Other common surface parameters are $\sigma = 0.4$ cm, $r = 0.5$ cm, and $\varepsilon = 6$. For each pair of solid or dashed curves the upper curve is vertical polarization.

Now we want to compare the two-frequency case by showing vertically polarized backscattering trends with the correlation length along different incident angles with the parameter values given in Figure 3.42. Results are shown in Figure 3.43, where we see that for both frequencies between 0 to 5 degrees the backscattering is increasing with L, and beyond 40 degrees it is decreasing with L. In between 5 and 40 degrees the backscattering trends at 2 GHz are different from those at 10 GHz. For example, at 25 degrees and 10 GHz, backscattering is decreasing as L increases, while at 2 GHz backscattering increases until $L = 4$ cm before it begins to decrease with the correlation length. Also, at 2 GHz and 15 degrees, backscattering is increasing with L until $L = 9$ cm before it falls back, while at 10 GHz backscattering is decreasing after $L = 4$ cm. There is also a significant difference in the angular shapes of the backscattering curves at these two frequencies. For L equal to or larger than 4 cm the shape of the backscattering curves at 10 GHz are mostly exponential, whereas at 2 GHz the curves are more Gaussian looking. The angular region over which the backscattering curves cross one another at 2 GHz is approximately from 8 to 50 degrees, while for 10 GHz the region is between 5 and 20 degrees.

It is well known that over small angles of incidence there is little difference between vertical and horizontal polarizations. The major difference between these two polarizations is that over the mid- to large angles of incidence, horizontal polarization generally drops off faster than vertical polarization. However, the relative position between backscattering signals with different correlation lengths is kept unchanged. Thus, the backscattering trends with correlation length are not affected by a change in polarization. Only the angular shapes are different. Figure 3.44 shows a comparison for horizontal polarization similar to the one given in Figure 3.43. It is seen that our conclusions about the backscattering trends with correlation length for vertical polarization are applicable to horizontal polarization in Figure 3.44.

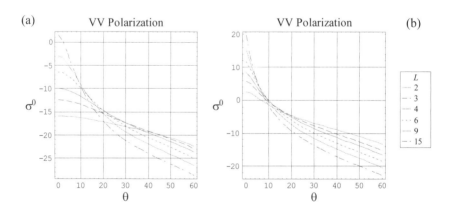

Figure 3.43 Vertically polarized backscattering coefficients computed with common parameters, $\varepsilon = 6$ cm, $\sigma = 0.4$ cm, and $r = 0.5$ cm at (a) $f = 2$ GHz and (b) $f = 10$ GHz.

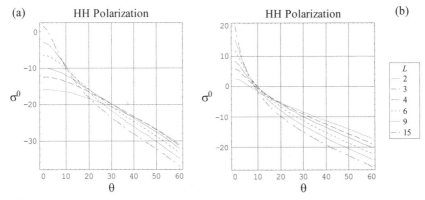

Figure 3.44 Horizontally polarized backscattering coefficients computed with common parameters, $\varepsilon = 6$ cm, $\sigma = 0.4$ cm, $r = 0.5$ cm at (a) $f = 2$ GHz and (b) $f = 10$ GHz.

3.2.4.2 Effect of rms Height on Correlation Length Dependence

Intuitively, surface features that are small compared with the incident wavelength will not have a significant impact on backscattering, because it cannot cause a significant phase change to be detected. To see how two different surface rms heights influence the dependence of backscattering on surface correlation length, we shall use the model parameters $f = 10$ GHz, $r = 0.5$ cm, and $\varepsilon = 6$ and two surface rms heights, $\sigma = 0.4$ cm and $\sigma = 0.6$ cm, to compute backscattering for $L = 3$, 6, and 9 cm. Results are shown in Figure 3.45. Note that a larger L decreases surface slope and alters the shape of surface correlation function. A larger σ will increase the surface rms slope and magnify the impact of surface correlation. It is one of the three model parameters (frequency, dielectric constant, and rms height) that can decrease the spacing between vertical and horizontal polarizations.

In Figure 3.45 as L increases, the surface rms slope decreases, causing backscattering to rise over small angles of incidence and to fall over large incident angles. A closer look also shows that a larger L can cause the spacing between polarizations to narrow. The impact of different rms heights also influences the spacing between polarizations. A larger rms height would cause the spacing to narrow also. Of course, a larger rms height leads to a larger rms slope, causing a lower backscattering at normal incidence and a larger return over large incident angles.

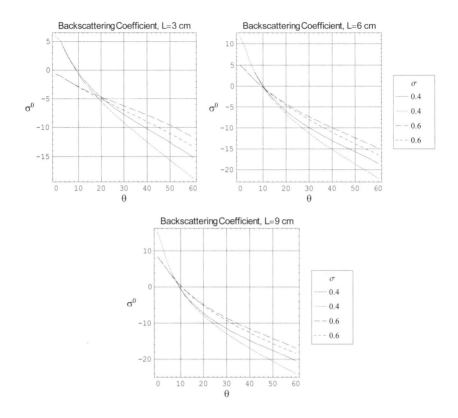

Figure 3.45 A comparison of vertical and horizontal backscattering coefficients from an expl-correlated surface operating at two different rms heights, 0.4 and 0.6 cm, as the surface correlation length changes from 3 to 9 cm. Other common surface parameters are f = 10 GHz, r = 0.5 cm, and ε = 6 . For each pair of solid or dashed curves the upper curve is vertical polarization.

To determine the backscattering trends with L along different incident angles for σ = 0.4 cm versus σ = 0.6 cm, we plot backscattering in Figure 3.46 using the same set of model parameters as in Figure 3.45 at 15 GHz. We see a clear difference between the curves in Figure 3.45(a, b) in both the signal level and the angular shape. However, the backscattering versus the correlation length trends within 5 degrees of normal incidence and beyond 40 degrees are the same in Figure 3.45(a, b), although the rates of change are different. Within the 5–40-degree region the angular curves are crossing one another in different ways in Figure

3.45(a, b). As a result, how the backscattering signal varies with L along an incident angle within this region is different between Figure 3.45(a, b). For example, along 30 degrees in Figure 3.45(a) backscattering is monotonically decreasing as L increases, while in Figure 3.45(b) it increases until $L = 4$ cm before it reverses direction. Along an incident angle of 20 degrees in Figure 3.45(a), backscattering is saturated at $L = 2$, 3, and 4 cm before it decreases. In Figure 3.45(b), backscattering signal actually increases with L until it saturates at $L = 6$ and 9 cm before it drops at $L = 15$ cm along the same angle of incidence.

For horizontal polarization we know that the backscattering characteristics are very similar to vertical polarization over small angles of incidence. Over mid- to large angles of incidence, generally horizontally polarized backscattering will drop off faster with the incident angle. However, the backscattering curves with different L do retain their relative positions similar to vertical polarization. Hence, the comments we made about vertical polarization are applicable directly here to horizontal polarization.

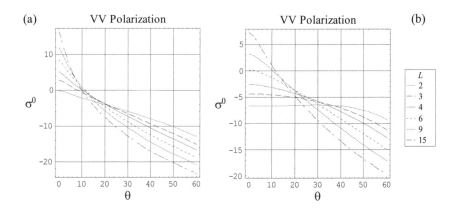

Figure 3.46 Vertically polarized backscattering coefficients computed with common parameters, $\varepsilon = 6$ cm, and $r = 0.5$ cm at $f = 15$ GHz: (a) $\sigma = 0.4$ cm, and (b) $\sigma = 0.6$ cm.

The analysis we have carried out so far has indicated that the model parameters that influence the spacing between the backscattering coefficients of vertical and horizontal polarizations are frequency, surface rms height, and dielectric constant. The sensitivity of backscattering to surface roughness or correlation parameters is dependent on the sensing wavelength. It is for this reason that we have chosen 15 GHz and a surface rms height of 0.6 cm to provide the illustrations in Figure 3.46. Had we used a lower frequency or a smaller surface rms height, we would not see as large a change as shown in Figure 3.46.

3.2.4.3 Effect of Correlation Parameter on Correlation Length Dependence

Recall that both the correlation parameter r and the correlation length L are responsible for the shape of the correlation function. When L is much larger than r the surface correlation length is determined by L. In this case the surface correlation function approaches the exponential function except around the origin region, the size of which is determined by r. When r is greater than L, the correlation function is closer to a Gaussian function in the region around the origin but will approach an exponential function over large lag distance. Hence, the true correlation length is determined by both r and L in this case. In most applications to multiscale surfaces, as we indicated in Chapter 1, the correlation function is close to an exponential function. Hence, our main interest will be dealing with $L > r$, although there are cases where the reverse is true.

Since a larger correlation parameter r would allow a larger portion of the correlation function to follow the Gaussian function, which does not have as many high-frequency spectral components as an exponential function, we know that backscattering will drop off more over large angles of incidence and have a small rise over small angles of incidence. For illustration, a case with $r = 0.1$ cm is compared with $r = 1.4$ cm in Figure 3.47 where other model parameters are chosen to be $f = 9$ GHz, $\sigma = 0.4$ cm, and $\varepsilon = 6$, as surface correlation length changes from 3 to 9 cm. As expected at $L = 3$ cm, backscattering curves with $r = 1.4$ cm are higher than those with $r = 0.1$ cm within the first 30 degrees for both vertical and horizontal polarizations. After about 35 degrees both polarization curves become lower than the corresponding curves with $r = 0.1$ cm. As L increases to 6 cm, backscattering near normal increases due to larger kL and smaller rms slopes, while the backscattering at large angles of incidence declines. The difference between the $r = 0.1$ cm and $r = 1.4$ cm sets of curves are no longer visible at normal incidence, because r is now smaller compared to L. The drop-off at large angles of incidence (beyond 40 degrees) is larger for the $r = 1.4$ cm surface relative to the $r = 0.1$ cm surface, resulting in a separation between the two sets of backscattering curves beyond 40 degrees. A further increase of L to 9 cm allows backscattering associated with the $r = 1.4$ cm surface to increase further at normal incidence and decline even faster over large incident angles, creating a greater and wider separation between the two sets of backscattering curves.

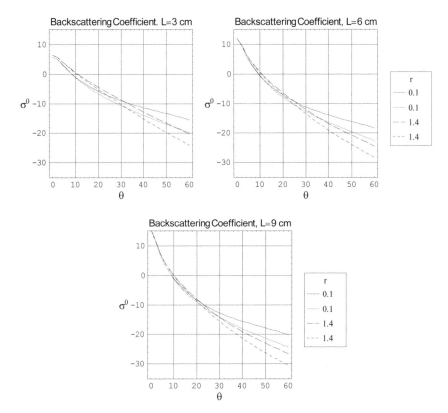

Figure 3.47 A comparison of vertical and horizontal backscattering coefficients from an expl-correlated surface operating at two different correlation parameter values, 0.1 and 1.4 cm, as the surface correlation length changes from 3 to 9 cm. Other common surface parameters are $f = 9$ GHz, $\sigma = 0.4$ cm, and $\varepsilon = 6$. For each pair of solid or dashed curves the upper curve is vertical polarization.

3.2.4.4 Effect of Dielectric Constant on Correlation Length Dependence

Dielectric constant is the model parameter that is independent of surface geometric parameters and is a generally fixed quantity at a given frequency and temperature. In Section 3.2.3 we found that backscattering changes with the correlation parameter r independently of the surface dielectric constant. We expect that the same will happen to the correlation length L (i.e., while both the dielectric constant ε and L can cause level and angular changes to backscattering, the changes due to one parameter are independent of the changes due to the other parameter). For this reason we shall not further illustrate the dielectric effects.

3.2.5 Summary Comments on Parameter Effects

This section summarizes the general influence of model parameters on backscattering in two practical situations in modeling applications. One common situation is that the data are acquired at a given frequency from a certain type of surface with vertical and horizontal polarizations over a large range of incident angles. This means that the incident frequency and the approximate dielectric values are fixed. Only the surface rms height σ, the correlation length L, and the correlation parameter r can be selected in the surface backscattering model. The other situation could be that an incident angle is chosen and measurements are performed over a range of frequencies. In both situations the model parameters that can be selected to match data are σ, L, and r.

3.2.5.1 Parameter Considerations with Angular Data

When $k\sigma < 0.6$, backscattering at normal incidence will increase with σ, but it will reverse direction when $k\sigma > 0.6$. Note that we select 0.6 to denote an approximate location where this transition occurs. The actual transition is gradual and does not change suddenly in backscattering. As the incident angle increases, this reference number for backscattering to change direction also increases when backscattering curves with larger $k\sigma$ values are present (Figure 3.17). Thus, when we increase σ values over normal incidence, backscattering may increase or decrease depending on $k\sigma$, but over incident angles of about 35 to 40 degrees, backscattering always increases with σ (Figure 3.17). Another point about increasing σ is that when $k\sigma > 2$, there is no need to increase σ further, because backscattering should saturate around this value, and there is no appreciable difference between vertical and horizontal polarizations. This means that when a given set of data shows a clear polarization difference, the $k\sigma$ value must be much lower than 2. We know that all three parameters, frequency, rms height, and dielectric constant, can influence the spacing between polarizations. However, when the incident frequency is given and the surface type is specified, only the surface rms height parameter is available to adjust the spacing between polarizations. Hence, the possible choices of σ values are restricted to a very narrow range when the spacing between polarizations is known. In other words, the spacing between polarizations determines the value of σ.

The effect of the correlation length L is simpler than σ. Generally, a larger L will raise the backscattering signal at and near normal incidence and reduce it over large angles of incidence. A larger L reduces the surface rms slope. This is why raising backscattering at near normal incidence also reduces backscattering at large incident angles.

One other model parameter available to choose to fit data is the correlation parameter r. When r is equal to 0.1 cm, it requires an incident wavelength of 1.5 cm to differentiate it from other r values (Figure 3.31). If so, it causes a higher backscattering level over large incident angles and a small drop near normal incidence. If the incident wavelength is 3 cm, then the small drop over small incident angles is not appreciable. Only the rise over large incident angles is significant (Figure 3.32). These backscattering changes come about because the correlation function behaves likes an exponential for small r, which helps to raise backscattering over large incident angles. Generally, a smaller r will cause backscattering to increase over large incident angles. However, this trend may reverse direction at some r value depending on the incident frequency.

3.2.5.2 Parameter Considerations with Frequency Data

Most of the backscattering versus frequency measurements have been taken at incident angles away from both near normal and near grazing angles. This is because near normal incidence there is the possibility of including an unknown amount of coherent scattering in the data, while near grazing there could be an unknown amount of volume scattering due to protuberances such as a spray or whitecap over the ocean surface. In the low-frequency region, backscattering should be rising with frequency because of increases in both $k\sigma$ and kL. A larger σ should start with a higher signal level because of $k\sigma$. It should also be higher over larger incident angles due to having a larger rms slope relative to a similar surface with a smaller σ. In general, it provides a rising curve with frequency showing signs of saturation at higher frequencies [Figure 3.48 (a)]. A lower σ surface on the other hand will start at a lower signal level in the low-frequency region and could rise over a wider frequency range before showing saturation. However, this rising trend with frequency as shown in Figure 3.48(b) changes very quickly as the incident angle increases from 20 to 30 degrees. At 30 degrees the frequency trend is flat after 15 GHz. At 40 degrees the frequency trend turns downward after about 6 GHz for vertical polarization and 15 GHz for horizontal polarization. In addition to having a smaller rms slope, another contributing cause to this downward movement is due to having $r = 1$ cm. This downward movement does not exist if we set $r = 0.5$ cm and keep all other model parameters unchanged. This result is illustrated in Figure 3.48.

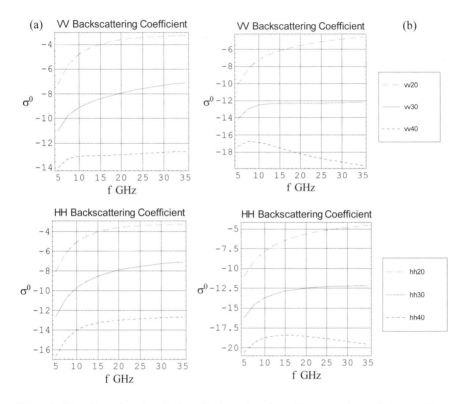

Figure 3.48 An illustration of vertically and horizontally polarized backscattering coefficients at 20, 30, and 40 degrees versus frequency for two surfaces with common parameters, $r = 1$ cm, $L = 7$ cm, $\varepsilon = 5$, and the expl correlation: (a) $\sigma = 0.6$ cm and (b) $\sigma = 0.4$ cm. Results indicate all backscattering curves in (a) have a rising trend with frequency, whereas in (b) backscattering declines at 40 degrees after frequency exceeds 10 GHz for vertical polarization and 15 GHz for horizontal polarization.

At 5 GHz the signal levels at 20, 30, and 40 degrees are very close to those in Figure 3.48. As frequency increases, signal begins to be more sensitive to the correlation function near the origin. The $r = 0.5$ cm correlation is more exponential like than the $r = 1$ cm correlation near the origin, thus causing signal to rise more. This is true for both vertical and horizontal polarizations. Hence, we do not see a decline for the 40-degree curve.

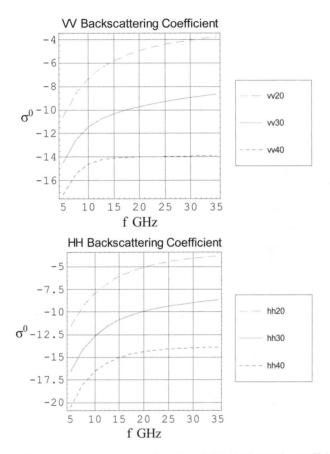

Figure 3.49 An illustration of vertically and horizontally polarized backscattering coefficients versus frequency with surface parameters, $r = 0.5$ cm, $\sigma = 0.4$ cm, $L = 7$ GHz, and $\varepsilon = 5$ and the expl correlation.

Finally, consider the influence of the correlation length L on backscattering versus frequency. We know its major impact is to increase backscattering near normal incidence and lower it at large incident angles starting from about 30 degrees and beyond. Hence, we choose 10, 30, and 50 degrees for this comparison. Results are shown in Figure 3.50, where we have $L = 3$ cm in Figure 3.50(a) and $L = 7$ cm in Figure 3.50(b). Other than the expected level difference at 10, 30, and 50 degrees, we see that the frequency trends at these angles are also different in the Figure 3.50(a, b). In particular, the 10-degree curve in Figure 3.50(a) has a decreasing trend after 15 GHz, whereas in Figure 3.50(b) it has an increasing trend.

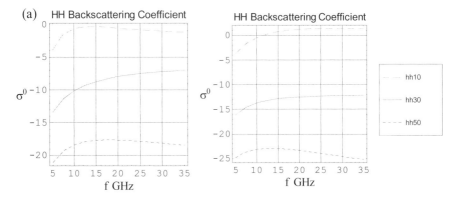

Figure 3.50 A comparison of horizontally polarized backscattering coefficients versus frequency with surface parameters, $r = 1$ cm, $\varepsilon = 5$, and $\sigma = 0.4$ cm and the expl correlation: (a) $L = 3$ cm, and (b) $L = 7$ cm.

3.3 COMPARISONS WITH DATA FROM SURFACES WITH UNKNOWN PARAMETERS

Two sets of data had been acquired at 8.6, 17, and 35.6 GHz. One is from a dry asphalt surface [Ulaby et al., 1986, p. 1809] and the other is from a loose dirt surface [Ulaby et al., 1986, p. 1810]. A significant point about the asphalt surface is that the measurements show a clear separation of 3 dB or more between the vertical and horizontal polarizations at 60 degrees as shown in Figure 3.51. This means that the $k\sigma$ value for the surface is significantly less than 1 or the incident wavelength can be 10 times the surface rms height. The fact that this surface is smooth to the wavelength is also evidenced by showing a strong a coherent backscattering at normal incidence at 8.6 and 17 GHz. Since the backscattering coefficient σ^0 represents only incoherent scattering, in our comparisons we shall ignore the data at normal incidence at these two frequencies. Over a 20-dB change between 0 and 10 degrees at 8.6 GHz is believed to be due to coherent contribution. A similar but smaller change also occurs at 17 GHz. At 35.6 GHz this change is down to 10 dB, which is still significant over a 10-degree range.

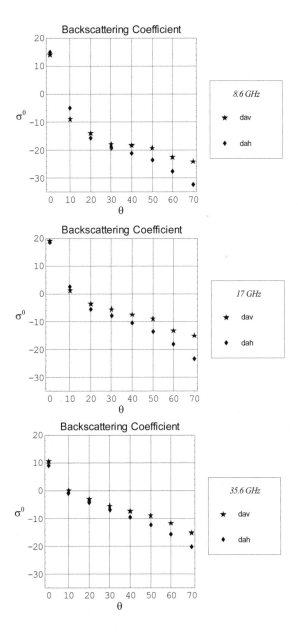

Figure 3.51 Data acquired over an asphalt surface at 8.6, 17, and 35.6 GHz reported by [Ulaby et al., 1986].

3.3.1 An Asphalt Surface

The dielectric value of asphalt is around 5 and 6. The incident frequency is known. Hence, the adjustable model parameters are σ, L, and r. The shape of the angular curves based on reported data is exponential. This implies a relatively small r. However, at 8.6 GHz, the data is known to be affected by a coherent return of an unknown amount, which could also influence the measurement at 10 degrees. This plus inherent data fluctuation makes it unclear whether in data matching we should focus on the 10-degree data or the 20-degree data. For this reason we shall show three different matching to illustrate the 8.6 GHz data. Results are shown in Figure 3.52. The different choices of model parameters in Figure 3.52 also serve to illustrate the impact of σ and L in data matching.

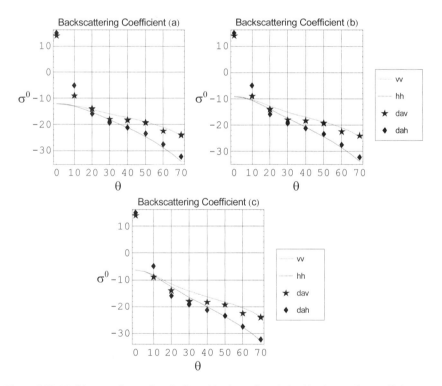

Figure 3.52 Model comparisons of vertically and horizontally polarized backscattering coefficients with data acquired from an asphalt surface at 8.6 GHz. Common surface parameters are $r = 0.09$ cm and $\varepsilon = 5$ with the expl correlation: (a) $\sigma = 0.13$ cm, $L = 0.6$ cm, (b) $\sigma = 0.14$ cm, $L = 0.8$ cm, and (c) $\sigma = 0.16$ cm, $L = 1.0$ cm.

In Figure 3.52(a) we have attempted to match the 8.6-GHz data, assuming that the 20-degree data is more reliable than the 10-degree data. Parameter values used are shown in the legend. The vertically polarized 30-degree data is off the model predicted value, but it is also off the angular trend established by other data points and fails to show a separation between vertically and horizontally polarized data. All other data points are in agreement with the model predicted level and angular trend. This is an acceptable model prediction excluding the data points at 0 and 10 degrees.

If we think data fluctuation has caused the 10-degree data to be higher and the 20-degree data to be lower, then Figure 3.52(b) provides a better agreement between the model and these data. In Figure 3.52(b) we have raised σ from 0.13 cm to 0.14 cm, causing the signal level to rise at 10 degrees and other angles. In order to bring back agreement over large incident angles, we have to increase L from 0.6 cm to 0.8 cm.

Finally, to further illustrate model behavior we assume the data at 10 degrees is more reliable than 20 degrees. If so, we have to increase σ further from 0.14 cm to 0.16 cm and lower backscattering at larger incident angles back to their original level by increasing L from 0.8 to 1.0. This new result is shown in Figure 3.52(c). The agreement between the model and data is good because we have left out the 20-degree data and we know the 30-degree data is questionable. A closer examination reveals that the agreement between the model and data at 40 degrees has deteriorated as compared to the comparison in Figure 3.52(a). This indicates that the assumption leading to the comparison in Figure 3.52(c) may not be a valid one, although the agreement with the intended data shows acceptable agreement.

In Figure 3.52 the largest value of the selected $k\sigma$ is 0.29. This means that it is the roughness smaller than the incident wavelength that is responsible for backscattering. As we mentioned before, the other indication that backscattering is due to the small roughness is having a large spacing between vertical and horizontal polarizations over large angles of incidence.

Next, we want to consider the data at 17 GHz. This data set also shows a clear significant separation between vertical and horizontal polarizations as shown in Figure 3.53. The data level at 20 degrees is about 10 dB higher than at 8.6 GHz, and, as shown in Figure 3.51, it is comparable to that at 35.6 GHz. We believe that this level is too high to be consistent with having as large a spacing between polarizations over large angles of incidence as shown in Figure 3.53. Assuming that the measured spacing is more reliable than the signal level, we shall perform only an angular trend comparison here. All model parameters used are given in the legend.

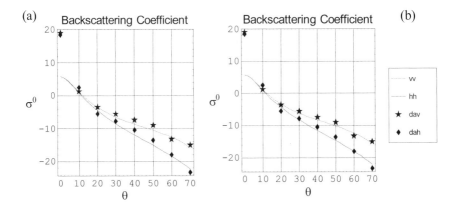

Figure 3.53 Angular trend comparisons of vertically and horizontally polarized backscattering coefficients with data acquired from an asphalt surface at 17 GHz. Common model parameters are $\sigma = 0.16$ cm, $L = 1.0$ cm, and $\varepsilon = 6$ with the expl correlation: (a) $r = 0.09$ cm and (b) $r = 0.15$ cm. The peaking at 10 degrees is due to kL being twice as large as its value at 8.6 GHz. The use of $r = 0.09$ cm in (a) results in a low prediction for vertically polarized backscattering at 30, 40, and 50 degrees. This difference in level can be improved by raising r to 0.15 cm as shown in (b). In general, increasing the value of r will cause backscattering to decrease over large incident angles but the exact location where the backscattered signal reaches a maximum is dependent on frequency. In the current case it is for r close to 0.15 cm.

We know that a higher frequency has a better resolution, meaning that unlike what happened to the 8.6-GHz data, the 10-degree data is not affected by the coherent contribution around normal incidence. It is possible that either the same or smaller roughness scales are responsible for backscattering at this frequency. We know that both larger surface rms height and higher frequency could narrow the spacing between polarizations. The spacing at 17 GHz is narrower than the one at 8.6 GHz but is still quite wide. Hence, we shall keep the surface rms height the same as at 8.6 GHz. In Figure 3.53(a) we show an angular trend comparison with the same model parameters as those used for the 8.6 GHz except we have raised the dielectric value from 5 to 6 to provide a somewhat higher signal level. Overall, the predicted signal levels at 30, 40, and 50 degrees appear low for vertical polarization and are also low at 40 and 50 degrees for horizontal polarization. For this reason we adjust r to 0.15 cm, which influences the signal level mainly over large incident angles. Note that a further increase in r will cause backscattering to decrease, because in general, larger r makes the correlation function more Gaussian like near the origin. The specific value of r where backscattering over large incident angles reaches a maximum is dependent on both the correlation function and the incident wavelength. The result of this comparison is shown in Figure 3.53(b), where a better overall angular agreement is obtained. In Figure 3.53 we have to raise the model predicted value by 3 dB to realize the agreement.

In our illustration of parameter effects in the previous section we encounter backscattering angular trends and signal levels similar to those shown in Figure 3.53, but the spacing between the vertical and horizontal polarizations is much smaller. This is because to have a high signal level over large incident angles requires a $k\sigma$ greater than 1.0. The large $k\sigma$ forces the spacing to be small. To enlarge the spacing $k\sigma$ must be lowered, causing the signal level to be lowered along with it. Thus, when we consider the 35.6-GHz data given in Figure 3.54, which has a high signal level along with a wide separation between polarizations, we choose to ignore the signal level and attempt to match only the angular trends.

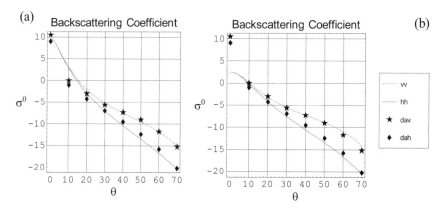

Figure 3.54 Angular trend comparisons of vertically and horizontally polarized backscattering coefficients with data acquired from an asphalt surface at 35.6 GHz. Common model parameters are $f = 35.6$ GHz, and $\varepsilon = 5$ with the expl correlation: (a) $\sigma = 0.09$ cm, $L = 0.67$ cm, and $r = 0.07$ cm and (b) $\sigma = 0.072$ cm, $L = 0.3$ cm, and $r = 0.05$ cm. In (a) we include the data at normal incidence. In (b) we ignore the data at normal incidence.

In Figure 3.54 the incident frequency is more than four times 8.6 GHz, and the wavelength is less than a quarter of the one at 8.6 GHz. It is unlikely that the radar will see the same set of surface parameters as those used in 8.6 GHz, because if it does $k\sigma = 1.19$, which will force the two polarizations to come together. Furthermore, there is a clear spacing between polarizations in this data set as shown in Figure 3.54. This means that the $k\sigma$ should be smaller than 1.0 and $kL < 5$. Investigators who acquired the data have indicated that there was a significant coherent contribution at normal incidence at 8.6 and 17 GHz. It is not clear whether the same problem exists at 35.6 GHz. Hence, we shall try to match these data in two ways: (1) include the data points at normal incidence in Figure 3.54(a) and (2) exclude them in Figure 3.54(b). The actual values chosen to match this data set are $\sigma = 0.09$ cm and $L = 0.67$ cm in Figure 3.54(a) and $\sigma = 0.072$ cm and $L = 0.3$ cm in Figure 3.54(b). Other model parameters are given in the legend.

In Figure 3.54(a) we try to fit the data points at normal incidence and miss the data points at 10 degrees. The difference between 0 and 10 degrees in data level is 10 dB or more, which seems excessive. Based on the angular trends established by data at other angles, it appears that the data at 10 degrees is too low. This is true when we assume the data level at normal incidence is correct. On the other hand, if we assume that the 10-degree data is correct and the high data level at normal incidence is due to coherent contribution, then we should choose a different set of model parameters as shown in the legend for Figure 3.54(b). In Figure 3.54(b) we assume a smaller σ to lower the predicted level around 10 degrees and a much smaller L to keep the backscattering over large incident angles from falling. The smaller σ has caused a wider separation between the polarizations relative to Figure 3.54(a), but the difference is within measurement error. Thus, depending on what we know about the data we shall have different choices of the model parameters. In either case, satisfactory agreement in angular trend between model and data is possible, as shown in Figure 3.54. The agreement shown requires us to raise the model predicted value by 4.5 dB. The requirement of a smaller set of surface parameters at 35.6 GHz confirms our belief that *wavelength filtering* is taking place here.

3.3.2 A Loose Dirt Surface

Measurements available at 8.6, 17, and 35.6 GHz from a loose dirt surface are shown in Figure 3.55. Unlike the asphalt surface, the separation between polarizations is small and the fluctuation in data level is as large or larger than the spacing between vertical and horizontal polarizations. Generally, the data trend is not clear within the first 40 degrees due to significant data fluctuation in this region. Beyond 30 or 40 degrees there is a clear angular trend. However, this angular trend over large angles cannot determine the correct angular trend over the smaller angles. Another significant point about this data set is that there is no sharp peak near normal incidence. Furthermore, the fluctuation in data is so large within the first 20 degrees that at 17 and 35.6 GHz the 10-degree data is higher than those at normal incidence This means that only incoherent scattering is present in this data set. Theoretically, the spacing between polarizations should be zero at normal incidence and increases gradually with the incident angle. This data set shows similar spacing throughout the entire range of incident angles. One possible interpretation is that there is really no significant separation between the polarizations and that the spacing is due to data fluctuation. Another possible interpretation is that the spacing over large angles starting at 50 degrees is real while the spacing at other angles is due to data fluctuation. For each frequency we shall consider both possibilities. Furthermore, over small incident angles there could be more than one way to fit the data, depending on our assumption about which data points are more likely to be correct.

Let us now consider the 8.6-GHz data. First, we assume that the spacing between polarizations is unimportant because it is uniformly the same throughout all angles (i.e., the spacing is caused by inherent fluctuations in data). If so, $k\sigma$ should be between 1 and 2 to force vertical and horizontal polarizations to come close to each other. Loose dirt should have a low dielectric constant due to air space between soil particles. In Figure 3.56(a) we choose $\sigma = 0.92$ cm and $\varepsilon = 2.8$. The correlation parameter r is chosen to be 1.3 cm to allow backscattering to drop over large incident angles and the correlation length is set to 4.2 cm to generate an angular curve shown in Figure 3.56(a). These choices of surface parameters indicate that the surface is very rough and has a large rms slope. The theoretical curve has been chosen to pass through the midpoint of the data at 20 degrees. Due to fluctuation in data it is above the data points at 10, 30, and 40 degrees. Should we choose to let the model curve pass through the 10-degree data and get closer to 30- and 40-degree data, we can increase σ to 0.95 cm and drop the dielectric constant to $\varepsilon = 2.6$. This choice will miss the data points at normal incidence but it does provide a good fit to all other data points. This case is shown in Figure 3.56(b) to indicate that data fluctuation can produce different model curves depending on our assumption as to which data we want to match and what data points are assumed to be reliable. In Figure 3.56 we have assumed that the spacing between data points is not real, because it is the same instead of increasing with the incident angle. Furthermore, it shows a separation at normal incidence quite similar to the separations at other incident angles. Theoretically, there is no difference in polarization at normal incidence for randomly rough surfaces.

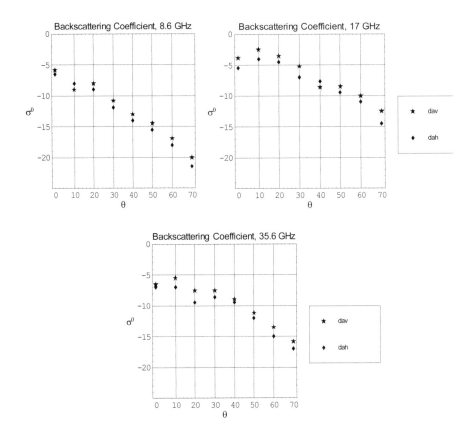

Figure 3.55 Data acquired over a loose dirt surface at 8.6, 17, and 35.6 GHz reported by [Ulaby et al., 1986]. A significant point about this data set is that the spacing between polarizations is about the same over most incident angles, whereas normal spacing is zero at normal incidence and increases gradually with the incident angle. Within 40 degrees there is a significant fluctuation in data, which causes an uncertainty in the angular trend in this region.

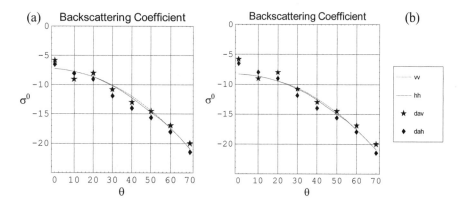

Figure 3.56 Comparisons of vertically and horizontally polarized backscattering coefficients with data acquired from a loose dirt surface at 8.6 GHz. Common model parameters are $r = 1.3$ cm, and $L = 4.2$ cm with the expl correlation: (a) $\sigma = 0.92$ cm, and $\varepsilon = 2.8$ cm and (b) $\sigma = 0.95$ cm, and $\varepsilon = 2.6$. In (a) we include the data at normal incidence. In (b) we ignore the data at normal incidence.

Another possible interpretation of the data at 8.6 GHz is that the small spacing between vertical and horizontal polarizations over large angles of incidence is real because the data there shows a clear angular trend, whereas over small angles of incidence there are large fluctuations. In order to allow a spacing between polarizations to appear we must reduce $k\sigma$ close to half of its value used in Figure 3.56. Lowering σ will cause a large rise near normal incidence. To compensate for this rise we have to lower L or r, or both. A possible choice of model parameters are $\sigma = 0.46$ cm, $L = 1.2$ cm, $r = 1$ cm, and $\varepsilon = 2.8$, the same dielectric value as in Figure 3.56(a). The comparison is shown in Figure 3.57. Clearly, the changes in σ, L, and r are very large as compared with the corresponding parameters in Figure 3.56. However, both the signal level and the angular trend here are similar and close to those in Figure 3.56(a). This means that the accuracy in measuring the relative spacing between polarizations is very important. It also indicates that when data fluctuation is of the same order as the spacing, there is a greater uncertainty in the estimation of surface parameters. Theoretically, the spacing between vertical and horizontal polarizations carries a very important piece of information about the surface roughness. Measurements must provide a reliable angular trend to be useful for estimating surface parameter values.

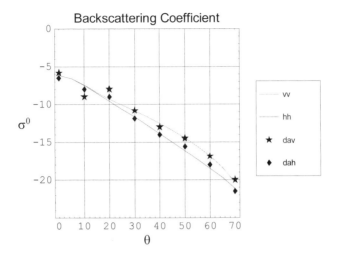

Figure 3.57 Comparisons of vertically and horizontally polarized backscattering coefficients with data acquired from a loose dirt surface at 8.6 GHz. Model parameters are $\sigma = 0.46$ cm, $\varepsilon = 2.8$, $r = 1.0$ cm, and $L = 1.2$ cm with the expl correlation.

Another point worth noting here is that in Figure 3.57 the values of L and r are not far apart. They are the quantities that determine the shape of the correlation function. It is possible to interchange their values, and the resulting correlation functions will stay close to each other. If we modify the change a little bit we can make the correlation functions, and the backscattering coefficients computed from them very close to each other. To demonstrate this point we show a comparison between the correlation functions with the values of L and r interchanged in Figure 3.58(a), where the solid line is the normalized correlation function with $r = 1$ cm and $L = 1.2$ cm, which are the values used in Figure 3.57, and the dashed line is with $r = 1.2$ cm and $L = 1.0$ cm. It is clear in Figure 3.58(a), the two correlation functions are close to each other. In Figure 3.58(b) we want to produce an even closer agreement by modifying L to $L = 1.1$ cm. Results indicate that when the values of L and r are close, both of them influence the correlation length. This is why different L and r values can generate similar correlations.

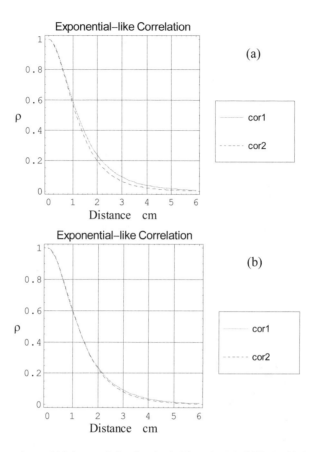

Figure 3.58 Comparisons of (a) the correlation function in Figure 3.57 (solid line) with the same correlation function (in dashes) but with the values of r and L interchanged and (b) similar comparison as in (a) but with the value of L increased from 1.0 to 1.1 cm for the correlation function represented by the dashed line. Results indicate that when the values of r and L are close, their roles are about the same. Furthermore, it is possible to make the correlation functions very close with a small adjustment.

Finally, we show that the correlation function with $r = 1.2$ cm and $L = 1.1$ cm can produce backscattering curves quite similar to those in Figure 3.57 where $r = 1.0$ cm and $L = 1.2$ cm. Results are shown in Figure 3.59(a). Figure 3.59(b) is a copy of Figure 3.57 to allow a more direct comparison.

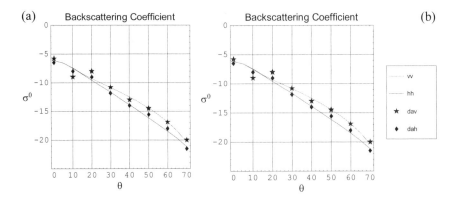

Figure 3.59 Comparisons of vertically and horizontally polarized backscattering coefficients with data acquired from a loose dirt surface at 8.6 GHz. Common model parameters are $\sigma = 0.46$ cm, and $\varepsilon = 2.8$ with the expl correlation: (a) $r = 1.2$ cm and $L = 1.1$ cm, and (b) $r = 1.0$ cm and $L = 1.2$ cm.

Now, we consider the data at 17 GHz shown in Figure 3.55. The level of this data set is higher than those at 8.6 and 35.6 GHz. For a very rough surface the signal level is determined by the surface rms slope and its dielectric constant. Here, the dielectric constant is limited to 4 or lower because it is loose dirt. The size of the slope is controlled by the shape of the angular curve. Thus, these quantities are interrelated. For this particular data set we believe the level is too high and we shall restrict ourselves to match only the angular trend. Similar to the 8.6-GHz data this set also has large fluctuations over small angles of incidence. There is a possibility that the $\sigma = 0.46$ cm that we used for the 8.6-GHz data also works at 17 GHz. We shall start with this rms height and adjust L to fit the angular trend. The correlation length comes to 1.95 cm with $r = 0.42$ cm. At this point the overall trend is correct but the level is low and we have to raise ε to 4 and add 2.5 dB to realize the matching shown in Figure 3.60. Similar to the asphalt data set the fluctuation in data is very large over small angles of incidence, and there is a clear angular trend over large incident angles along with some separation between polarizations. However, it is unlikely that the separation between polarizations is real. First, there is no angular trend showing that the spacing is decreasing toward smaller incident angles. Second, if the spacing over large angles is real the surface would have to be sufficiently smooth because $k\sigma$ should be smaller than 1.0. If so, we should see a maximum at normal incidence. Instead, the data has a dip at normal incidence. The dip of data at 40 degrees along with a reversal in the level of vertical and horizontal polarizations has disrupted the data trend. If we leave out the 40-degree data and the peaking at 10 degrees, then the general data trend should be what we show in Figure 3.60.

For a loose dirt surface there is one more possibility (i.e., due to difference in penetration over small versus large angles of incidence, the incident wave actually sees several different surfaces). If so, a much smoother surface is seen over 50 to 70 degrees, and this is why there is a clear angular trend and some separation between the polarizations. The large variation in data over smaller angles is due to seeing different surfaces.

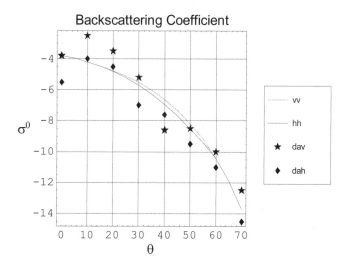

Figure 3.60 Comparisons of vertically and horizontally polarized backscattering coefficients with data acquired from a loose dirt surface at 17 GHz. Model parameters are $\sigma = 0.46$ cm, $\varepsilon = 4$, $r = 0.42$ cm, and $L = 1.95$ cm with the expl correlation.

One more loose dirt data set to consider is at 35.6 GHz, which is also given in Figure 3.55. The general appearance of this data set is similar to the 17-GHz data but it is at a lower level. There is a clear separation between the vertical and horizontal polarizations at every incident angle but the amount of separation does not form an angular trend. Theoretically, this separation should be zero at normal incidence and increase with the incident angle. This theoretical angular trend is not exhibited by the data. Thus, we ignore the presence of spacing between polarizations and try to match only the overall angular trend. Based on the wavelength filtering concept when we used $\sigma = 0.92$ cm at 8.6 GHz, we should select approximately $\sigma = 0.46$ cm at 17 GHz and $\sigma = 0.23$ cm at 35.6 GHz. The specific selected model parameters at 35.6 GHz are $\sigma = 0.23$ cm, $L = 0.95$ cm, $r = 0.23$ cm, and $\varepsilon = 3.8$. These selections of surface rms height lead to $k\sigma$ values larger than 1.6 and the two polarizations to come close to each other. The comparison for the 35.6-GHz case is shown in Figure 3.61. Model predictions are tracking the overall angular trend of the data and are at the same level as the average data.

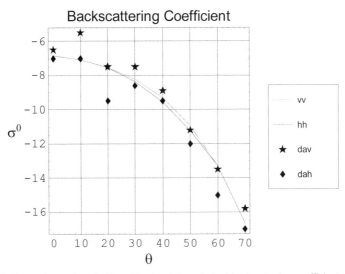

Figure 3.61 Comparisons of vertically and horizontally polarized backscattering coefficients with data acquired from a loose dirt surface at 35.6 GHz. Model parameters are $\sigma = 0.23$, $L = 0.95$ cm, $r = 0.42$ cm, and $\varepsilon = 3.8$ with the expl correlation.

3.4 COMPARISONS WITH DATA FROM SURFACES WITH MEASURED PARAMETERS

Backscatter measurements have been performed from the L-band through the X-band on surfaces with $k\sigma < 1$, $k\sigma \approx 1$ around C-band, and $k\sigma \approx 1$ near L-band by [Oh et al., 1992]. Profiles of surface heights were taken and surface rms heights and correlation lengths were computed along with dielectric values at the three bands. Theoretically, these are known surfaces because all the surface parameters needed in the backscattering model are available. However, whenever $k\sigma > 1$ and backscattering fails to approach GO, a smaller set of surface parameters must be used due to the *wavelength filtering* effect. We shall see in the following studies that in a natural environment, roughness scales smaller than a wavelength are usually present. This is why backscattering does not approach GO. However, for a man-made, machine-milled surface there are no smaller roughness scales beyond a certain wavelength. Hence, we can clearly see that as the incident frequency increases, backscattering is converging to the GO in the high-frequency region.

3.4.1 A Surface with $k\sigma < 1$

A three-frequency set of measurements were acquired by [Oh et al., 1992] from a randomly rough surface with $\sigma = 0.4$ cm, and $L = 8.4$ cm at frequencies of 1.5, 4.75, and 9.5 GHz. The corresponding dielectric constants are $15.6 - j3.7$, $15.4 - j2.15$, and $12.3 - j3.55$. Based upon the overall angular shape of the data and reported correlation function computed from surface height profiles, the exponential correlation function is a good candidate to use. A comparison between the backscattering model in (2.1) and the measurements of the first two frequencies is shown in Figure 3.62(a, b). All surface parameters are fixed so that the good agreement shown in Figure 3.62 for both polarizations, frequencies, and incident angles indicates that both the model and the data are quite accurate. According to [Oh et al., 1992] the 10-degree data point at 1.5 GHz is high and off the angular trend of the rest of the data because of the coherent contribution from normal incidence via a wide antenna beamwidth. At 9.5 GHz, the $k\sigma = 0.796$, which is less than unity. Hence, we expect backscattering to be caused by the same set of roughness scales as at lower frequencies. Indeed, in Figure 3.62(c) we continue to see a very good agreement between the model prediction and the measurements at 9.5 GHz. In the event where the incident frequency is much higher such that $k\sigma$ is larger than 1.0, we expect either wavelength filtering to occur or backscattering to approach the geometric optics condition. (Note that the $k\sigma = 1$ is just a convenient reference number. As we have illustrated in Chapter 2, all transitions between roughness scales and changes in angular trends are gradual.) Generally, the GO will lead to a bell-shaped backscattering curve independent of polarization. If this is not the case due to the presence of smaller scales of roughness not yet accounted for, then wavelength filtering will occur. If so, the reported parameter values should be reduced accordingly to reflect the presence of these smaller roughness scales.

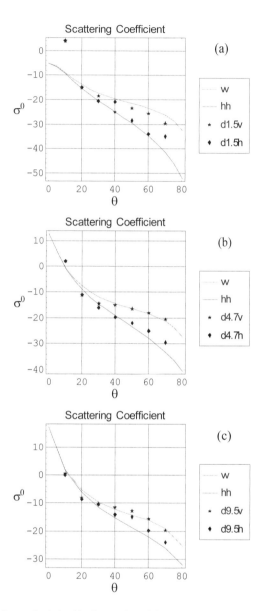

Figure 3.62 Comparisons of polarized backscattering with measurements from a surface with $\sigma = 0.4$ cm and $L = 8.4$ cm at (a) 1.5 GHz and $\varepsilon_r = 15.6 - j3.7$, and (b) 4.75 GHz and $\varepsilon_r = 15.4 - j2.15$, and (c) 9.5 GHz and $\varepsilon_r = 12.3 - j3.55$.

3.4.2 A Surface with $k\sigma \approx 1$ Near C-Band

A set of data to illustrate the *wavelength filtering* phenomenon was acquired by [Oh et al., 1992] and is available in [Qin et al., 2002]. This data set was taken from a randomly rough surface with $\sigma = 1.12$ cm, and $L = 8.4$ cm at frequencies of 1.5, 4.75, and 9.5 GHz and the corresponding dielectric constants are $15.3 - j3.7$, $12 - j2.12$, and $10 - j3.7$. The $k\sigma$ values at these frequencies are 0.35, 1.11, and 2.22, respectively. Hence, we expect that at 4.75 GHz we have a marginal case beyond which these surface parameters are no longer responsible for backscattering. The reported correlation function is an exponential function with which we obtain the matching shown in Figure 3.63.

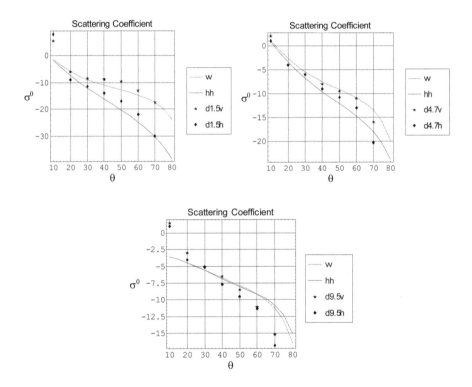

Figure 3.63 Comparisons of polarized backscattering with measurements from a surface with $\sigma = 1.12$ cm and $L = 8.4$ cm at 1.5 GHz, 4.75 GHz, and 9.5 GHz. It is clear that disagreement between model and data begins at 70 degrees, 4.75 GHz, and higher frequencies or angles.

In Figure 3.63 the general behavior of the scattering model is in agreement with data until the incident angle reaches 70 degrees at 4.75 GHz, where we see a large difference between data and model predictions. The exponential correlation is known to have a wide spectrum that can cause overestimation when frequency is high and the incident angle is large. This is one of the reasons why the exponential function is not suitable for high-frequency calculations. A correlation function that limits the high-frequency components of the surface is the mexp. If we keep the same surface parameters and use the mexp instead, we should be able to do better at 4.75 GHz. At 9.5 GHz we must reduce the size of the surface parameters because of *wavelength filtering*. Smaller roughness scales are now responsible for scattering at 9.5 GHz. With the mexp correlation and reported surface parameters, we can choose $z = 0.01$ at 1.5 GHz and $z = 0.035$ at 4.75 GHz. At 9.5 GHz we use a smaller set of surface parameters, $\sigma = 0.69$ cm, $L = 5.63$ cm, and $z = 0.02$. There is no change in the reported dielectric values at the three frequencies under consideration. The comparisons using the mexp are shown in Figure 3.64.

With either the exponential or the mexp correlation function, the comparisons between model predictions and data at 1.5 GHz are generally poor in the midangular range, 40–60 degrees. At 4.75 GHz the mexp correlation function allows better agreement at 70 degrees than the exponential correlation but not as good an agreement at the midangular range, 50–60 degrees. At 9.5 GHz smaller surface parameters do produce an agreement with data, but once again there is some disagreement in the midangular range, 40–50 degrees. This consistently poorer agreement in the midangular range suggests that the exponential correlation needs be modified in a different way to improve agreement in the midangular range. Generally, higher data level in the midangular range is not the character of an exponential function. We see this type of disagreement in the comparison with the 1.5-GHz data in Figures 3.63 and 3.64. The mexp correlation function can help to reduce high-frequency components over large incident angles in backscattering, but its influence on backscattering over the midangular range is not different from an exponential correlation function. In other words, to obtain a better agreement over the midangular range, we need a correlation function that provides a different type of transition between the exponential correlation function and the Gaussian correlation function.

A possible correlation function to consider is the exponential-like correlation function that behaves like a Gaussian near the origin and an exponential over a large lag distance. This function was presented in Chapter 1.

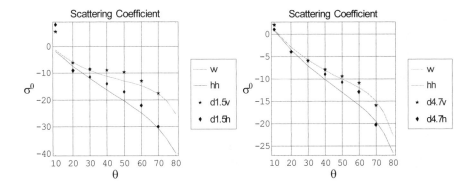

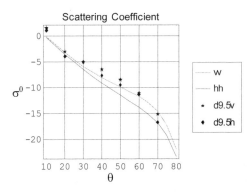

Figure 3.64 Comparisons of polarized backscattering measurements using an mexp correlation with $\sigma = 1.12$ cm, $L = 8.4$ cm, and $z = 0.01$ at 1.5 GHz; $z = 0.035$ at 4.75 GHz. At 9.5 GHz reduced values are used with $\sigma = 0.69$ cm, $L = 5.63$ cm, and $z = 0.02$. Dielectric values are as reported in [Oh et al., 1992].

Let us consider the application of the exponential-like correlation function to the data set in Figure 3.63. It has the form,

$$R(\xi) = \sigma^2 \exp\left[-\frac{\xi}{L}(1 - \exp[-\xi/r])\right], \, L > r \tag{3.1}$$

By choosing a small value for r and letting $r \ll L$, this function behaves like an exponential except over a short distance represented by r. For the current problem we use the reported $L = 8.4$ cm and $\sigma = 1.12$ cm for both 1.5 and 4.75

GHz. At 1.5 GHz we let $r = 0.25$ cm and at 4.75 GHz we set $r = 0.065$ cm. The value of r determines how fast the transition takes place from a Gaussian function into an exponential function. All dielectric values remain unchanged. At 9.5 GHz, a reduced set of rms surface height and correlation distance is chosen (i.e., we let $\sigma = 0.68$ cm, $L = 4.5$ cm, and $r = 0.088$). The computed backscattering at the three frequencies along with the data is shown in Figure 3.65.

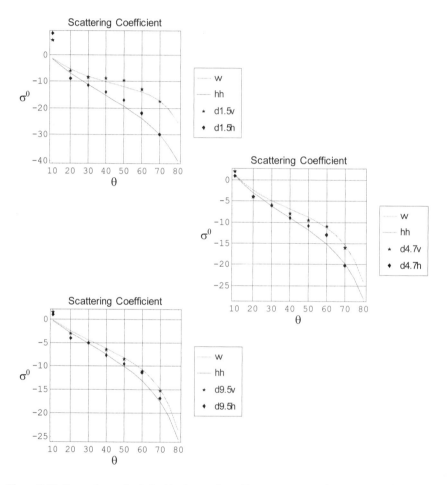

Figure 3.65 Comparisons of polarized backscattering with measurements using an exponential-like correlation function. A much better agreement is realized here relative to the use of either the expl or the mexp.

In Figure 3.65 we see that both vertical and horizontal polarization at 1.5 GHz are much closer to the data over the midangles than is possible with the exponential correlation or the modified exponential correlation shown in Figures 3.63 and 3.64. This improvement is due to a change in the shape of the angular backscattering curves resulting from using the exponential-like correlation function. Better agreements are achieved also at 4.75 and 9.5 GHz than those in Figures 3.63 and 3.64.

The above study shows that backscattering measurements can indicate what size of roughness scale is responsible for backscattering at a given angle and frequency. Generally, the roughness scale will agree with ground-truth measurements. However, when dealing with a multiscale surface and operating at a frequency where wavelength filtering is taking place, the roughness scale responsible for backscattering can be different from the ground-truth measurement, because certain large roughness scale or scales are no longer responsible for backscattering. We have been emphasizing that large roughness scales are being excluded by wavelength filtering, mainly because this change is not intuitively obvious. Actually, wavelength filtering has a bandpass effect. A roughness scale too small or smooth to make a significant contribution at some frequency is automatically excluded by wavelength filtering also. Thus, surface parameters computed from surface height profiles are applicable approximately in the frequency range where $k\sigma \leq 1$. If this condition is not satisfied, there is no practical way to exclude the large roughness scale required by the wavelength filtering phenomenon in ground-truth measurement at this time. Our current study indicates that surface parameters in modeling generally are effective parameters responsible for backscattering at the incident frequency. They may or may not agree with the ground-truth measurements.

Another example indicating that measured surface parameters are not applicable when $k\sigma > 1$ can be found in the roughest surface reported in [Oh et al., 1992]. We shall consider this case in Section 3.4.3.

3.4.3 A Surface with $k\sigma \approx 1$ Near L-Band

A very rough Gaussian distributed surface with a correlation function that is in between a Gaussian and an exponential was reported by [Oh et al., 1992]. It has $\sigma = 3.02$ cm and $L = 8.8$ cm. At 1.5, 4.75, and 9.5 GHz the values of $k\sigma$ are 0.95, 3, and 6.01, and the dielectric constants are $8.92 - j2.24$, $9.64 - j1.19$, and $7.57 - j1.99$, respectively. At 1.5 GHz we expect the model to work with the reported surface parameters, and we shall test different correlation functions beginning with the Gaussian and the modified exponential correlation as shown in Figure 3.66.

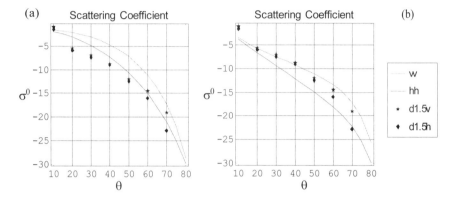

Figure 3.66 Comparisons of polarized backscattering with measurements from a very rough Gaussian distributed surface with σ = 3.02 cm and L = 8.8 cm. Assume (a) Gaussian correlation and (b) modified exponential correlation with z = 0.2 .

The specific angular trend of the data in Figure 3.66 calls for a drop from 10 to 20 degrees. Then there is some separation opening up between vertical and horizontal polarizations as the incident angle increases. The first feature is not in the Gaussian-correlated backscattering curve but the second one could be as shown in Figure 3.66(a). In Figure 3.66(b) we used the modified exponential correlation with z = 0.2, which is a very large modification of the exponential function. It allows the small angular region to be dominated by the exponential correlation function and forces the angular curve beyond 20 degrees downward to approximate the Gaussian correlation effect. Much better agreement is obtained with the modified exponential correlation with z = 0.2 than the Gaussian, but the angular bending is too much for some smaller incident angles and not quite enough at 70 degrees.

Next, we consider using the exponential and the exponential-like correlation functions at 1.5 GHz for this surface. Results are shown in Figure 3.67(a, b). As expected, the exponential correlation can provide a good fit over the small angular region. This region corresponds to the region where the effective wavelength is large (i.e., the low-frequency region where the entire correlation function is contributing to the scattering integral). At large incident angles, the effective wavelength is shorter, and the portion of the exponential correlation function close to the origin is the dominant contributor to the scattering integral. The exponential function has a sharp peak at the origin corresponding to a wide, slow-decaying spectrum. This is the reason why the model prediction is too high in the large angular region. When this peaked portion of the exponential correlation is replaced by a Gaussian-like function such as in the exponential-like function, then backscattering will decrease much faster with the incident angle leading to a good agreement with measurements. With the exception of 10 degrees, which is affected by coherent contribution at normal incidence, the exponential-like correlation provides the best fit to this data set. It is able to fit data before 40 degrees and then bends down far enough to fit data at 70 degrees for vertical and horizontal polarizations. Hence, we can conclude that the model given in (2.1) and the data are in agreement.

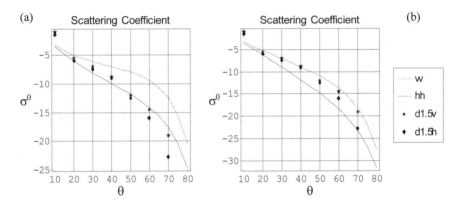

Figure 3.67 Comparisons of polarized backscattering with measurements from a very rough surface with $\sigma = 3.02$ cm and $L = 8.8$ cm: (a) exponential correlation and (b) exponential-like correlation with $r = 0.06$.

Both the modified exponential and exponential-like correlation functions are functions in between the exponential and the Gaussian. Hence, they have the best chance to match data acquired from natural surfaces. At 4.75 GHz, the large $k\sigma$ should lead to either the geometric optics result for a single-scale surface or a reduced set of surface parameters for a multiscale surface. In the former case, there is no distinction between vertical and horizontal polarization, and there should be a sharp drop-off in backscattering with angle because the probability of having many large slopes should be small.

Next, we carry out similar comparisons at 4.75 GHz and 9.5 GHz. Results at 4.75 GHz are shown in Figure 3.68. In Figure 3.68(a), we keep the same surface parameters as given in [Oh et al., 1992], and in Figure 3.68(b) we reduce both the surface rms height and the correlation length. All other model parameters remain unchanged between Figure 3.68(a, b).

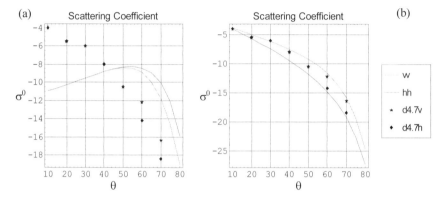

Figure 3.68 Comparisons between model and measurements using surface parameters (a) as reported by [Oh et al., 1992] with $r = 0.08$ cm and (b) with the values of the rms height and correlation length reduced to 1.2 cm and 4 cm, respectively. Incident frequency is 4.75 GHz.

In Figure 3.68(a) we see that both the level and the angular trends are completely different between the model predictions and the measurements. The low predicted level at 10 degrees indicates that the surface rms height used in the model is too large. The predicted rise with the incident angle confirms that energy is being transferred to larger angles by a very rough surface. Such predicted behavior is not what is observed. Hence, the reported roughness scale is not the one responsible for the observed data. After we reduce the rms height from 3.02 cm to 1.2 cm and the correlation length from 8.8 cm to 4 cm, we obtain a very nice agreement between the model and measurements shown in Figure 3.68(b). All other surface parameters remain the same in Figure 3.68(a, b) indicating that the radar is seeing a smaller roughness scale as required by wavelength filtering. The measured σ and L are not the cause of backscattering at or beyond 4.75 GHz.

At 9.5 GHz we expect smaller roughness scale to be the cause of backscattering similar to what we saw at 4.75 GHz. To convince us that the measured parameters are not the cause, again we showed the model prediction due to them in Figure 3.69(a). Here, the use of such a large rms height causes the model prediction to be more than 7 dB lower than the data at normal incidence. Furthermore, the model-predicted angular trend is upward between 0 and 60 degrees, and at 60 degrees the predicted value is 6 dB higher than the measurement. Clearly, there is no similarity between the model prediction and the data. However, after we reduce the rms height from 3.02 cm to 0.62 cm and the correlation length from 8.8 cm to 1.9 cm, we obtain a very good matching as shown in Figure 3.69(b). Other surface parameters are identical in Figure 3.69(a, b). Here again we have shown that shorter incident wavelength has eliminated the large-scale roughness from being the source of scattering even though they are present on the surface.

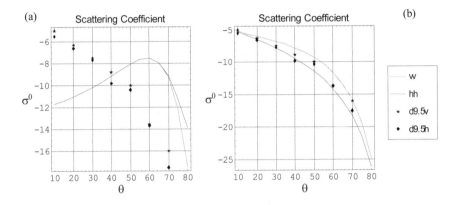

Figure 3.69 Comparisons between model and measurements using surface parameters (a) as reported by [Oh et al., 1992] with $r = 0.11$ cm and (b) with the values of the rms height and correlation length reduced to 0.62 cm and 1.9 cm respectively. Incident frequency is 9.5 GHz.

The last two examples serve to demonstrate the effects of wavelength filtering in surface scattering from multiscale surfaces. As stated in Chapter 2 when $k\sigma$ is larger than one, another possible result is for the measurement to approach the GO. This can be the case if there are no roughness scales smaller than a wavelength on the surface. Should this happen, it would occur at 9.5 GHz. We want to consider this possibility because the maximum spread between the vertical and horizontal polarizations is less than 2 dB. The GO for backscattering from surfaces with a Gaussian height distribution takes the following form [Fung, 1994],

$$\sigma^0 = \frac{S(\theta)R^2}{2\sigma_s^2 \cos^4\theta} \exp\left[-\frac{\tan^2\theta}{2\sigma_s^2}\right] \tag{3.2}$$

where $S(\theta)$ is the shadowing function given by [Smith, 1967]; R^2 is the reflectivity at normal incidence; σ_s^2 is the variance of surface slope; and θ is the angle of incidence. According to [Oh et al., 1992] this surface has a correlation function that lies in between a Gaussian and an exponential height distribution and its height distribution is close to a Gaussian. Hence, we also want to consider a GO with a modified exponential distribution given by [Fung, 1994]:

$$\sigma^0 = \frac{3S(\theta)R^2}{2\sigma_s^2 \cos^4\theta} \exp\left[-\frac{\sqrt{3}\tan\theta}{\sigma_s}\right] \tag{3.3}$$

If GO is applicable, the data should be lying in between the above two models. For the rms slope we use surface parameters reported by [Oh et al., 1992], $(\sigma\sqrt{2})/L = 0.485$ as a reference number, and we calculate backscattering coefficients at 30% higher and lower values of this rms slope to give an idea how the scattering coefficients vary. The results for the Gaussian model are given in Figure 3.70(a) and for the modified exponential model in Figure 3.70(b).

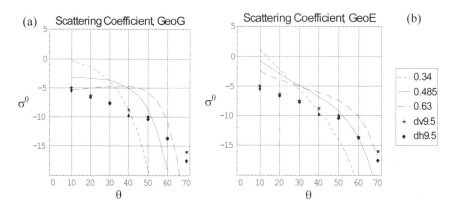

Figure 3.70 Comparisons between the geometric optics models and measurements using (a) Gaussian distribution and (b) the modified exponential distribution. The solid line is with rms slope computed with surface parameters as reported by [Oh et al., 1992], while the rms slope with the short dashes is 30% smaller and with the long dashes is 30% larger. Data shown are at 9.5 GHz.

Clearly, the geometric optics model with Gaussian distribution does not fit the data. The modified exponential model fits better, but it is also too high over small angles of incidence or too low at 70 degrees. The data fails to fall in between the two models and assumes a different angular trend from the models. Hence, we conclude that the data is not converging to geometric optics due to the presence of smaller roughness on the surface.

3.4.4 A Man-Made Known Surface

The surfaces we considered in previous sections are soil surfaces with surface parameters computed from surface profiles. The presence of small-scale roughness with rms heights around half a centimeter is difficult to resolve and not recognized through surface profile measurements. To be sure there is no small-scale roughness, we now consider a surface machine-milled to have an exponential-like surface correlation with $\sigma = 0.9$ cm, $L = 3$ cm, and $r = 1.8$. It was made by the European Microwave Signature Laboratory (EMSL) at the Joint Research Center in Italy. Measurements were taken from 1 to 19 GHz for both vertical and horizontal polarizations at incident angles of 40 and 50 degrees. For computational convenience we assume it has an average dielectric constant of 4.7. The data have been made available at the website, http://www-emsl.jrc.it. At 19 GHz, $k\sigma = 3.58$. In the absence of additional small roughness scales, we expect the measurement to approach the geometric optics model. There is no report on the slope distribution, but we expect that the data at 19 GHz should lie between the predictions of the geometric models given by (3.2) and (3.3). For this particular surface its rms slope is given by

$$\sqrt{\frac{2}{rL}}\sigma = 0.365 \qquad (3.4)$$

In Figure 3.71 we show a comparison of the backscattering model defined by (2.1) with the data at 40-degree incidence over the frequency range from 1 to 19 GHz. An average dielectric constant for all frequencies is assumed to be 4.7. Very good agreement is obtained in both polarizations and frequency trends. Both data and model show convergence toward -7.5 dB at 19 GHz. The limiting geometric optics value with Gaussian height distribution computed with (3.2) is -6.93 dB. The computation with the geometric optics model given by (3.3) with a modified exponential height distribution yields -8.5 dB. As we expect, the measured value is in between the two geometric optics models.

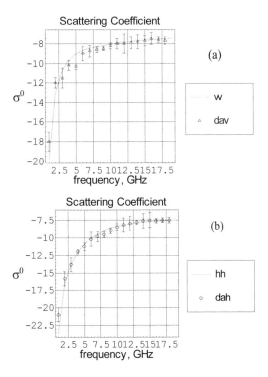

Figure 3.71 Comparisons of polarized backscattering with measurements from a man-made exponential-like correlated surface with $\sigma = 0.9$ cm, $L = 3$ cm, and $r = 1.8$ at 40 degrees: (a) vertical polarization and (b) horizontal polarization.

Next, we repeat a similar comparison as in Figure 3.71 but at 50 degrees. To see a more direct comparison between vertical and horizontal polarizations, we use the same range on the vertical axis for displaying the two polarizations. Results are shown in Figure 3.72. Here again, a good agreement is obtained between the model and the measurements. As expected, vertical polarization is generally higher than horizontal polarization in backscattering. As frequency increases, they approach each other heading toward -10 dB. The rate with which they reach the same value depends on the spectral content of the surface. Fewer high-frequency components will allow a faster convergence to the same value. For this man-made surface there are no unknown small spectral components present on the surface. Thus, we know backscattering must converge to geometric optics at sufficiently high frequency.

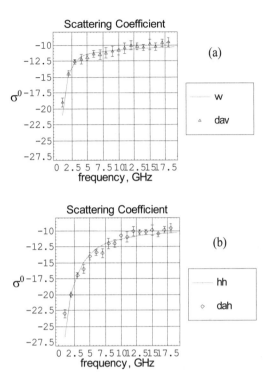

Figure 3.72 Comparisons of polarized backscattering with measurements from a man-made exponential-like correlated surface with $\sigma = 0.9$ cm, $L = 3$ cm, and $r = 1.8$ at 50 degrees: (a) vertical polarization and (b) horizontal polarization.

3.5 CONCLUDING REMARKS

In illustrating how backscattering depends on model parameters we have examined the backscattering trend versus each model parameter and whether or not this trend and the angular shape of the backscattering curve are affected by other model parameters. Of the five model parameters three relate to the surface geometry or roughness properties: surface rms height σ, correlation length L, and correlation parameter r. One relates to surface dielectric property ε, and one is the system frequency f. The change of any one of the three roughness parameters will change the surface geometry. This change may or may not affect backscattering noticeably, depending on the size of the change relative to the sensing wavelength. The dielectric constant can cause changes in the level and angular shape of the backscattering coefficient, and it is generally a function of frequency and temperature. The change in backscattering caused by the dielectric constant is independent of the changes due to surface geometric parameters.

The comparisons we have shown with known rough surfaces include exponential and exponential-like correlated surfaces for both vertical and horizontal polarizations over angular ranges from near normal to 70 degrees. Additional comparisons with known surfaces and computer simulations can be found in [Koudogbo et al., 2004] and [Fung and Chen, 2009], where more applications to other types of Earth terrains are demonstrated. These comparisons indicate that the backscattering model in (2.1) is applicable to randomly rough surfaces in general. For natural multiscale surfaces with a large rms height so that the $k\sigma$ value can be much larger than one, *wavelength filtering* would occur. In this case the surface parameters to be used in the surface scattering model should satisfy $k\sigma \leq 1$ and will not agree with measured surface parameters, because backscattering is no longer caused by the large-scale roughness. This means that the surface parameters retrieved from model applications are generally *effective parameters* indicating the roughness scale that is *responsible* for the measured data. However, as shown in Section 3.4, model-retrieved surface parameters can agree with those based on surface profile measurements, when $k\sigma \leq 1$. In short, the incident wavelength is the quantity that determines which roughness scale in a multiscale rough surface is responsible for backscattering.

References

Fung, A. K., *Microwave Scattering and Emission Models and Their Applications,* Norwood, MA: Artech House, 1994.

Fung, A. K., and K. S. Chen, *Microwave Scattering and Emission Models for Users,* Norwood, MA: Artech House, 2009.

Joint Research Center, European Microwave Signature Laboratory (EMSL) website, http://www-emsl.jrc.it.

Koudogbo, F., P. F. Combes, and H. J. Mametsa, "Numerical and Experimental Validations of IEM for Bistatic Scattering from Natural and Man-made Rough Surfaces," *Progress in Electromagnetic Research,* PIER 46, 2004, pp. 203–244.

Oh, Y., K. Sarabandi, and F. T. Ulaby, "An Empirical Model and an Inversion Technique for Radar Scattering from Bare Soil Surfaces," *IEEE Transactions on Geoscience and Remote Sensing,* Vol. 30, No. 2, March 1992, pp. 370–381.

Qin, L., J. Shi, and K. S. Chen, "A Generalized Power Law Spectrum and Its Applications to the

Backscattering of Soil Surfaces Based on the Integral Equation Model," *IEEE Transactions on Geoscience and Remote Sensing,* Vol. 40, No. 2, 2002, pp. 271–280.

Smith, B. G., "Geometrical Shadowing of a Random Rough Surface," *IEEE Transactions on Antenna and Propagation*, Vol. AP-15, 1967, pp. 668–671.

Ulaby, F. T., R. K. Moore, and A. K. Fung, *Microwave Remote Sensing,* Chapter 21, Vol. 3, Norwood, MA: Artech House, 1986.

Chapter 4

Backscattering from the Sea Surface

4.1 INTRODUCTION

It is known that the sea surface is a time-varying, anisotropic, and skewed rough surface affected by the local wind and waves propagating from other parts of the sea into the region of interest. Clearly, it is a very different and much more complex rough surface than that of the land surface. Figure 4.1 shows a sea surface with capillary waves of many sizes riding on large-scale waves also of many sizes. A practical question of interest is to be able to determine the local wind with radar measurements. A desirable wind sensor should detect mainly the wave sizes that are sensitive to the wind, which are the capillary waves. For this reason a better choice of sensing frequency should be equal to or higher than the C-band, and the incident angle should be larger than 30 degrees according to the backscattering properties we discussed in the previous chapters. Note that, near nadir, significant coherent contribution may come from reflection due to large waves and from neighboring angles due to finite beamwidth. The definition of the backscattering coefficient excludes coherent contribution, which is not easy to exclude in measurements. Also, the effective wavelength is longer than the physical wavelength for incident angles smaller than 30 degrees in backscattering. These are the reasons why smaller incident angles are not good choices for sensing wind speeds over the ocean surface.

In microwave backscattering from multiscale rough surfaces away from nadir, only roughness scales comparable to or smaller than the incident wavelength are important, because the larger roughness scales will generate reflections and scattering mostly in the forward direction and cause tilting of the smaller scales that ride on them. Their net contribution to backscattering is generally negligible [Nghiem et al., 1993]. This finding from experimental data is in agreement with the wavelength filtering phenomenon mentioned in Chapter 1. Physical mechanisms that contribute to backscattering are diffraction and incoherent scattering. These mechanisms are activated by the waves comparable to or smaller than the incident wavelength. This makes the microwave scatterometer a viable candidate for sensing wind speeds over ocean. Wind direction can also be determined with airborne radar flying in a circular path, because radar backscattering in the upwind direction is always much higher than the crosswind. It is also larger than the downwind but the difference is generally smaller [Schroeder et al., 1985].

Figure 4.1 A sea surface.

Within a selected time frame and a localized region, we can assume that the roughness on a sea surface is generated by a stationary random process. Although this is only approximately correct, useful estimates of wind speed can be obtained in practice. To calculate backscattering, we need either the surface correlation function or its Fourier transform, the roughness spectrum. In Chapter 1 we demonstrated that the correlation function of all multiscale surfaces is likely to have an exponential appearance, but it is not a simple exponential function. The sea surface is clearly a multiscale surface. Hence, along a given azimuth direction the sea surface correlation function for short waves including the capillary waves can be approximated better by an expl function as demonstrated in Chapter 2. It is known that for any surface the correlation function is centro-symmetric. Hence, a possible approximate representation of the sea surface correlation for a portion of the small waves on the sea surface is

$$R(\xi, \phi) = \sigma^2 \exp\left[-\frac{\xi}{L}\left(1 - e^{-\frac{\xi}{r}}\right)\right] \tag{4.1}$$

where $L = L_u|cos\phi|^a + L_c|sin\phi|^2$ is the correlation length along ϕ direction; L_u is the correlation length along the upwind direction chosen to be at $\phi = 0^0$; L_c is the correlation length along the crosswind direction; $2 \leq a \leq 4$ is the *azimuth parameter* that controls the width of the azimuth lobes around upwind and downwind directions; and σ^2 is the surface height variance. It is expected that $L_c > L_u$, and both of them are decreasing functions of wind speed, while σ^2 is an increasing function of wind speed. We shall demonstrate that they can be calibrated with radar measurements in Chapter 5. As discussed in previous chapters, the correlation parameter r allows $R(\xi, \varphi)$ to behave like a Gaussian function over a lag distance proportional to r. We have found that $a \approx 2$ for most individual data sets, but when large volumes of data are used to develop empirical models, $a > 2$.

We should emphasize here that due to *wavelength filtering*, at a given frequency only a portion of the small waves on the sea surface is important to backscattering. This is the reason why we can use this simple expression given by (4.1) instead of a full-blown expression for the real sea surface correlation function or its spectrum, which is very complex. Using (4.1) greatly simplifies the calculation of the backscattering coefficients for the sea surface. In the past such computations were so extensive that it was not feasible to do in practice. As we shall see in Chapter 5, for many applications where backscattering varies with the azimuth angle it is possible to fix r at a very small number such as 0.02 cm and determine all other parameters in (4.1) as a function of wind speed based on measurements.

Next, we want to address the surface skewness effect. In a stationary random process its moments are related to its second-order and third-order cumulant functions, also known as correlation and bicoherence function in the literature. The Fourier transform of these two functions are the spectrum and bispectrum in the random process. Early studies of the bicoherence function had been carried out by many investigators [Longuet-Higgins, 1963; Hasselmann et al., 1963; Srokosz and Longuet-Higgins, 1980; Masoda and Kuo, 1981]. The application of this function to radar scattering was reported by [Chen and Fung, 1990], [Fung and Chen, 1991], and [Chen et al., 1992]. An investigation of the form and properties of the bicoherence function was carried out by [Amar, 1989]. The bicoherence function has vanishing first and second derivatives at the origin and can be written as the sum of a symmetric and an antisymmetric functions. The symmetric function is responsible for vertical skewness, and the antisymmetric function is for horizontal skewness. As a third-order function the impact of the symmetric function on scattering is small compared with the surface correlation function. Hence, it can be ignored in scattering calculations. Our major interest here is in the antisymmetric function. In modeling radar backscattering, this is the function causing the upwind return to be higher than the downwind. It has no influence in the crosswind direction. We shall refer to it as the skewness function. Its Fourier transform, the bispectrum, is purely imaginary. A summary of Amar's work on skewness is available in Appendix 7A of [Fung, 1994], where a suggested form for the skewness function is

$$S(r, \phi) = \sigma^3 \left(\frac{r \cos \phi}{s_0} \right)^3 \exp \left[-\left(\frac{r}{s_0} \right)^2 \right] \tag{4.2}$$

where the skewness parameter s_0 is also a function of wind speed.

4.2 A SEA SURFACE SCATTERING MODEL

Before 1992 available radar surface scattering models including the skewness effect were restricted mainly to the small perturbation model for small roughness scales [Chen and Fung, 1990] and the Kirchhoff model for large roughness scales [Fung and Chen, 1991]. Based on what we discussed in Section 4.1, in backscattering, the small perturbation model should be almost adequate except that it cannot handle roughness size comparable to the wavelength and does not account for higher order spectra. It was clear to most investigators that a scattering model that could account for the roughness size comparable to the incident wavelength was needed. Such a model became available in 1992 when the integral equation governing the surface current was used by [Fung et al., 1992] to provide a better estimate of the surface current induced by the incident wave. Their model is able to bridge the gap between the perturbation and the Kirchhoff model and includes these models as special cases in the low- and high-frequency regions. Hence, there is no need to use either of these models anymore. Furthermore, their surface scattering model is in an algebraic form in terms of the surface spectrum and its higher orders for both vertical and horizontal polarizations. Thus, it is fairly easy to compute. For backscattering from the sea surface this integral equation model (IEM) for the backscattering coefficient without the skewness part is [Fung, 1994]

$$\sigma^0_{pp}(\theta) = \frac{k^2}{2} exp(-2k^2 \sigma^2 \cos^2 \theta) \sum_{n=1}^{\infty} \frac{\left| I^n_{pp} \right|^2}{n!} W^{(n)}(K, \phi) \tag{4.3}$$

where $p = v, h$ denotes vertical or horizontal polarization,

$$I_{pp}^n = (2k\cos\theta)^n f_{pp} \exp(-k^2\sigma^2\cos^2\theta) + (k\cos\theta)^n F_{pp}$$

$$f_{vv} = (2R_v)/\cos\theta$$

$$f_{hh} = -(2R_h)/\cos\theta$$

$$F_{vv} = \frac{\sin^2\theta}{\cos\theta}\left[\left(\frac{\mu_r\varepsilon_r - \sin^2\theta - \varepsilon_r\cos^2\theta}{\varepsilon_r^2\cos^2\theta}\right) + \left(1 - \frac{1}{\varepsilon_r}\right)\right](1 + R_v)^2$$

$$F_{hh} = \left(-\frac{\sin^2\theta}{\cos\theta}\right)\left[\left(\frac{\mu_r\varepsilon_r - \sin^2\theta - \mu_r\cos^2\theta}{\mu_r^2\cos^2\theta}\right) + \left(1 - \frac{1}{\mu_r}\right)\right](1 + R_h)^2$$

In the above, k is the wavenumber, θ is the incident angle, σ is the surface rms height, R_p is the Fresnel reflection coefficient, ε_r is the surface dielectric constant, and

$$W^{(n)}(K, \phi) = \frac{1}{2\pi}\int_0^{2\pi}\int_0^\infty R(r, \varphi)^n e^{-jKr\cos(\phi - \varphi)} r\,dr\,d\varphi, \quad n = 1, 2, 3, \ldots$$

where $R(r, \varphi)$ is the surface correlation function given by (4.1).

For the computation in the next section we choose the expl spectrum given in (1.8) as the form for $W^{(n)}(K, \phi)$. When we compare model predictions with azimuth data for incident angles greater than 30 degrees we may use (1.9) or a much simpler form of $W^{(n)}(K, \phi)$, which is based solely on the exponential correlation function. It has been successfully used in many surface scattering computations. It is

$$W^{(n)}(K, \phi) = n(\sigma L)^2[n^2 + (KL)^2]^{-1.5} \tag{4.4}$$

where $L = L_u|\cos\phi|^a + L_c|\sin\phi|^2$. It is important to note that this spectrum is to approximate only a portion of the sea spectrum representing wave sizes in the range of centimeters in the microwave range. It does not include either the lower or the higher end of the wavenumber spectrum of the sea surface. The rms height σ ; azimuth parameter a ; and correlation lengths, L_u in the upwind direction and L_c in the crosswind direction, are to be determined by radar measurements to be shown in a later section. Modified and extended alternatives to (4.4) were discussed in Chapter 1 and given as (1.8) and (1.9). Equations (1.8) and (1.9) are more general than (4.4) because they contain another correlation parameter that allows an adjustment to the surface correlation function to become more Gaussian-like. They are needed to interpret some backscattering versus the incident angle curves near normal incidence. On the other hand, when the problem is about backscattering versus the azimuthal angle beyond 30 degrees incidence, (4.4) or (1.9) is generally adequate. Chapter 3 provides examples where (1.8) works better than (4.4) for some problems.

The skewness part of the backscattering coefficient [Fung, 1994] is

$$\sigma^0_{pp}(S) = \frac{k^2}{2}|f_{pp}|^2 \exp(-4k^2\sigma^2\cos^2\theta) \sum_{n=1}^{\infty} \frac{(-8k^3\cos^3\theta)^n}{n!}B^{(n)}(K,\phi)$$

$$+\frac{k^2}{2}\mathrm{Re}(f_{pp}{}^* F_{pp})\exp(-3k^2\sigma^2\cos^2\theta) \sum_{n=1}^{\infty} \left[\frac{(-3k^3\cos^3\theta)^n}{n!}B^{(n)}(K,\phi)\right.$$

$$+\frac{k^2}{8}|F_{pp}|^2\exp(-2k^2\sigma^2\cos^2\theta) \sum_{n=1}^{\infty} \frac{(-k^3\cos^3\theta)^n}{n!}B^{(n)}(K,\phi) \qquad (4.5)$$

where

$$B^{(n)}(K,\phi) = \frac{-j}{2\pi}\int_0^{2\pi}\int_0^{\infty} S(r,\phi)^n e^{-jKr\cos(\phi-\phi)}r\,dr\,d\phi$$

and $S(r,\phi)$ is given by (4.2).

4.3 PARAMETER EFFECTS ON BACKSCATTERING FROM AN ANISOTROPIC SKEWED SURFACE

In this section we want to consider parameter effects due to surface anisotropy and skewness on backscattering from a general anisotropic, skewed surface with the azimuth parameter a set to 2 except in Section 4.3.6. The illustrations are dealing with a general anisotropic, skewed surface such as a windblown sand surface that has a small dielectric constant or the sea surface with a large dielectric constant. We let the maximum skewness effect occur along the azimuth angle $\phi = 0$. Thus, along $\phi = 90$ degrees, there is no skewness effect on backscattering. In fact, the backscattering coefficient along this particular direction is the same as the backscattering from an isotropic surface with the same model parameters. Hence, it can serve as a reference to indicate changes due to both anisotropy and skewness as we move away from this direction. In sea surface scattering this is the crosswind direction, and the sea surface correlation length is a maximum along this direction. The surface correlation length reaches its minimum value at $\phi = 0$, while the skewness effect reaches its maximum value at this location. For an anisotropic surface, backscattering due to the skewness effect is added on to the backscattering due to the surface correlation in the angular range, $\phi = 0-90$ degrees and is subtracted from the surface correlation contribution in the angular range, $\phi = 90 - 180$ degrees. This is why in the upwind direction ($\phi = 0$ degrees) backscattering reaches its maximum, while in the downwind direction ($\phi = 180$ degrees) backscattering is smaller than its value at upwind. The difference between upwind and downwind is generally not very large because the skewness is a higher order effect. In our illustrations in this chapter, the shadowing effect is ignored and we restrict our largest incident angle to 60 degrees.

It is important to emphasize that physically the skewness is a higher order effect compared with the surface correlation function. Mathematically, its contribution is required to be smaller than the contribution from the surface correlation function. In selecting the skewness parameter care must be exercised to keep the skewness effect smaller than that of the surface correlation to avoid obtaining a nonphysical answer, especially for horizontal polarization.

4.3.1 Skewness and Anisotropic Effects on Frequency Dependence

Chapter 3 illustrates how backscattering normally varies with frequency for isotropically rough surfaces and how this variation is affected by other model parameters. Here, we want to see in what way this variation is affected by anisotropy and skewness with the azimuth parameter a set to 2, which works for all airplane measurements. Consider the case of backscattering along the $\phi = 90$ degree direction where $r = 0.1$ cm, $\sigma = 0.4$ cm, $L = 3(cos\varphi)^2 + 7(sin\varphi)^2$ cm, $s_0 = 0.13$ cm, and $\varepsilon = 6$ with frequency varying from 4 to 16 GHz. The corresponding case for the isotropic surface will have the same model parameters except that it has no skewness contribution or a skewness parameter s_0 and its correlation length does not change with the azimuth direction. We may view the $\phi = 90$ degrees as equivalent to the isotropic case because there is no skewness contribution at this azimuth angle. When the azimuth angle changes from $\phi = 90$ to 40 degrees, skewness contribution will appear along with a change in backscattering due to anisotropy. Hence, the difference in backscattering due to anisotropy and skewness at $\phi = 40$ degrees can be found by comparing the backscattering signals at $\phi = 90$ degrees with those at $\phi = 40$ degrees as shown in Figure 4.2. Approximately before the incident angle reaches 10 degrees, the signal rises from 4 GHz to 8 GHz and falls back down at 16 GHz. Beyond 10 degrees, backscattering signal rises with frequency. Near normal incidence the signal is higher at $\phi = 90$ degrees than $\phi = 40$ degrees, and it becomes lower after the incident angle exceeds 20 degrees.

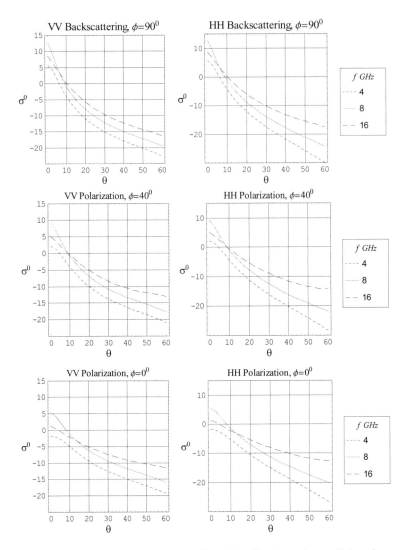

Figure 4.2 A comparison of vertically and horizontally polarized backscattering coefficients from an anisotropically rough surface at ϕ = 90 , 40, and 0 degrees. Model parameters are r = 0.1 cm, $L = 3(cos\varphi)^2 + 7(sin\varphi)^2$ cm, σ = 0.4 cm, ε = 6 , and s_0 = 0.13 cm. The choice of a small r here forces the correlation function to be more exponential-like.

In practice, most measurements taken over anisotropic surfaces are between 30 and 50 degrees. Hence, we can focus more on the backscattering behavior at or over 30 degrees. In this incident angular range, backscattered signal at $\phi = 0$ degrees is at a maximum and it reaches a minimum at an azimuth angle at or larger than $\phi = 90$ degrees. The anisotropic properties we just described do not influence the frequency trend. A closer comparison between the backscattering curves at $\phi = 40$ and 90 degrees shows that the rate of change with frequency in the two cases are different especially in horizontal polarization over large angles of incidence. This significant difference in the rate of change with frequency is due to the skewness effect.

Over the range of incident angles, 30 to 60 degrees, backscattering is increasing as ϕ decreases from 90 to 0 degrees. This increase is due to anisotropy and happens to all three frequencies. Over the same range of incident angles and at a given ϕ angle, backscattering is also higher at higher frequencies as shown in Figure 4.2. The differences in signal level and angular trends between backscattering at $\phi = 90$ versus $\phi = 40$ and $\phi = 0$ degrees are due to the combined effects of anisotropy and skewness.

Next, we want to compare the spacing between polarizations to see what changes may take place due to anisotropy and skewness. For the isotropic surface represented by $\phi = 90$ degrees in Figure 4.3, we know that the spacing between polarizations in backscattering at a given frequency generally will increase with the incident angle and decrease with an increase in frequency. For a skewed surface the spacing should be the same as the isotropic surface over small incident angles up to 40 degrees. Between 40 and 50 degrees, the skewness effect may begin to show up, which tends to slow down the widening in spacing. This effect may not be obvious visually because the widening in spacing is continuing. If we compare the cases, $\phi = 90$ with $\phi = 40$ degrees or with $\phi = 0$ degrees in Figure 4.3 and incident frequencies of 8 and 16 GHz up to 60 degrees in incidence, we see that the growth in spacing has stopped at 8 GHz and has reversed direction at 16 GHz. These changes are observable beyond 50 degrees especially at 16 GHz. The reason for narrowing in spacing at large incident angles is that horizontal polarization has increased more than vertical polarization at these angles. Another obvious effect due to skewness is the slowdown in the incident angular trend beyond 50 degrees and at frequencies 8 or higher in Figure 4.3. At 4 GHz the change in spacing or angular trends is less noticeable because the skewness effect is smaller at lower frequencies, although the effect is similar to what happens at higher frequencies. When the incident angle is greater than 20 degrees, signal level increases as ϕ decreases from $\phi = 90$ degrees toward $\phi = 0$ degrees as shown in Figure 4.3. This is due entirely to anisotropy.

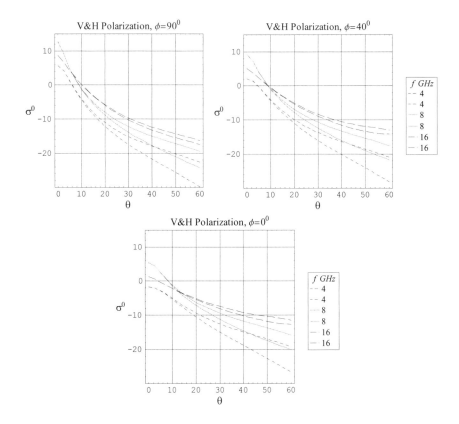

Figure 4.3 An illustration of changes in the spacing between vertically and horizontally polarized backscattering coefficients due to skewness and anisotropy at ϕ = 0 and 40 degrees with the case ϕ = 90 degrees serving as a reference. Model parameters are r = 0.1 cm, L = $3(cos\varphi)^2 + 7(sin\varphi)^2$ cm, σ = 0.4 cm, ε = 6, and s_0 = 0.13 cm. For each polarization pair the upper curve is vertical polarization. Major differences in backscattering occur only over large angles of incidence and at higher frequencies.

The skewness impact on backscattering over the azimuth angle between 90 and 180 degrees is to reduce the backscattered signal caused by the roughness spectrum. Over this azimuth angular range the influence of anisotropy is the same as between 0 and 90 degrees (i.e., the backscattered signal will rise from 90 to 180 degrees due to surface anisotropy). Figure 4.4 illustrates these described results.

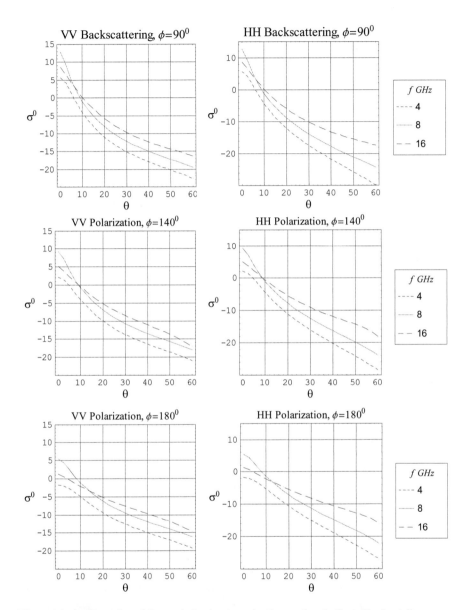

Figure 4.4 An illustration of changes in level and angular shapes of vertically and horizontally polarized backscattering coefficients as ϕ increases from 90 to 180 degrees. The model parameters are $r = 0.1$, $\sigma = 0.4$ cm, $L = 3(cos\phi)^2 + 7(sin\phi)^2$ cm, $\varepsilon = 6$, and $s_0 = 0.13$ cm with the expl correlation.

For ease of reference we have repeated the case at $\phi = 90$ degrees in Figure 4.4. For incident angles beyond 30 degrees, backscattering at $\phi = 140$ and 180 degrees is higher than that at $\phi = 90$ degrees, and their angular trends are turning downward after the incident angle exceeds 50 degrees due to surface skewness. Such a change is clearer at higher frequencies at $\phi = 140$ and 180 degrees for both vertical and horizontal polarizations because the skewness effect is larger at higher frequencies.

A further increase in ϕ beyond 90 degrees leads to backscattering with a decreasing correlation length. As expected from our study in Chapter 3, this will cause a decrease in backscattering over small incident angles and an increase over large incident angles resulting in flatter angular curves versus the incident angle. This general trend holds for both vertical and horizontal polarizations. Such a result is shown in Figure 4.4. Similar to ϕ in the 0–90 degree range, the frequency trend is the same at all incident angles beyond 15 degrees, but the rate of change of backscattering with frequency is different because of the influence of both anisotropy and skewness.

Next, we want to consider the influence of anisotropy and skewness on the spacing between polarizations in the azimuth angular range, 90–180 degrees. One way to show these effects is to compare the spacing behavior here with that shown in Figure 4.3. That is, we are comparing the angular region smaller than $\phi = 90$ degrees with the one that is greater than $\phi = 90$ degrees in Figure 4.5. Results indicate that while the spacing becomes narrower at an incident angle of 60 degrees for cases with $\phi < 90$ degrees, it becomes wider at the same incident angle location for cases with $\phi > 90$ degrees. The reason is the contribution from skewness to backscattering is positive in the range $0 < \phi < 90$ degrees and is negative in the range $90 < \phi < 180$ degrees. Horizontal polarization being at a significantly lower signal level than vertical polarization, whenever the dielectric constant is large, it is affected more by skewness. Even at a dielectric value of 6 in Figure 4.5 we can see that at 8 GHz, the spacing between vertical and horizontal polarization is much wider at $\phi = 180$ than at $\phi = 0$ degrees over incident angles from 50 to 60 degrees. A similar result is observed when we compare the cases, $\phi = 40$ and $\phi = 140$ degrees. A closer look at these two cases indicates that the cause is largely due to the changes in the signal level associated with horizontal polarization. The vertical polarization being four or more decibels higher is less affected by skewness at 8 GHz. At 16 GHz the major skewness impact between incident angles of 50 and 60 degrees is on the angular trends. For both cases, $\phi = 0$ and $\phi = 40$ degrees, the angular trends are nearly flat between 50 and 60 degrees incidence, while there is a clear downward bending trend for the cases, ϕ = 140 and ϕ = 180 degrees.

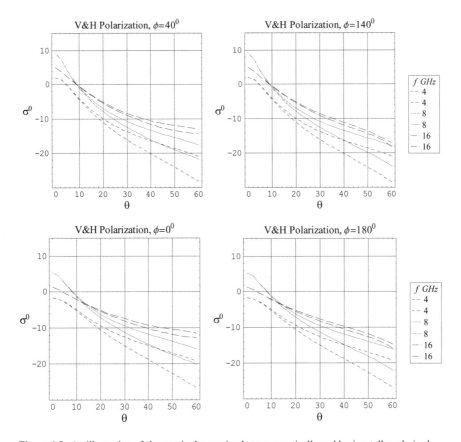

Figure 4.5 An illustration of changes in the spacing between vertically and horizontally polarized backscattering coefficients due to skewness anisotropy at ϕ = 140 and 180 degrees are compared with cases at ϕ = 40 and 0 degrees. Model parameters are r = 0.1 cm, L = $3(cos\varphi)^2 + 7(sin\varphi)^2$ cm, σ = 0.4 cm, ε = 6, and s_0 = 0.13 cm. For each polarization pair the upper curve is vertical polarization. Major differences in backscattering occur only over large angles of incidence and at higher frequencies. The small spacing at 140 and 180 degrees in azimuth at 16 GHz is due to a combined effect of frequency and anisotropy.

The incident angular curves we have shown can provide changes due to anisotropy over all the incident angles of interest but cannot show the skewness effect very well because it is a higher order effect. A better way to show skewness and anisotropy effects is to do our plots in azimuth angle at only one incident angle (i.e., by giving up changes in the incident angle). For example, if we select an incident angle of 45 degrees and use the same set of model parameters as we did in Figure 4.5, we would obtain Figure 4.6, where we show vertical and horizontal polarizations separately.

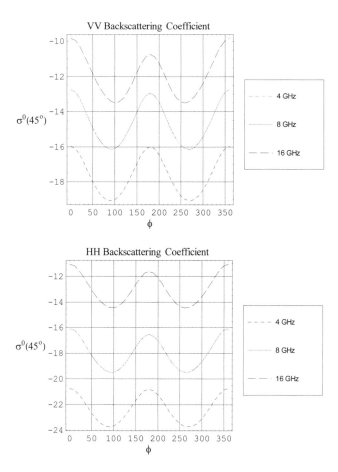

Figure 4.6 An illustration of changes in level and angular shapes of vertically and horizontally polarized backscattering coefficients due to skewness $s_0 = 0.13$ cm and surface anisotropy as ϕ changes. The common model parameters are $r = 0.1$ cm, $L = 3(cos\phi)^2 + 7(sin\phi)^2$ cm, $\sigma = 0.4$ cm, and $\varepsilon = 6$ with the expl correlation. Major variations of the backscattering coefficient with ϕ are due to surface anisotropy, and the difference between the signal levels at 0 and 180 is due to skewness, which has an increasing trend with the incident frequency.

At 4 GHz and VV polarization in Figure 4.6 there is no appreciable difference between backscattering at 0 and 180 degrees in azimuth. This means the skewness effect is negligible at this frequency. As frequency increases to 8 and 16 GHz, it is obvious that backscattering at 0 degrees is higher than at 180 and this difference is larger at higher frequencies, implying that the skewness effect is stronger at higher frequencies. Another obvious feature in this type of plot is that the minimum backscattering does not occur at 90 or 270 degrees for vertical polarization when the skewness effect is noticeable but is shifted toward the location of 180 degrees. This shift is larger at higher frequencies. We may view the backscattering curve at 4 GHz as representing only the effect of surface anisotropy, because the skewness effect is nearly negligible here. At 4 GHz the backscattering curve appears to be symmetric about 90 and 270 degrees. The variation in backscattering from 90 to 180 degrees is quite similar to the variation from 90 to 0 degrees for both polarizations. These changes therefore represent surface anisotropy. When the surface minimum moves away from 90 degrees toward 180 degrees, this move is caused by the skewness effect. This effect causes both a loss of symmetry around 90 degrees in backscattering and an observable difference between backscattering at 0 and 180 degrees. These are general statements that hold true in most cases. However, these effects are nonlinear. For example, the 8-GHz case does not show as much difference in backscattering between 0 and 180 in vertical as in horizontal polarization. There is also a greater shifting of the minimum for vertical than horizontal polarization at 16 GHz. Otherwise, the effects of both skewness and anisotropy are similar in both polarizations as frequency changes.

To show the effect of the incident angle on anisotropy and skewness in azimuthal plots we show backscattering behavior versus the azimuth angle at 55 degrees incidence at 4, 8, and 16 GHz in Figure 4.7. The level difference in vertical and horizontal polarizations is made clear by using the same vertical scale for both polarizations. In Figure 4.7 we see a strong nonlinear behavior in skewness effect at 8 GHz and vertical polarization leading to a much higher backscattering around 180 degrees than what should occur based on the signal levels at 4 and 16 GHz. Another unexpected nonlinear behavior is the large shift of the minimum backscattering signal from 90 to about 120 at 16 GHz in vertical polarization. These large changes are caused by skewness effects. We also see a large-level difference between vertical and horizontal polarizations occurring at 4 GHz where $k\sigma = 0.33$, $kL = 2.5$ at $L = 3$ cm, and $kL = 5.86$ at $L = 7$ cm. The small $k\sigma$ and the small to medium kL are in or close to the small perturbation range, which is the cause of the large difference between vertical and horizontal polarizations at large angles of incidence. At 16 GHz, $k\sigma = 1.34$. This is why the

Backscattering from the Sea Surface

two polarizations are much closer together.

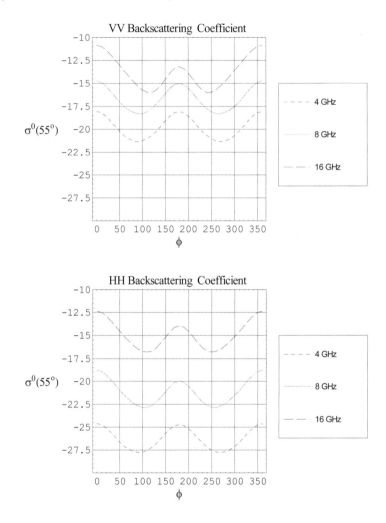

Figure 4.7 An illustration of changes in level and angular shapes of vertically and horizontally polarized backscattering coefficients due to skewness $s_0 = 0.13$ cm and surface anisotropy as ϕ changes. The common model parameters are $r = 0.1$ cm, $L = 3(cos\phi)^2 + 7(sin\phi)^2$ cm, $\sigma = 0.4$ cm, and $\varepsilon = 6$ with the expl correlation. Major variations of the backscattering coefficient with ϕ are due to surface anisotropy, and differences between the signal levels at 0 and 180 are due to skewness, which has an increasing trend with the incident frequency. Large differences in signal level between vertical and horizontal polarizations occur at lower frequencies, especially 4 GHz.

4.3.2 Skewness and Anisotropic Effects on rms Height Dependence

Chapter 3 illustrated how backscattering normally changes with surface rms height for isotropically rough surfaces. Here, we want to see how these changes are affected by anisotropy and skewness. Consider the case of backscattering along the $\phi = 90$ direction where $r = 0.1$ cm, $f = 8$ GHz, $s_0 = 0.13$ cm, $L = 3(cos\varphi)^2 + 7(sin\varphi)^2$, and $\varepsilon = 6$, with surface height varying from 0.2 to 0.6 cm. The corresponding case for the isotropic surface will have the same model parameters except it has no skewness parameter s_0, and its correlation length is fixed at 7 cm. Since skewness does not contribute at $\phi = 90$ degrees, this is the equivalent isotropic case although we are using an anisotropic, skewed surface to do the computation. Figure 4.8 compares backscattering at $\phi = 90$, 40, and 0 degrees for three different rms height surfaces. It is seen that before 20 degrees incidence backscattering coefficients for horizontal and vertical polarizations are very similar. The decrease in signal level close to normal incidence and the rise in signal levels beyond 30 degrees for $\phi = 40$ and 0 degrees relative to the case $\phi = 90$ degrees are due to anisotropy. The angular curves are also getting flatter as ϕ decreases, which is due to both anisotropy and skewness effects. These indicated changes in signal level and angular trends, however, do not change the trends of backscattering with the surface rms height.

Next, we want to compare the spacing between polarizations to see what changes may take place. For the isotropic surface we know that the spacing between polarizations in backscattering at a given frequency generally will increase with the incident angle. For a skewed surface the spacing should be the same as the isotropic surface over small to midsize angles. Around angles 40 degrees or more, the spacing increase should slow down, stop increasing, or change from an increasing to a decreasing trend depending on the surface rms height and the size of the skewness parameter. For the surface rms height and the choice of the skewness parameter given in Figure 4.8, the actual changes in spacing are shown in Figure 4.9 for backscattering in the $\phi = 0$, 40, and 90 degrees. At $\sigma = 0.2$ cm the increase of spacing with the incident angle at $\phi = 90$ degrees has slowed down from 7 dB to about 6 dB at 60 degrees incidence at $\phi = 0$ and 40 degrees. For $\sigma = 0.4$ cm we see that the spacing at $\phi = 0$ and 40 degrees is nearly a constant beyond 50 degrees. At $\sigma = 0.6$ cm, the spacing at $\phi = 0$ and 40 degrees appears to be a constant also in the region from 50 to 60 degrees. More evidence that there is no further increase in spacing between incident angles of 50 and 60 degrees is that the spacings between the backscattering curves at $\phi = 0$ and 40 degrees do not increase as fast with the incident angle as in the $\phi = 90$ degrees case. These changes are the result of the skewness effect.

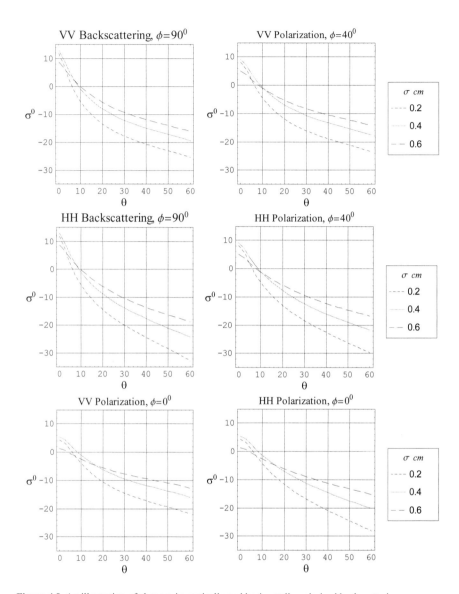

Figure 4.8 An illustration of changes in vertically and horizontally polarized backscattering coefficients due to skewness and anisotropy at $\phi = 0$ and 40 degrees relative to the case $\phi = 90$ degrees, which serves as a reference. Model parameters are $r = 0.1$ cm, $L = 3(cos\varphi)^2 + 7(sin\varphi)^2$ cm, $f = 8$ GHz, $\varepsilon = 6$, and $s_0 = 0.13$ cm. Beyond 30 degrees incidence backscattering generally rises as the azimuth angle ϕ decreases.

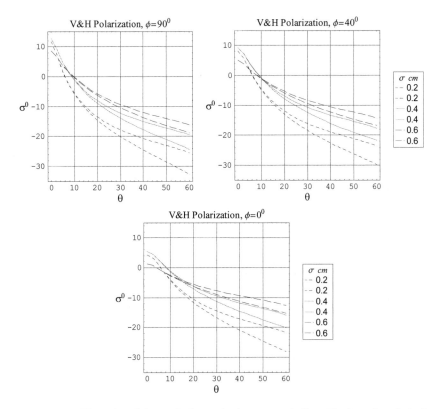

Figure 4.9 An illustration of changes in the spacing between vertically and horizontally polarized backscattering coefficients due to skewness and anisotropy at $\phi = 0$ and 40 degrees with the case $\phi = 90$ degrees serving as a reference. Model parameters are $r = 0.1$ cm, $\sigma = 0.4$ cm, $\varepsilon = 6$ $s_0 = 0.13$ cm, and $L = 3(cos\varphi)^2 + 7(sin\varphi)^2$ cm. For each polarization pair the upper curve is vertical polarization. Major differences in backscattering occur only over large angles of incidence and at higher frequencies.

For ϕ angles larger than 90 degrees, the influence of skewness is to decrease backscattering at large angles of incidence. The amount of decrease is dependent on the incident angle, surface rms height, and incident frequency. An illustration of the backscattering for azimuth angle ϕ larger than 90 degrees under different rms height conditions is shown in Figure 4.10 for both vertical and horizontal polarizations. Comparing vertical polarization between the $\phi = 140$ and 90 degrees cases we see that anisotropy has caused a drop near normal incidence and a rise over large incident angles in backscattering.

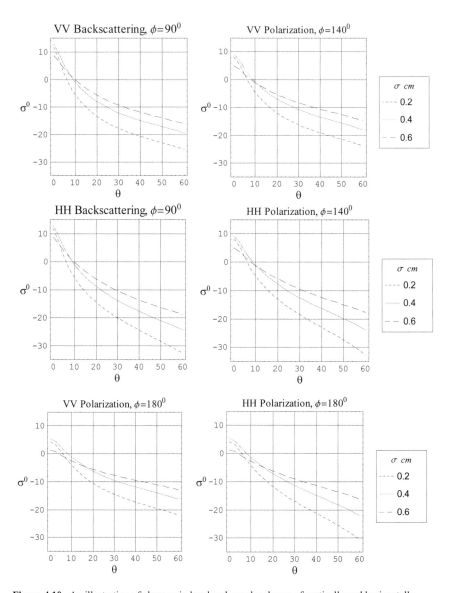

Figure 4.10 An illustration of changes in level and angular shapes of vertically and horizontally polarized backscattering coefficients as ϕ increases from 90 to 180 degrees. The model parameters are $r = 0.1$, $\sigma = 0.4$, $L = 3(cos\phi)^2 + 7(sin\phi)^2$ cm, $\varepsilon = 6$, and $s_0 = 0.13$ cm with the expl correlation. As ϕ increases from 90 degrees, the correlation length decreases and the skewness effect increases.

Based on the graphs in Figure 4.10 we cannot see a clear drop-off at large incident angles due to skewness for any one of the three surfaces. This is because the angular shape created by the shorter correlation length due to anisotropy is moving upward over large angles of incidence, while the one created by skewness is moving downward. The same situation exists for the ϕ = 180 degrees case. When we compare horizontal polarization, we can see that the backscattering curves with σ = 0.2 and 0.4 cm do bend downward between incident angles of 50 and 60 degrees for the cases with ϕ = 140 and ϕ = 180 degrees. This means that the skewness effect is large enough to be seen in these cases. For backscattering with σ = 0.6 cm we do not see a downward-bending angular trend at either polarization, meaning that the skewness effect is smaller for surfaces with a larger rms height. Note that a smaller skewness effect does not mean a smaller skewness parameter, because the significance of skewness is dependent upon the relative strength of skewness contribution and backscattering contribution from the correlation term.

Next, we want to illustrate the anisotropic and skewness effect by displaying backscattering coefficients versus the azimuth angle at incident angles of 40 and 50 degrees. There should be a small skewness effect at 40 degrees and a more noticeable skewness effect at 50 degrees for the cases we have presented in Figures 4.9 and 4.10. From Figure 4.11 we see clear variations of backscattering versus the azimuth angle due to surface anisotropy in both vertical and horizontal polarizations. The general picture is that the backscattering signal is highest at ϕ = 0 degrees and the next highest level is at ϕ = 180 degrees, while the two minimum signal levels are in the regions close to $\phi \geq 90$ and $\phi \leq 270$ degrees. The effect of skewness, causing backscattering at ϕ = 180 degrees to be smaller than at ϕ = 0, is visible for all three surfaces with different rms heights in horizontal polarization at an incident angle of 50 degrees. At an incident angle of 40 degrees, it is still visible for the two smoother surfaces in horizontal polarization, while a closer examination is needed to see the much smaller difference for the σ = 0.6 cm surface. For vertical polarization the results are less clear, especially for the incident angle of 40 degrees. However, a closer examination indicates that the backscattered signal at ϕ = 0 is higher than at ϕ = 180 degrees for all three surfaces and at both incident angles of 40 and 50 degrees. Experimentally, these fine distinctions should be buried in the noise. Another higher order effect that has been observed in measurements is the location of signal minima. The general trend is that the larger the skewness effect, the closer the signal minima is located toward the downwind location (ϕ = 180 degrees). A closer examination of horizontal polarization at 50 degrees will show this. Experimental confirmation can also be found when we show [Masuko et al., 1986] data for horizontal polarization at 52 degrees and 10 GHz.

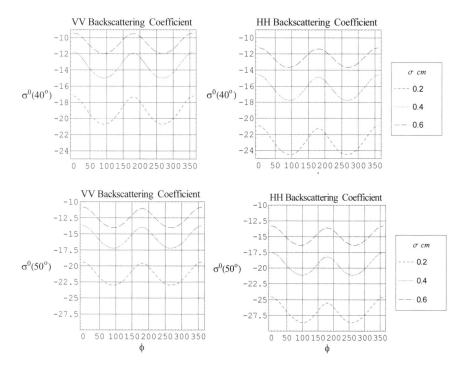

Figure 4.11   An illustration of changes in level and angular shapes of vertically and horizontally polarized backscattering coefficients due to skewness $s_0 = 0.13$ cm and surface anisotropy as ϕ changes. The common model parameters are $r = 0.1$ cm, $L = 3(cos\phi)^2 + 7(sin\phi)^2$ cm, $\sigma = 0.4$ cm, and $\varepsilon = 6$ with the expl correlation. Major variations of the backscattering coefficient with ϕ are due to surface anisotropy, and any difference between the signal levels at 0 and 180 is due to skewness, which has a decreasing trend with the surface rms height.

4.3.3 Skewness and Anisotropic Effects on Correlation Parameter Dependence

Changes in the correlation parameter change the properties of the correlation function. It can cause the expl correlation function to move from mostly an exponential function toward a much more Gaussian-like function. This is illustrated in Chapter 1. We shall consider backscattering corresponding to three different values of the correlation parameter, $r = 0.2, 1.0$, and 1.5 cm, and examine how it is affected by anisotropy and skewness. An illustration of this problem is given in Figure 4.12.

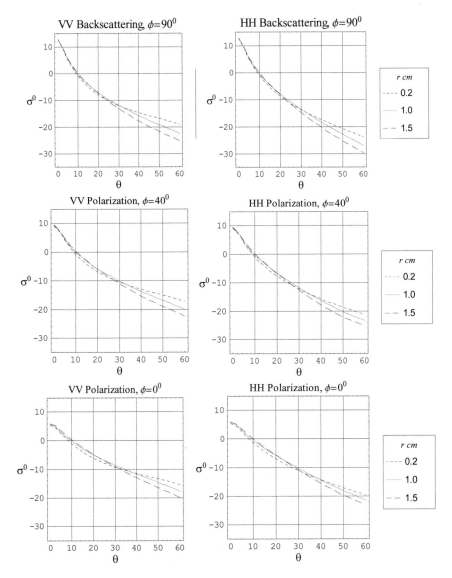

Figure 4.12 Backscattering coefficient variations due to skewness and anisotropy. Model parameters are $r = 0.1$ cm, $L = 3(cos\varphi)^2 + 7(sin\varphi)^2$ cm, $f = 8$ GHz, $\varepsilon = 6$, and $s_0 = 0.13$ cm. Beyond 30 degrees incidence backscattering generally rises as the azimuth angle ϕ decreases.

Differences in the values of the correlation parameter do not affect backscattering at normal incidence for vertical or horizontal polarization. A small r can cause a decrease over small angles of incidence relative to a large r, which can cause an increase over the same region. The role of the small and large r is then reversed over large angles of incidence starting near incident angles of 30–35 degrees for both polarizations. The obvious impact of surface anisotropy is to cause backscattering to decrease with decreasing azimuth angle between 0 and 90 degrees at normal incidence. This backscattering trend is reversed after the incident angle exceeds 20 degrees. The effect of skewness should be largest at $\phi = 0$ degrees and over large incident angles, and it decreases gradually with decreasing incident angle and as the azimuth angle moves away from the $\phi = 0$ position as shown in Figure 4.12. A better way to see the skewness effect is through comparing the case at $\phi = 40$ to $\phi = 140$ degrees. This is shown in Figure 4.13.

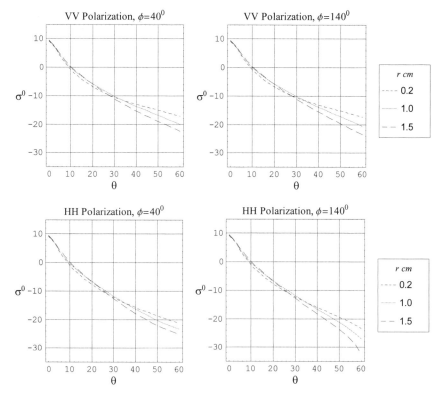

Figure 4.13 Effects of skewness and anisotropy on backscattering coefficients with different correlation parameters.

In Figure 4.13 the model parameters chosen are $r = 0.1$ cm, $L = 3(cos\varphi)^2 + 7(sin\varphi)^2$ cm, $\sigma = 0.4$ cm, $\varepsilon = 6$, and $s_0 = 0.13$ cm. For vertical polarization there is basically no change in the backscattering coefficients for $\phi = 40$ and $\phi = 140$ degrees in the incident angular range from 0 to 40 degrees. Over large incident angles we can see that the backscattering coefficients drop off more when $\phi = 140$ degrees than when $\phi = 40$ degrees due to the skewness effect. When it comes to horizontal polarization, the influence of skewness becomes much clearer. Although at incident angles less than 40 degrees there is no appreciable difference between the backscattering coefficients, the backscattering curves at $\phi = 40$ degrees are turning upward after the incident angle exceeds 40 degrees. While at $\phi = 140$ degrees, the backscattering curves are turning decisively downward. For the $r = 1.5$ cm case, the difference between the backscattering coefficients at 60 degrees is as much as 7 dB, whereas for the $r = 0.2$ cm case the difference is about 3 dB.

When we compare the backscattering curves at $\phi = 0$ with $\phi = 180$ degrees, we should see a similar picture to that in Figure 4.13.

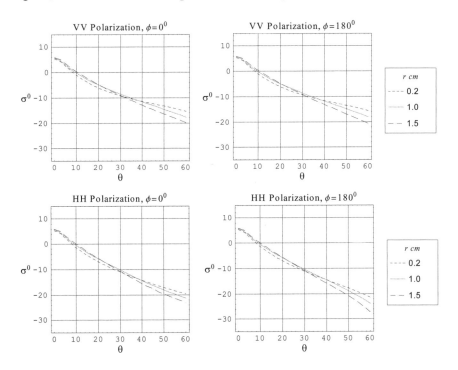

Figure 4.14 An illustration of the skewness effect between the two cases, $\phi = 0$ and 180 degrees.

In Figure 4.14 an additional point to note is that the $r = 0.2$ and $r = 1.0$ cm curves cross each other at an incident angle of 40 degrees for both $\phi = 0$ and 180 degrees in horizontal and vertical polarization. When we view the same problem over all azimuth angles at incident angles of 40 and 50 degrees, the difference becomes self-evident in Figure 4.15. As r increases, the signal level generally drops over large incident angles along with an increase in the difference between upwind and downwind and a shift of the minima toward the downwind location.

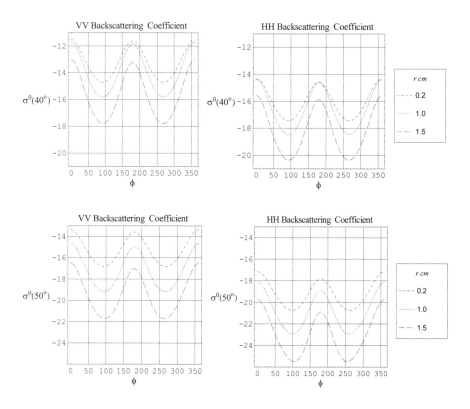

Figure 4.15 An illustration of changes in level and angular shapes of vertically and horizontally polarized backscattering coefficients due to skewness $s_0 = 0.13$ cm and surface anisotropy as ϕ changes. The common model parameters are $r = 0.1$ cm, $L = 3(cos\phi)^2 + 7(sin\phi)^2$ cm, $\sigma = 0.4$ cm, and $\varepsilon = 6$ with the expl correlation. Major variations of the backscattering coefficient with ϕ are due to surface anisotropy, and any difference between the signal levels at 0 and 180 is due to skewness, which has a decreasing trend with a decreasing correlation parameter.

In Figure 4.15 at an incident angle of 40 degrees, we see that the anisotropic behavior of the surface is affected by the surface correlation properties defined by $r = 0.2$ and 1.0 cm, which force backscattering at 0, 180, and 360 degrees in azimuth to have essentially the same backscattering signal level for the $r = 0.2$ and $r = 1$ cm curves in horizontal polarization. Our normal expectation is for a more expl correlation function to generate a higher level return over large angles of incidence than a more Gaussian-like correlation. The incident angle of 40 degrees happens to be in the transition region. At an incident angle of 50 degrees in Figure 4.15 we have what we expect to see, that the $r = 0.2$ cm curve is at a higher level than the $r = 1.0$ cm curve, which, in turn, is higher than the $r = 1.5$ cm curve. Figure 4.15 alone does not show the complete picture of what is happening, but with Figure 4.14 showing incident angle dependence, the explanation provided here becomes clear.

4.3.4 Skewness and Anisotropic Effects on Correlation Length Dependence

Similar to the model parameters r and σ that we have considered, the correlation length parameter is another one that changes the shape of the surface correlation function. For anisotropic surfaces there are two correlation lengths along orthogonal directions. We label the shorter one L_u. The longer one L_c is taken to be twice the size of L_u in the example considered in this section. Backscattering from three surfaces with L_u equal to 2, 4, and 6 cm is shown in Figure 4.16. All model parameters are given in the legend. For each value of ϕ we show backscattering from three surfaces with different correlation lengths. The longer correlation length causes higher backscattering near normal incidence and lower backscattering over large angles of incidence. As ϕ decreases from 90 to 0 degrees, the effective correlation length is reduced due to surface anisotropy. Hence, we see a decrease in backscattering near normal and an increase in backscattering over large incident angles when we compare $\phi = 0$ with $\phi = 40$ or 90 degrees. All these obvious changes in signal level and angular trends are due to anisotropy. Actually, there is also a change due to the skewness effect, but it is not obvious in the examples in Figure 4.16 because it is a higher order effect.

A better way to see this effect is to compare the vertically and horizontally polarized backscattering coefficient pairs at $\phi = 40$ with $\phi = 140$ degrees or $\phi = 0$ with $\phi = 180$ degrees over a wide range of incident angles. The reason is that backscattering coefficients for ϕ angles less than 90 degrees are being strengthened by contributions from surface skewness, while the backscattering coefficients for ϕ angles larger than 90 degrees are reduced by contributions from skewness. Results are shown in Figure 4.17.

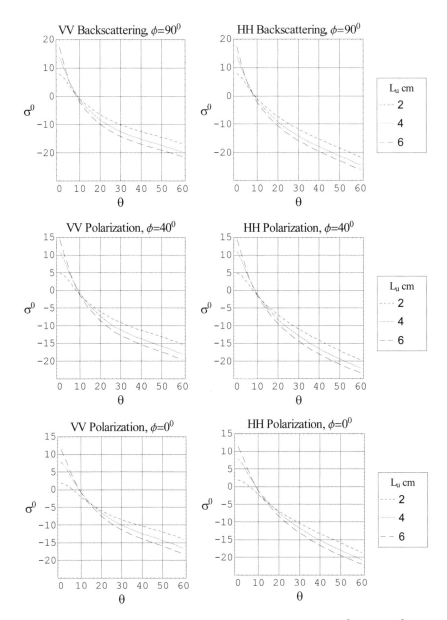

Figure 4.16 Backscattering with $f = 8$ GHz, $\sigma = 0.4$ cm, $L = L_u(cos\phi)^2 + L_c(sin\phi)^2$ cm, $L_c = 4, 8$, and 12 cm, $r = 0.2$ cm, and $s_0 = 0.13$ cm for dielectric values of 6. The case with azimuth angle $\phi = 90$ degrees is unaffected by skewness. Hence, we use it as a reference.

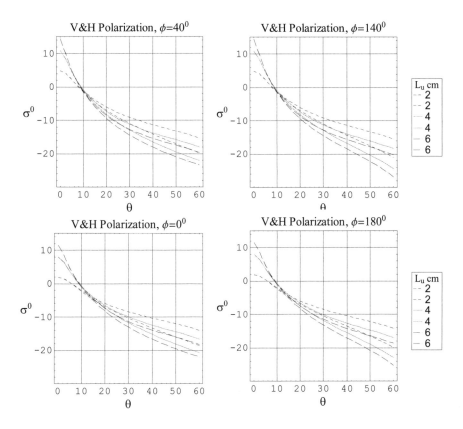

Figure 4.17 An illustration of changes in level and angular shapes of vertically and horizontally polarized backscattering coefficients as ϕ increases from 0 to 180 degrees. The model parameters are r = 0.2 cm, σ = 0.4 cm, $L = L_u(cos\phi)^2 + L_c(sin\phi)^2$ cm, ε = 6, and s_0 = 0.13 cm with the expl correlation. Differences between ϕ = 0 and 180 or ϕ = 40 and 140 degrees cases are due to surface skewness.

In Figure 4.17 we see that backscattering over small angles of incidence up to about 40 degrees is very similar between the cases, ϕ = 40 and 140 degrees. At incident angles beyond 40 degrees, the angular trends of the backscattering curves for ϕ = 40 degrees are slowing down in their downward trends relative to those for ϕ = 140 degrees, where there is a further increase in the downward bending of the backscattering curves. This difference is caused by the surface skewness, and the effect is larger for horizontal polarization and longer correlation lengths.

Similar situations exist when we compare the cases, $\phi = 0$ degrees with $\phi = 180$ degrees.

Another way to show the effects of skewness and anisotropy is to use azimuth plots. Here, we select 35 and 45 degrees of incidence and show backscattering variations over 0 to 360 degrees in the azimuth angle. These illustrations are given in Figure 4.18.

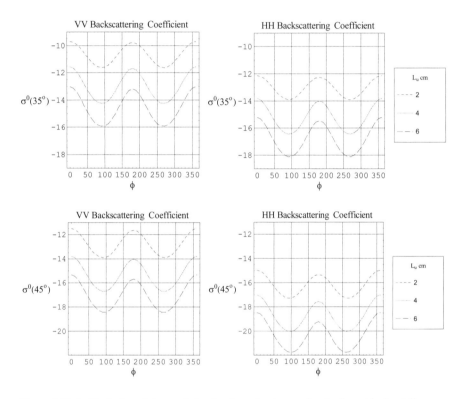

Figure 4.18 An illustration of changes in level and angular shapes of vertically and horizontally polarized backscattering coefficients due to skewness $s_0 = 0.13$ cm and surface anisotropy as ϕ changes. The common model parameters are $r = 0.1$ cm, $L = L_u(cos\phi)^2 + L_c(sin\phi)^2$ cm, $L_c = 2L_u$, $\sigma = 0.4$ cm, and $\varepsilon = 6$ with the expl correlation.

Generally, we cannot see visually any skewness effect at an incident angle of 35 degrees in a backscattering coefficient plot versus the incident angle. However, in azimuth plots given in Figure 4.18 we can see the skewness effect manifesting in two ways: it causes a signal level difference between $\phi = 0$ and 180 degrees and a shift in the locations of signal minima toward the ϕ = 180-degree location. In Figure 4.18 at an incident angle of 45 degrees, there is a small drop at ϕ = 180 degrees relative to 0 degrees even in vertical polarization for the L_u = 4 cm case. The difference between 0 and 180 degrees in horizontally polarized backscattering is generally larger and clearer, especially for surfaces with longer correlation lengths. We use the same vertical scale in both polarizations to show that the horizontally polarized backscattering coefficient is always lower than the corresponding vertical polarization at large incident angles. When the incident angle is increased from 35 to 45 degrees, the skewness effect is stronger. Greater differences in signal level are seen between 0 and 180 degrees in azimuth for both polarizations. The shift in signal minima toward the ϕ = 180-degree location can also be seen visually with an incident angle of 45 degrees in horizontal polarization. In summary, the skewness effect increases with the incident angle and the correlation length and is larger for horizontal polarization.

4.3.5 Skewness and Anisotropic Effects on Dielectric Constant Dependence

In this section we want to examine backscattering behaviors due to changes in the dielectric constant and in what way they are modified by anisotropy or skewness. The dielectric constant is a completely different parameter from those we have considered in our parameter study in that it is unrelated to and independent of surface geometry. However, backscattering angular trends generated by different dielectric values will be affected by surface anisotropy and skewness in different ways. Results are shown in Figure 4.19 and model parameters used are given in the legend.

According to our previous study, as ϕ decreases from 90 to 0 degrees, we expect the backscattering signal near normal incidence to decrease while the signal over large incident angles increases. This is true for all surfaces with three different dielectric values and it is caused by surface anisotropy. We also know that the angular curves at ϕ = 0 and 40 degrees should drop off more slowly over large incident angles than those at ϕ = 90 due to the combined effects of skewness and anisotropy. Unlike correlation parameters, the relative spacings among the three different backscattering curves remain unchanged. We know the changes due to skewness are of a higher order and hence are not obvious in Figure 4.19. A better way to see the skewness effect over a large range of incident angles is to compare both vertical and horizontal polarizations for all three different dielectric surfaces at ϕ = 40 with ϕ = 140 degrees and at ϕ = 0 with ϕ = 180 degrees. Results are shown in Figure 4.20. Model parameters are given in the legend.

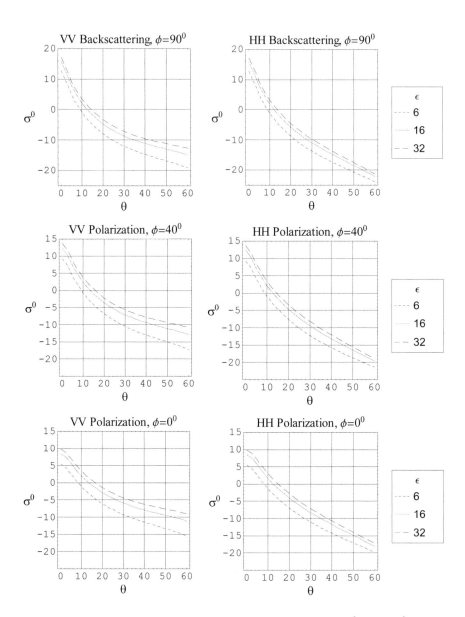

Figure 4.19 Backscattering with $f = 8$ GHz, $\sigma = 0.4$ cm, $L = 3(cos\phi)^2 + 7(sin\phi)^2$ cm, $r = 0.1$ cm, and $s_0 = 0.13$ cm for dielectric values of 6, 16, and 32. The case with azimuth angle $\phi = 90$ degrees is unaffected by skewness. Hence, we use it as a reference.

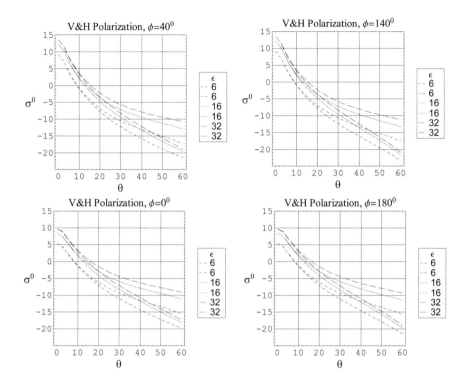

Figure 4.20 Variations in level and angular shapes of vertically and horizontally polarized backscattering coefficients as ϕ increases from 0 to 180 degrees. The model parameters are $r = 0.2$ cm, $\sigma = 0.4$ cm, $L = 3(cos\phi)^2 + 7(sin\phi)^2$ cm, $\varepsilon = 6$, and $s_0 = 0.13$ cm with the expl correlation.

When we compare the cases, $\phi = 40$ with $\phi = 140$ degrees in Figure 4.20, a clear difference exists in horizontal polarization after the incident angle exceeds about 40 degrees. The backscattering curves at $\phi = 140$ degrees have a faster drop-off than those at $\phi = 40$ degrees. A similar effect also occurs in vertical polarization, but it is on a much smaller scale. These changes are due to the skewness effect. In comparison to a similar illustration in Figure 4.17, the downward bending of the horizontally polarized curves at $\phi = 140$ degrees for all three dielectric surfaces appears to move together, keeping their relative spacings the same as for the $\phi = 40$ degrees case. This is where dielectric changes are different from those parameters sensitive to the geometric properties of the rough surface. In Figure 4.17 the relative spacings between the two polarizations with the three surfaces for the ϕ = 40 degrees case are visually narrower than those for the ϕ = 140 degrees case.

For the cases ϕ = 0 and ϕ = 180 degrees in Figure 4.20, we expect to see similar properties as we saw in the cases ϕ = 40 and ϕ = 140 degrees. The only difference seems to be that for horizontally polarized backscattering we can visually see that the curve with ε = 32 at ϕ = 180 degrees begins to deviate from the corresponding curve at ϕ = 0 degrees when the incident angle exceeds 30 degrees. Further examination shows that the other two horizontally polarized curves have a similar property (i.e., the similarity between the two cases, ϕ = 0 and ϕ = 180 degrees, ends at a smaller incident angle than the other two cases, ϕ = 40 and ϕ = 140 degrees).

When we change the surface correlation length, the skewness and anisotropy effects change with it. When we change the surface dielectric constant, both skewness and anisotropic effects remain the same. This point is illustrated with a backscattering plot versus the azimuth angle in Figure 4.21. The model parameters used are given in the legend. The amount of skewness taken to be the difference between 0 and 180 degrees for either vertical or horizontal polarization is the same, when the dielectric constant changes from 6 through 16 to 32.

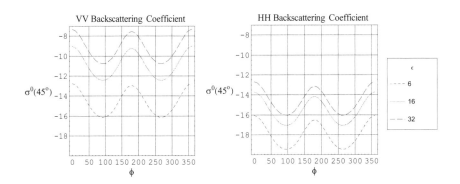

Figure 4.21 An illustration of changes in level and angular shapes of vertically and horizontally polarized backscattering coefficients due to skewness s_0 = 0.13 cm and surface anisotropy as ϕ changes. The common model parameters are f = 8 GHz, σ = 0.4 cm, ε = 6, r = 0.1 cm, and $L = 3L_u(cos\phi)^2 + 7(sin\phi)^2$ cm with the expl correlation. The difference in the backscattering coefficients between 0 and 180 degrees in azimuth does not change when the dielectric constant changes from 6 to 32.

4.3.6 Azimuth Parameter Effect

Up to this point, our discussions of parameter effects have dealt with signal level and incident angle changes. The sole parameter that affects the shape of the azimuth lobe around the upwind-downwind locations is the azimuth parameter a. Changes in the width of this lobe will automatically influence the lobe around the crosswind region. Thus, separate consideration is not needed for the crosswind region. In Figure 4.22(a) we see that as a changes from 2 to 4, the lobes around upwind and downwind widen, while the lobe around crosswind narrows. Other model parameters are given in the legend. In Figure 4.22(b) we increase the skewness parameter from 0.05 to 0.1 cm. The large skewness value has caused a small change in the locations and values of signal minima.

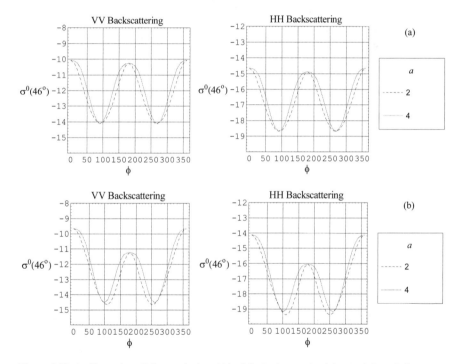

Figure 4.22 An illustration of changes in the width of the backscattering lobe around upwind-downwind directions due to the azimuth parameter a changing from 2 to 4 and the impact of skewness. The common model parameters are f = 13.4 GHz, σ = 0.33 cm, $L = 8|cos\phi|^a + 18|sin\phi|^2$ cm, z = 0.005 cm, and ε = 48, with the mexp correlation function: (a) skewness s_0 = 0.05 cm and (b) skewness s_0 = 0.1 cm.

4.4 COMPARISONS WITH RADAR MEASUREMENTS OVER OCEAN

This section considers comparisons of the model given by (4.3) and (4.5) with data varying with the azimuth angle and the incident angle at various wind speeds. Unlike land surfaces the sea surface varies continuously with time. We assume that its roughness follows a stationary process, but this is only an assumption. We do not know how well that holds true. Wind speed and direction may also fluctuate or vary during measurements. Stability of the airplane may also contribute to error. Despite all these uncertainties, consistent trends of the backscattering coefficient in incident angle, azimuth angle, and wind speed have been reported by [MacDonald, 1956], [Grant and Yaplee, 1957], [Wiltse et al., 1957], [Jones et al., 1977], [Schroeder et al., 1985], and [Masuko et al., 1986].

4.4.1 General Characteristics of Radar Sea Return

Based upon the backscattering measurements taken by [Wiltse et al., 1957] and [Grant and Yaplee, 1957] at 10 GHz and [Jones et al., 1977] at 13.9 GHz shown in Figure 4.23, we see that for incident angles less than 25 degrees, the surface backscattering is controlled by a Gaussian correlation function resulting in a bell-shaped backscattering curve. Beyond 30 degrees backscattering has an exponential shape, indicating that backscattering may come from an exponentially correlated surface.

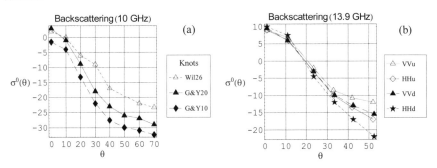

Figure 4.23 (a) Data acquired at 10 GHz by [Wiltse et al., 1957] at 26 knots (13.4 m/s) and [Grant and Yaplee, 1957] at 20 and 10 knots (5.15 m/s). (b) Data acquired at 13.9 GHz by [Jones, Schroeder, and Mitchell, 1977] at 13.9 m/s.

This angular shape is observed over a range of wind speeds and at X- and Ku-bands. This angular shape is very different from those we considered in Chapter 3 for soil surface where the backscattering curves are closer to an exponential. In Chapter 1 we introduced an expl correlation function with two parameters, L and

r. Figure 1.3 illustrates that when r is significant compared to L or $r > L$, this correlation function is close to a Gaussian function over small lag distances and approaches an exponential function over large lag distances. Hence, it is a good candidate to produce a backscattering curve over incident angles that can match backscattering from the sea surface. In the next paragraph we shall demonstrate this point with the data acquired by [Jones et al., 1977].

The data acquired by [Jones et al., 1977] in Figure 4.23 include both the upwind and downwind cases. This means that the model parameters should be the same for these two cases with the exception of the skewness parameter s_0. The comparison between the model and this data set is given in Figure 4.24. Selected model parameters are $\sigma = 0.23$ cm, $L_u = 0.4$ cm, $L_c = 0.4$ cm, $\varepsilon = 46 - j39$, $r = 6.5$ cm, and $s_0 = 0.12$ cm for upwind and $s_0 = 0.02$ cm for downwind. The azimuth parameter $a = 2$.

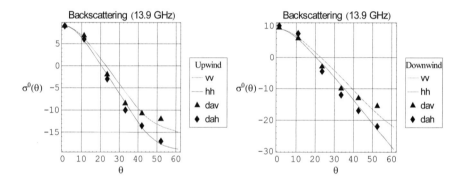

Figure 4.24 Comparison of sea scatter model prediction based on (4.3) and (4.5) with measurements acquired by [Jones, Schroeder, and Mitchell, 1977] at 13.5 m/s for the upwind and downwind cases. Over the first 25 degrees or so the angular shape appears to be Gaussian, while over larger incident angles the shape of the backscattering curve is exponential for both upwind and downwind cases.

When the parameter L is less than r, the theoretical curves do take a Gaussian shape over small incident angles and an exponential shape after 30 degrees. Thus, the theoretical model has the capability to match backscattering trends from the sea surface. Note that for incident angles 30 or more, the backscattering angular trend is exponential. Hence, we may have the option to use a simple exponential correlation function to account for surface backscattering at large enough incident angles over all 360 degrees in azimuth. This would represent some simplification in model and its evaluation in applications to problems involving large incident angles, which is the case in many satellite observations over the sea surface.

For the upwind case there is a sharp bending after 40 degrees due to skewness. This bending will be less sharp if the data level near 40 and 50 degrees is lower. An examination of the data trend indicates that over the first 35 degrees the data trend is different from the trend indicated by the data near 40 and 50 degrees. Currently, data matching is able to include the first 10 degrees and 40 to 50 degrees but misses the data in between because they follow a different trend. A similar situation exists in the comparison with the downwind data. There is the possibility that the data near 20 and 30 are somewhat low and that those near 40 and 50 are higher than they should be for both the downwind and the upwind cases. To account for this possibility, we shall match the data, assuming that the 20-degree and 30-degree data are somewhat higher and that the data near 40 and 50 degrees is lower. The matching is shown in Figure 4.26 after increasing r to 7.5 and reducing σ to 0.22 cm, while keeping all other parameters unchanged.

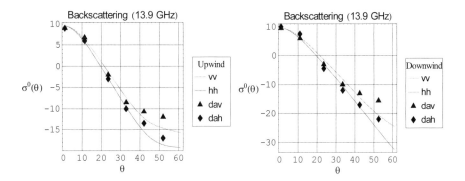

Figure 4.25 Comparison of sea scatter model prediction based on (4.3) and (4.5) with measurements acquired by [Jones, Schroeder, and Mitchell, 1977] at 13.5 m/s for the upwind and downwind cases. In matching data it has been assumed that the data near 20 and 30 is a bit higher than those shown in the figure and that the data near 40 and 50 degrees is somewhat lower in level than those shown in the figure. The azimuth parameter $a = 2$.

We have demonstrated how far a more Gaussian-weighted expl correlation function can fit the data with our backscattering model. Clearly, it cannot go very far. In Section 4.4.3 we shall also investigate how far a more exponential-weighted expl correlation function can fit the data with our model. At incident angles larger than 30 degrees, there is the possibility of using only a simple exponential correlation function when the variation is over the azimuth angle. Examples are shown in Section 4.4.2.

4.4.2 Variations of Backscattering with the Azimuth Angle

This section considers measurements by [Masuko et al., 1986] and [Jones et al., 1977], who designed airborne circle-flight radar experiments to acquire wind speed and direction over all azimuth angles. Their data shows that radar return is maximum along the upwind direction and reaches a minimum near the crosswind direction generally shifted toward the downwind direction when the skewness effect is significant. Along the downwind direction the return is usually smaller than the return in the upwind direction. We believe that this is due to the skewness in the wave created by the wind. The incident angle chosen for wind speed and direction measurements is usually around 30 degrees or larger. In part, this is because over smaller angles of incidence there is not enough difference between upwind and crosswind to provide a clear picture of changes in wind direction.

Let us apply the surface scattering model to the data from [Masuko et al., 1986] at 10 GHz and incident angles of 32 and 52 degrees for VV and HH polarizations using the simple exponential correlation function. The dielectric constant of sea water can be estimated by a dielectric model given in Appendix 4A. At 20°C, a salinity of 32.54 parts per thousand, and 10 GHz, the dielectric constant is estimated to be $56.2 + j37.4$. The sizes of roughness responsible for scattering are determined by frequency, incident angle, and wind speed. In the scattering model the signal level at upwind is controlled mainly by the correlation length L_u. When the incident angle exceeds 30°, an increase in L_u will cause the signal to decrease. The signal level at crosswind is controlled by L_c in a similar way. Intuitively, L_c is always larger than L_u. The quantity that determines the upwind-downwind difference is s_0. A larger value will cause a larger increase in upwind and a larger decrease in downwind. Usually, the value of s_0 is below 0.2 under low wind conditions. Finally, the scattering level at all azimuth angles rises or falls with the rms height σ, which affects the overall signal level. In most cases, $k\sigma$ is less than one. Three wind speeds, 3.2, 9.3, and 14.5 m/s, are available from [Masuko et al., 1986]. A comparison between the model and measurements for vertical polarization at an incident angle of 32 degrees is shown in Figure 4.26 with a simple exponential correlation function, which appears to work here.

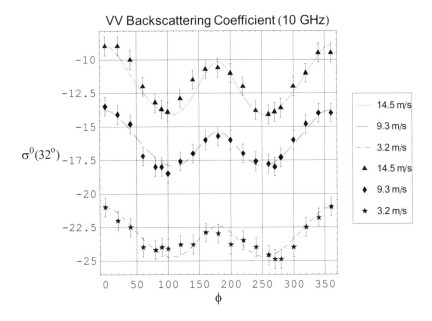

Figure 4.26 A comparison between the IEM surface scattering model with a vertically polarized data set collected by [Masuko et al., 1986] at an incident angle of 32 degrees. Results indicate that there are clear trends of σ^0, L_u, L_c, and σ with wind speed. Model predictions are in solid and dashed lines, and symbols are the data points. The azimuth parameter $a = 2$.

In Figure 4.26 σ increases with wind speed from 0.125 cm through 0.19 cm to 0.29 cm. Simultaneously, L_u decreases from 30 cm through 13 cm to 9 cm, while L_c changes from 58 cm through 28 cm to 25 cm. All three parameters have a clear increasing or decreasing trend with wind speed. The skewness parameter also has an increasing trend here. It goes from $s_0 = 0.13$ cm at a low wind speed through $s_0 = 0.17$ to 0.18 cm at a high wind speed. Note that a higher s_0 value at a higher wind speed does not necessarily mean a larger upwind-downwind difference because the backscattering coefficient is larger at a higher wind speed. Data show a decreasing upwind-downwind difference from 3.5 dB at 3.2 m/s, 3 dB at 9.3 m/s to 0.5 dB at 14.5 m/s, but s_0 does not decrease with wind speed. In fact, because signal level is much higher at 9.3 m/s than at 3.2 m/s, s_0 has to increase from 0.13 to 0.17 to generate the 3-dB difference at a higher wind speed. Then, at

14.5 m/s wind speed, we need $s_0 = 0.18$ to cause a 0.5-dB difference between upwind and downwind. Hence, it is clear that the decrease in upwind-downwind difference is due more to the increase in the return signal level than the size of the skewness parameter. In fact, it is possible for s_0 to continue to increase with wind speed while the difference between upwind and downwind gets smaller. Overall, there is a good agreement in angular trends for all three wind speeds.

The upwind-crosswind difference seems to stay around 4 to 5 dB at wind speeds between 3.2 m/s and 14.5 m/s. Another point worth noting is that the minimum radar return does not occur at crosswind locations. Instead, it is shifted toward the downwind location, and this is quite apparent under low wind conditions. Overall, the model is able to match the data behavior very well. Hence, our choice of the function for the surface spectrum given by (4.4) can adequately represent the intended portion of the sea spectrum. Another factor that allows (4.4) to work is that both the incident frequency and the incident angle are fixed, thus fixing the size of roughness at each wind speed.

Next, we want to consider backscattering at another incident angle, 52°. Normally, for an isotropically rough surface one set of surface parameters is used for all incident angles as demonstrated in Chapter 3. This is also true for the sea surface excluding the skewness effect, when data is taken along the incident angle direction and viewed from upwind, downwind, or crosswind directions as shown later with the FASINEX [Li et al., 1989; Weissman, 1990] data. For data acquired along the azimuth direction with circle flights, we can only expect the correlation lengths along the upwind and downwind directions to remain the same for different incident angles at a given wind speed. The main focus with circle flights is to maintain the correct signal level along the azimuthal direction. In [Masuko et al., 1986] the incident angle is estimated through some averaging scheme. Thus, the signal level along the incident angle direction has some uncertainties causing the rms height parameter at 32 degrees to be different from the one at 52 degrees. In fact, [Masuko et al., 1986] reported incident angle to be near 32° and near 52° instead of 32° and 52°. A comparison of some model parameters for vertical and horizontal polarizations at the three wind speeds is given in Table 4.1. Both L_u and L_c remain unchanged with the incident angle and polarization as required by the physical model. However, all σ values for horizontal polarization are higher than vertical polarization and vary with the incident angle with only one exception in the 9.3 m/s case for vertical polarization. This means that most of the horizontally polarized data is set too low relative to vertical polarization.

Table 4.1 A Comparison of Some Model Parameters

		$32°$ σ cm	L_u	L_c	$52°$ σ	L_u	L_c
3.2 m/s	VV	0.125	30	58	0.07	30	58
	HH	0.178	30	58	0.13	30	58
9.3 m/s	VV	0.19	13	28	0.19	13	28
	HH	0.27	13	28	0.29	13	28
14.5 m/s	VV	0.29	9	25	0.23	9	25
	HH	0.37	9	25	0.35	9	25

We know that the signal level at 52° incidence is much lower than that at 32°. Hence, the skewness parameter should be smaller here. This means that the skewness parameter is actually a function of wind speed, the incident angle, and polarization, because its contribution [based on (4.5)] must be smaller than the contribution from (4.3) to remain as a higher order effect. For the two low wind speeds we let s_0 = 0.09 and 0.093 cm and use a larger value, 0.097 cm, at 14.5 m/s. By adjusting the rms heights at wind speeds of 3.2 m/s and 14.5 m/s from 0.125 to 0.07 cm and 0.29 to 0.23 cm, respectively, and keeping the same rms height for 9.3 m/s, we obtain the matching shown in Figure 4.27. The matching is quite good at both the high and the low wind cases. At 9.3 m/s wind speed, the data seems to fall into two groups with different signal levels. More specifically, some data points around the crosswind direction are shifted down relative to the rest of the data. Hence, the matching can be very good only when those data points are excluded. We believe these data points are too low because the same correlation length and rms height at 9.3 m/s work at 32 degrees incidence around the crosswind direction. Hence, they should be outliers.

The above analysis shows that when there is an uncertainty in the incident angle, under the same wind conditions, the rms surface height will take on different values at different incident angles and polarizations. This is not the case for incident angle data, at least for low wind speeds, because as we shall see with FASINEX [Li et al., 1989; Weissman, 1990] data and [Jones et al., 1977] data, there is a unique set of surface parameters associated with a given wind speed for all incident and azimuth angles of interest as long as the skewness effect is small. However, for azimuth angle data, there is enough uncertainty in the signal level to change σ.

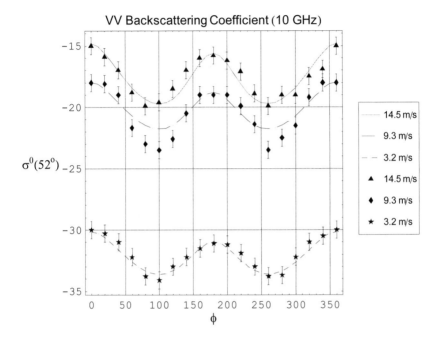

Figure 4.27 A comparison between the IEM surface scattering model for the sea surface and a vertically polarized data set collected by [Masuko et al., 1986] at an incident angle of 52 degrees. Results indicate that there are clear trends of σ^0, L_u, L_c, and σ with wind speed. There is a clear shift of the minimum toward the downwind direction in the data especially under low wind conditions. Model predictions are in solid and dashed lines, and symbols are the data points. Only a simple exponential correlation function is needed here. The azimuth parameter $a = 2$.

Now, we consider horizontal polarization. Again, we believe that the correlation lengths along the upwind and downwind directions should remain the same as in vertical polarization at a given wind speed. The rms height values have to be adjusted because of the uncertainty in the incident angle signal level in [Masuko et al., 1986]. Here, rms height values must be increased for horizontal polarization. For the skewness parameter little or no change is necessary at 32° incidence, because the signal levels for vertical and horizontal polarizations do not differ much over small angles of incidence, although horizontal polarization is expected to be somewhat lower at 32°. At 52° incidence, vertical polarization can be several decibels higher than horizontal polarization. Hence, smaller values for the skewness parameter are expected for horizontal polarization.

For the same three wind speeds as in vertical polarization, we show a comparison of our model predictions with horizontally polarized circle flight data at 32° in Figure 4.28. The rms height values used for the three wind speeds from low to high are 0.178, 0.27, and 0.37 cm as shown in Table 4.1. They are different from and larger than what we used for VV polarization (i.e., the signal level acquired through the HH channel is not calibrated to maintain a proper relation with the VV channel). Hence, we do not know which channel has the correct signal level based on these data. We do know that the two polarizations should have the same rms height based on incident angle measurements or the physical model.

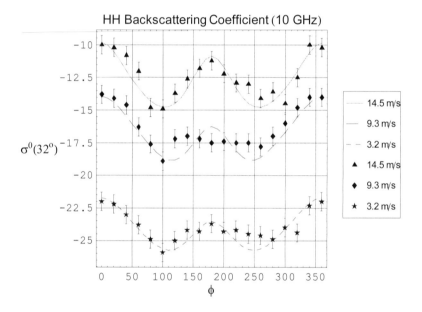

Figure 4.28 A comparison between the IEM surface scattering model for the sea surface and a horizontally polarized data set collected by [Masuko et al., 1986] at an incident angle of 32 degrees. Results indicate that there are clear trends of σ^0, L_u, L_c, and σ with wind speed. Model predictions are in solid and dashed lines, and symbols are the data points. Only a simple exponential correlation function is needed here. The azimuth parameter $a = 2$.

The high and low wind data fit the model very well near the upwind and downwind region. For all three wind speeds, there is some scatter in data around the crosswind regions. At the 9.3 m/s wind speed, the correct angular shape is lost in the crosswind and downwind regions due to significant scatter in data. However, very good matching is realized in the upwind direction and this good agreement extends out to 100 degrees in azimuth on both sides of the upwind direction. For the low wind speed case, very good matching is seen from 0 to 200 degrees in azimuth, beyond which the data loses track of its proper angular shape until it reaches the upwind region once again. For the two high wind speeds the values of the skewness parameter are the same as in vertical polarization. At 3.2 m/s wind speed, this parameter is 0.11 cm, which is smaller than 0.13 cm selected in vertical polarization. Thus, the increasing trend with wind speed is almost the same in both polarizations.

For the horizontally polarized 52° incidence data we also keep the same correlation lengths in the upwind and crosswind directions for the three wind speeds as we did for vertical polarization. These data have clear angular trends in azimuth and have very little scatter. The selected rms heights from low to high winds are 0.13, 0.29, and 0.35 cm. Except for the low wind case, these rms height values are very close to those used at 32° incidence, but as expected they are very different from those for VV polarization as shown in Table 4.1. It seems that calibration was done within each polarization channel independently without regard to the proper relation between the two polarizations. Due to low signal levels at large incident angles the skewness parameter must take on smaller values than for vertical polarization. For the three wind speeds from low to high, s_0 = 0.065, 0.08, and 0.06 cm. This is the only case where s_0 fails to increase at a higher wind speed. A comparison between model and measurements for this case is shown in Figure 4.29.

An excellent matching is achieved at 14.5 m/s where not only are agreements obtained at upwind, downwind, and crosswind directions, but also the specific angular shape along the azimuth direction is closely followed. Note that the specific angular shapes are different at different wind speeds because of the changes in the amount of skewness causing both a different amount of upwind-downwind difference and a shift in signal minima. Due to the small amount of scatter in the data we are able to see the angular shape very clearly. In particular, as the wind speed decreases, there is a gradual shift in the minimum return from the crosswind direction toward the downwind direction and an increase in the upwind-downwind difference. These gradual changes define the angular shape of the backscattering curve along the azimuth direction very clearly.

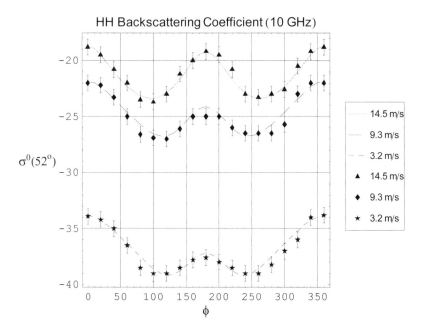

Figure 4.29 A comparison between the IEM surface scattering model for the sea surface and a horizontally polarized data set collected by [Masuko et al., 1986] at an incident angle of 52 degrees. Results indicate that there are clear trends of σ^0, L_u, L_c, and σ with wind speed. Model predictions are in solid and dashed lines, and symbols are the data points. Only a simple exponential correlation function is needed here. The azimuth parameter $a = 2$.

Next, we want to consider the data acquired by [Jones et al., 1977]. Their data includes vertically polarized measurements at two wind speeds, 6.5 and 15 m/s, at an incident angle of 33.5 degrees and a set of vertically and horizontally polarized measurements at a wind speed of 12.8 m/s and an incident angle of 40 degrees. All measurements were acquired at 13.9 GHz. In Figure 4.30 we show our model comparison with the vertically polarized data at 6.5 and 15 m/s. The agreement between model and data at 6.5 m/s is quite good between 0 and 130 degrees and between 250 to 360 degrees in azimuth (i.e., the agreement is good around both the upwind and crosswind regions). In the downwind region the data appears to have been distorted and fails to show a local maximum in the downwind direction. We know the data is distorted in this region because the same problem does not exist in the 15-m/s data.

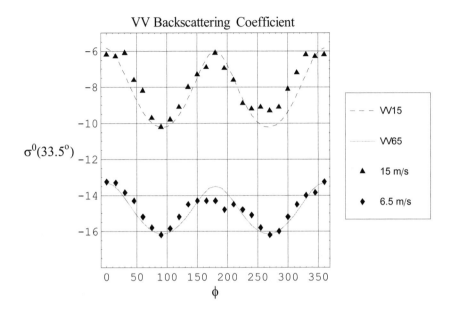

Figure 4.30 A comparison between the IEM surface scattering model for the sea surface and a set of vertically polarized data collected by [Jones et al., 1977] at an incident angle of 33.5 degrees. Model parameters for the 15 m/s data are f = 13.9 GHz, σ = 0.18 cm, L_u = 1.7 cm, L_c = 5.2 cm, ε = 48 − j39, and s_0 = 0.09 cm. Model parameters for the 6.5 m/s data are f = 13.9 GHz, σ = 0.12 cm, L_u = 5 cm, L_c = 9.5 cm, ε = 48 − j39, and s_0 = 0.07 cm. Model predictions are in solid and dashed lines, and symbols are the data points. Only a simple exponential correlation function is needed here. The azimuth parameter a = 2 .

Examination of the 15-m/s case shows that there is a much better agreement around the downwind region between the model and measurements than at 6.5 m/s and that there is a local maximum at 180 degrees. However, a large disagreement exists in the region between 250 and 330 degrees. It appears that the data has been shifted upward in this region by about 0.7 dB. The same problem also exists between 20 to 60 degrees. At 6.5 m/s we see that the two crosswind regions provide the same level of return as predicted by the model. The fact that at 15 m/s the data at the two crosswind locations is at different levels could be due to some difference in local surface conditions. The general shape of the 6.5-m/s data and much of the data acquired by [Masuko et al., 1986] indicate that the expected backscattering from the ocean surface should be symmetrically distributed with respect to 180 degrees in azimuth.

[Jones et al., 1977] acquired both vertically and horizontally polarized data over all azimuth angles at the same incident angle. As indicated by [Masuko et al., 1986], the incident angle for azimuth measurements is an averaged value. Hence, unlike measurements taken over the incident angle, we cannot expect the same set of model parameters to be applicable to both polarizations, although both polarizations are assumed to be taken from the same incident angle. Figure 4.31 shows a comparison of the sea scatter model with their measurements.

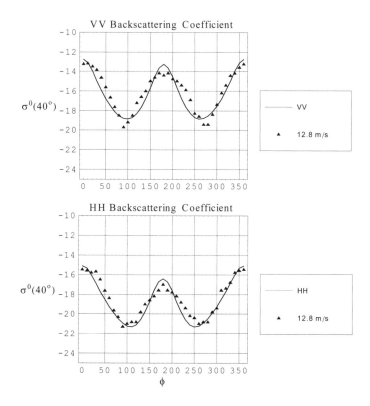

Figure 4.31 A comparison of the model based on (4.3) and (4.5) with measurements acquired by [Jones, Schroeder, and Mitchell, 1977] at 12.8 m/s over all azimuth angles. Only a simple exponential correlation function is needed here. The azimuth parameter $a = 2$.

For the vertically polarized case we use the model parameters, f = 13.9 GHz, σ = 0.15 cm, L_u = 5 cm, L_c = 19 cm, ε = $48 - j39$, and s_0 = 0.08 cm, and for horizontal polarization we use σ = 0.2 cm, L_u = 5 cm, L_c = 17 cm, ε = $48 - j39$, and s_0 = 0.09 cm. There is a clear disagreement around the crosswind region between the model and measurements, because some data points seem to have dropped off from the trends established by other data. At the downwind location the local peak is also missing in the data. For a stationary randomly rough surface the data distribution should be symmetric with respect to the downwind location (ϕ = 180°). This assumption about the sea surface being stationary in modeling does not hold very well for this data set. Hence, only a very general agreement is achieved in this comparison. Differences around 1 dB in level exist in the angular regions, $\phi = 30°$ to $\phi = 60°$, $\phi = 120°$ to $\phi = 130°$, and $\phi = 220°$ to $\phi = 240°$. For horizontal polarization the agreement between model and measurements is much better. Except for a few isolated data points, only one region, $\phi = 220°$ to $\phi = 250°$, shows a level difference around 1 dB. While a 1-dB shift causes a clear change in angular shape, such a difference is not considered large in measurements.

4.4.3 Variations of Backscattering with the Incident Angle

This section analyzes incident angle data available from four different sources, early measurements by [Grant and Yaplee, 1957] and later measurements by [Jones et al., 1977], [Masuko et al., 1986], and [Weissman, 1990]. The basic difference between the incident angle data versus the azimuth angle data is that whenever vertical and horizontal measurements are taken together in incident angle measurements, the spacing between the two polarizations will follow the model-predicted angular behavior. This property does not hold for azimuth angle data in general, because the emphasis there is on azimuth angle variation and the reported incident angle is an average over several incident angles. Furthermore, with the exception of the skewness parameter upwind, downwind and the two polarizations share the same model parameters over all incident angles at a given wind speed.

We have noted that for each wind speed the correlation lengths in the upwind and crosswind directions should not change with the incident angles. This should also be true of the surface rms height for all incident angles. On the other hand, the skewness parameter may change with the incident angle and polarization because it is subtracted from the correlation contribution on the downwind side, and physically it represents a higher order effect relative to the correlation term (i.e., contribution to backscattering from the skewed portion of the sea surface must be smaller than that of the symmetric portion). Hence, s_0 should be adjusted to fit its proper role at each incident angle and polarization when needed. However, in this book we have been choosing just one s_0 for all incident angles.

[Grant and Yaplee, 1957] reported backscatter measurements over the ocean at two wind speeds in the upwind direction. The incident angular shape of their measurements is quite representative of the characteristics of the ocean surface in that it takes on a bell shape over small incident angles and an exponential shape over large incident angles. In particular, there is an unusual sharp bend in the angular curve between 30 and 50 degrees. We want to show that with the expl correlation function it is possible to match this data. The comparison is shown in Figure 4.32(a) for their data at 10.28 m/s (20 knots) acquired at 10 GHz under upwind conditions with vertical polarization.

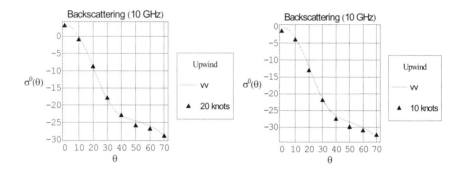

Figure 4.32 A comparison between the IEM surface scattering model for the sea surface and a vertically polarized data set for the upwind case collected by [Grant and Yaplee, 1957]. Wind speed is (a) 10.28 m/s and (b) 5.14 m/s. Results indicate that the sea surface backscattering has the special characteristics of possessing both a Gaussian-like angular shape in the small incident angle region and an exponential angular shape over large incident angles. These characteristics call for the use of an expl correlation function. Unlike the azimuth angle data the same rms height and correlation parameters should work for all incident angles. The azimuth parameter $a = 2$.

The data in Figure 4.32(a) appears to follow a smooth bell-shaped curve from 0 to about 30 degrees. Then, it turns into a slow decaying plateau region. The selected parameters for our model are $\sigma = 0.09$ cm, $L_u = 0.43$ cm, $r = 13$ cm, and $s_0 = 0.25$ cm. Here, r is much larger than L_u, forcing the region of the correlation function near the origin to look like a Gaussian function, while the large lag distance region remains like an exponential. The sharp turn is due to the combined effect of the correlation function and the skewness effect leading to this much slower decay of the backscattering signal after the turn. The matching between the model and the measurements is excellent, especially when data fluctuation is taken into account. Figure 4.32(b) shows a similar plot for the 5.14 m/s (10 knots) data. The angular shape of this data set is very similar to the one in Figure 4.32(a) except the signal level is lower and the drop-off at 70 degrees is smaller. A lower wind speed should imply a flatter surface, a smaller σ, and a larger correlation length, which is defined by the combined effect of r and L_u. As we mentioned in Chapter 1 for two parameter correlation functions, the correlation length is defined by both parameters.

[Jones et al., 1977] acquired a pair of vertically and horizontally polarized backscattering data for crosswind at 13.5 m/s and 13.9 GHz. The crosswind direction is not influenced by skewness. The controlling parameters are L_c and r, while $\sigma = 0.23$ cm, the same as for upwind and downwind given in Figure 4.24. The dielectric constant is $46 - j39$, fixed by the incident frequency and the water temperature taken to be $20°C$. For the sea surface the dielectric constant is large enough so that a $\pm 10\%$ change has little influence on backscattering. For the comparison between model and data shown in Figure 4.33, we select $L_c = 0.4$ cm and $r = 8.5$ cm.

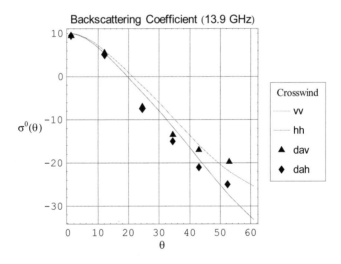

Figure 4.33 A comparison of the model based on (4.3) and (4.5) with measurements acquired by [Jones, Schroeder, and Mitchell, 1977] at 13.5 m/s for the crosswind case. There is only a general agreement between the model and the data. The azimuth parameter $a = 2$.

It is clear that the matching in Figure 4.33 misses the data near 20 and 30 degrees. Visually, we can see that these pieces of data are low compared to the angular trend established by the data near 0, 10, 40, and 50 degrees. The quality of the matching is similar to those in Figure 4.24. Basically, when we match the data over 0 and 10 degrees, we can only choose to match either the data near 20 and 30 degrees as done in Figure 4.25 or the data near 40 and 50 degrees but not both. The reason is the data at 0 and 10 degrees has established a Gaussian angular shape that has to be changed to an exponential over large angles of incidence. Allowing the Gaussian shape to continue through 20 and 30 degrees will miss the data at 40 and 50 degrees. On the other hand, when we focus on matching the 40-degree and 50-degree data, the data near 20 and 30 degrees may appear low to the angular trend, because the data between 20 and 60 degrees is forming an exponential angular trend by itself. Hence, the matching we did in Figures 4.24 and 4.33 indicates the difficulty in matching the transition region.   An alternative is to ignore the data point at normal incidence and see how well we can match the rest of the data. The reason for ignoring the data at normal incidence is that in many applications the normal incidence data is not used, because it may either contain a coherent scattering component or include backscattering contributions from nearby angles due to finite beamwidth.

We now consider matching the same data set by [Jones et al., 1977] at 13.9 GHz for upwind, downwind, and crosswind *excluding* the data at normal incidence. This is because the data when the incident angle exceeds 10 degrees appears to have a simple exponential shape. A close fit here may allow the model to be used in applications excluding the region where the incident angle is less than 10 degrees. The crosswind case is shown in Figure 4.34.

In Figure 4.34 very good agreement is realized between model and measurements within the 10–60-degree region. The selected model parameters are $\sigma = 0.37$ cm, $L_c = 10$ cm, $r = 1.4$ cm, and $\varepsilon = 46 - j39$. Note that the value of r is significant relative to the value of L_c, and it controls the backscattering signal over large incident angles. The next question is whether the same approach can provide a similar matching of the model with data acquired for upwind and downwind. We know that upwind and downwind share the same model parameters except for the skewness parameter, which could be smaller on the downwind side. Also, the same rms height should apply to upwind, downwind, and crosswind. The comparisons are shown in Figure 4.35 where we select $\sigma = 0.37$ cm, $L_u = 8$ cm, $r = 1.0$ cm, $\varepsilon = 46 - j39$, and $s_0 = 0.11$ cm for upwind and $s_0 = 0.02$ cm for downwind.

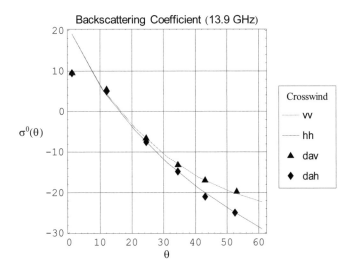

Figure 4.34 A comparison of sea scatter model prediction based on (4.3) and (4.5) with measurements acquired by [Jones, Schroeder, and Mitchell, 1977] at 13.5 m/s for the upwind case. Data at normal incidence is excluded. The azimuth parameter $a = 2$.

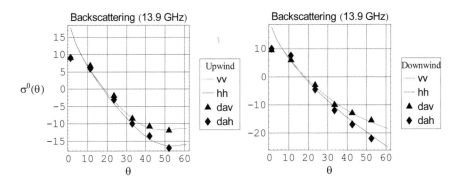

Figure 4.35 Comparison of sea scatter model prediction based on (4.3) and (4.5) with measurements acquired by [Jones, Schroeder, and Mitchell, 1977] at 13.5 m/s for the upwind and downwind cases. After excluding the data at normal incidence, all data points lie along an angular trend modified by skewness, which is responsible for the sharp bending between 40 and 50 degrees in the upwind case. Overall agreement is excellent. This approach is restricted to applications where data at normal incidence is not used. The azimuth parameter $a = 2$.

Results in Figures 4.34 and 4.35 indicate that in backscattering from the sea surface the same model parameters should apply to both vertical and horizontal polarizations and all incident angles considered. These properties should help recognize outliers in analyzing data. Note that with the other approach in matching data shown in Figures 4.33 and 4.24 it is also true that the same model parameters apply to vertical and horizontal polarizations and all incident angles (i.e., these properties are the nature of the backscattering data being exposed by the model). Hence, all properly analyzed backscattering data should have these properties.

[Jones et al., 1977] also acquired incident angle data in the upwind direction at two wind speeds, 6.5 and 15 m/s, and 13.9 GHz with vertical and horizontal polarizations. This data confirms again that the two polarizations should share the same model parameters and that these model parameters are good for all incident angles considered in the same problem. The implication here is that when one set of model parameters for vertical polarization is known, the corresponding backscattering behavior in horizontal polarization can be predicted, because physically they should share the same set of model parameters excluding the skewness parameter. A comparison of our model with their data is shown in Figure 4.36 to demonstrate this fact. In Figure 4.36 there is just one set of model parameters at each wind speed for both polarizations and all incident angles considered. Only the datapoints close to 20 degrees at 15 m/s are off the predicted angular trend. Other datapoints are either close to or on the predicted trends. The parameters used for the 6.5 m/s wind speed are $f = 13.9$ GHz, $\sigma = 0.18$ cm, $L_u = 1.5$ cm, $r = 3$ cm, $\varepsilon = 46 - j39$, and $s_0 = 0.09$ cm, and for the 15 m/s wind speed they are $f = 13.9$ GHz, $\sigma = 0.26$ cm, $L_u = 1.0$ cm, $r = 2.8$ cm, $\varepsilon = 46 - j39$, and $s_0 = 0.09$ cm. For both wind speeds we choose the azimuth parameter to be $a = 2$.

[Masuko et al., 1986] investigated changes in the incident angle when the azimuth angle is fixed in the downwind direction. They provided such angular data for the three wind speeds, 3.2, 9.3, and 14.5 m/s in horizontal polarization between incident angles of 20 to 65 degrees in their Figure 9. For the high and medium wind cases the signal level remains relatively high, so that we can let $s_0 = 0.06$ cm for all incident angles. For the low wind case we decrease the size of s_0 to 0.045 cm. The specific values of the rms height used for the three wind speeds from low to high are 0.145, 0.26, and 0.35 cm, which are similar to but not the same as what we used before due to fluctuations in data at each incident angle. For L_u we use 30, 13, and 9 cm for the three wind speeds and the same dielectric constant as we did in Section 4.4.2 dealing with azimuth angle data for HH polarization.

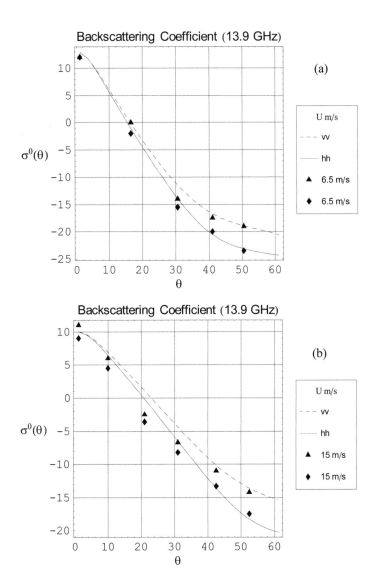

Figure 4.36 A comparison of sea scatter model predictions based on (4.3) and (4.5) with upwind measurements acquired by [Jones, Schroeder, and Mitchell, 1977]. (a) Parameters at 6.5 m/s are $f = 13.9$ GHz, $\sigma = 0.18$ cm, $L_u = 1.5$ cm, $r = 3$ cm, $\varepsilon = 46 - j39$, and $s_0 = 0.09$ cm. (b) Parameters at 15 m/s are $f = 13.9$ GHz, $\sigma = 0.26$ cm, $L_u = 1.0$ cm, $r = 2.8$ cm, $\varepsilon = 46 - j39$, and $s_0 = 0.09$ cm. The azimuth parameter $a = 2$.

A comparison with the [Masuko et al., 1986] incident angle data in their Figure 9 is shown in Figure 4.37. Good agreement is obtained for all cases, especially at the 14.5 m/s wind speed. One exception is at 20 degrees for the 9.3-m/s wind speed. This datapoint coincides with the datapoint for 14.5 m/s. Hence, we believe that it could be an outlier because it is also off the angular trend of all other data for the 9.3-m/s wind speed. Both the data and the model indicate a clear wind dependence for the backscattering coefficient. Furthermore, better sensitivity to wind speed occurs at larger incident angles. However, the signal level is also lower at larger incident angles. Thus, in practice, a good compromise for sensing wind speed should be between 30 and 50 degrees.

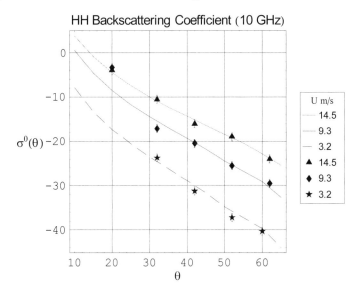

Figure 4.37 A comparison between the IEM surface scattering model for the sea surface and a horizontally polarized data set for the downwind case collected by [Masuko et al., 1986]. Results indicate that due to inherent fluctuations in data the use of any two incident angle data at a given wind speed will lead to two different rms height values unless the two data points fall on the model predicted curve, which is true here at 14.5 m/s wind speed. For the three wind speeds from low to high $\sigma = 0.145, 0.26, 0.350$ cm, $L_u = 30, 13, 9$ cm, and $\varepsilon_r = 56 - j37$. The azimuth parameter $a = 2$.

The agreement obtained in Figure 4.37 is in the general incident angular trend, not the individual incident angle at a specific azimuth angle. Similarly, when we fit the general azimuth angular trend at a specific incident angle we cannot, in general, fit each individual azimuth angle. This is why the rms height did not come out the same at the 32° and 52° incident angles when we did the matching over azimuthal trends. When the data at a specific incident angle is selected, it may not fall on the general incident angle trend, which is based on all acquired incident angle data. Furthermore, two pieces of selected incident angle data could end up with one above and the other one below the general angular trend as shown in Figure 4.37 for the 3.2-m/s wind speed case, thus forcing the surface height parameters to be different. One way to avoid introducing this type of problem is not to use data at a specific angle to determine signal level. Instead, use an acceptable angular trend based on all pieces of acquired incident angle data such as the one given by the model in Figure 4.37. If so, signal levels of all incident angles at a given wind speed share the same set of surface parameters, and any error introduced by normal fluctuations in data at a specific angle is avoided. This scheme to avoid fluctuations in data at an incident angle can be applied to azimuth angles as well.

The Frontal Air-Sea Interaction Experiment [Li et al., 1989; Weissman, 1990] (FASINEX) was performed at 14.6 GHz and 7-m/s wind speed. A smaller size of scatterers is responsible for scattering at this frequency. It turns out that no adjustment in the skewness parameter is needed even at 60 degrees for the downwind case here. Angular data is available between 20 and 60 degrees. Comparisons with the model given in this chapter were made in [Fung, 1994] using the capillary spectrum proposed by [Pierson and Moskowitz, 1964]. Numerical computation was very intensive because higher order roughness spectra had to be computed when only the roughness spectrum was available. Here, we shall use all orders of the roughness spectrum corresponding to the expl correlation given in (1.7). This makes the computation of backscattering very efficient, and we know it can give a good approximation to a portion of the real sea spectrum in the capillary region. At 14.6 GHz, a salinity of 32.54 parts per thousand and 20° C, the dielectric constant is $\varepsilon_r = 44.9 - j39$. This quantity controls the reflectivity of the surface and the spacing between vertical and horizontal polarizations. A larger value of the dielectric constant will cause a wider separation between the two polarizations and a higher backscattering level. The surface parameters σ, L_u, L_c, and r should remain the same for all incident angles considered and for all three azimuth viewing directions if data is taken from the same region and satisfies the stationary assumption. On the other hand, the skewness parameter s_0 is dependent on the azimuth viewing directions because the surface is skewed. It should be different when viewed from different directions. Here, the values of the four parameters that should remain the same are taken to be 0.22, 2.9, 6.2, and 1.8 cm, respectively. For the upwind case we shall let $s_0 = 0.053$ cm for all angles and polarizations considered. The backscattering coefficients for vertical and horizontal polarizations computed from our model are shown in Figure 4.38. The agreement between model predictions and measurements is quite good, including the bending between 40 and 60 degrees. This bending does not occur for most land surfaces because it is influenced by the contribution from skewness, which is caused by the wind.

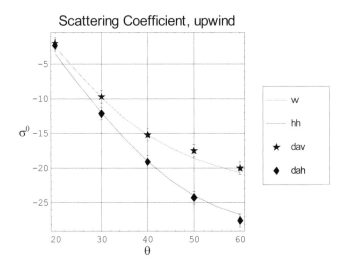

Figure 4.38 A comparison between the IEM surface scattering model for the sea surface and upwind measurements from FASINEX [Li et al., 1989]. Surface parameters are taken to be $\sigma = 0.22$, $L_u = 2.8$, $L_c = 6.2$, $r = 1.8$, and $s_0 = 0.048$ cm, and $\varepsilon_r = 44.9 - j39$ for both polarizations and all incident angles shown. The azimuth parameter $a = 2$.

Next, we compare the same model parameters with the downwind measurements. Indeed, with the exception of the skewness parameter needed to account for the skewed property of the surface, no change in any of the other surface parameters is necessary. Thus, it appears that our assumption of stationarity is justified. Results are shown in Figure 4.39. The agreement between model and measurements is excellent except at 60 degrees. There the spacing between VV and HH polarization is smaller than those at 40 and 50 degrees. Physically, the spacing between the data points for vertical and horizontal polarizations should be larger at higher incident angles. The data point for vertical polarization at 60 degrees should also be higher in order to match the data trend established at other angles. Thus, we believe the model predictions, which are in good agreement with data at other angles, to be correct, although the cause for the disagreement at 60 degrees is not known.

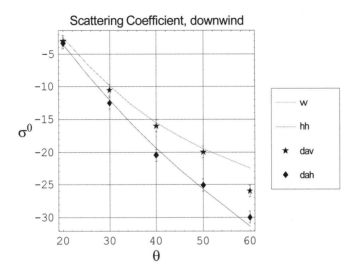

Figure 4.39 A comparison between the IEM surface scattering model for the sea surface and downwind measurements from FASINEX [Li et al., 1989]. Surface parameters are chosen to be $\sigma = 0.22$, $L_u = 2.8$, $L_c = 6.2$, $r = 1.8$, $s_0 = 0.01$ cm, and $\varepsilon_r = 44.9 - j39$ for both polarizations and all incident angles shown. The azimuth parameter $a = 2$.

For crosswind backscattering the selection of the same surface parameters works in a way similar to the upwind and downwind cases. Results are shown in Figure 4.40. The agreement is quite good except at 60 degrees for horizontal polarization. However, the data at 60 degrees is clearly off the data trend established by data at other angles. Furthermore, physically, the spacing between vertical and horizontal polarizations should be larger at higher incident angles. Hence, we believe the predicted value should be correct, although the cause for the difference is not known.

The analysis of the data from the Frontal Air-Sea Interaction Experiment indicates that the same set of surface parameters, excluding the skewness parameter, is expected to stay the same at a given wind speed, when the incident angle, azimuth angle, or polarization changes. This is true only when we use the angular trends established by all the acquired data instead of the signal level at any individual angle. It is also clear from this study that the reason why the rms height changed when we matched the azimuth angle data at two different incident angles is that we used the signal levels at those two incident angles instead of the signal level associated with the general angular trend. The value of the rms height also changed when we worked on the azimuth angle data at two different polarizations. According to the Frontal Air-Sea Interaction Experiment data, surface rms height value should not change when we change polarization. However, the Frontal Air-Sea Interaction Experiment was conducted at a 7-m/s wind speed. At higher wind speeds the sea surface is more skewed so that different polarizations may excite very different surfaces. As we have seen from the data presented in this section, angular trends established with all available data are much more reliable than the signal level at a given angle.

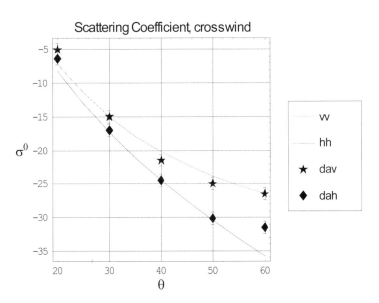

Figure 4.40 A comparison between the IEM surface scattering model for the sea surface and crosswind measurements from FASINEX [Li et al., 1989]. The surface parameters are chosen to be $\sigma = 0.22$, $L_u = 2.8$, $L_c = 6.2$, $r = 1.8$ cm, and $\varepsilon_r = 44.9 - j39$ for both polarizations and all incident angles shown. Note that skewness is an upwind-downwind phenomenon. It does not affect the crosswind. The azimuth parameter $a = 2$.

4.5 INTERNAL CONSISTENCY IN DATA LEVEL

In Sections 4.4.2 and 4.4.3, we have considered model applications to both the incident angle data and the azimuth angle data. One obvious problem is that the rms height obtained through matching the azimuth angle data changes with the incident angle and polarization. On the other hand, the FASINEX data and the data from [Jones et al., 1977] show that the surface rms height should remain the same for all incident angles; azimuth angles along upwind, downwind, and crosswind directions; and for both vertical and horizontal polarizations at a given wind speed. In practice, there is always some fluctuation in data, and it is quite difficult to determine the correct signal level at a single angle for various reasons. One way to obtain a self-consistent data set along the azimuth direction is to first establish an incident angle trend based on all available data for each polarization. This process will remove data fluctuation and establish consistency in signal levels over different incident angles. The same objective can be achieved by fitting an applicable surface scattering model to the data similar to what we did in Figures 4.38–4.40, where the relative signal level in both the incident angle and the spacing between vertical and horizontal polarizations at a given wind speed and azimuth direction was established. The results can then be applied to the azimuth angle data at a given wind speed and incident angle to establish a consistent set of surface parameters. In other words, after data at different incident angles, wind speeds, azimuth angles, and polarizations are obtained as in [Masuko et al., 1986], we should first rearrange them as a function of the incident angle for vertical and horizontal polarizations at each wind speed. Then, through curve fitting based on all available data, we can establish a self-consistent relative signal level in the incident angle and spacing between polarizations. When the data at a fixed incident angle is rearranged versus the azimuth angle, we use the established signal level instead of the original signal level at an individual angle. This way the surface parameters will remain the same as we change the incident angle. A similar process can also be applied to establish consistency in the level along the azimuth direction. If this internal consistency check is not done and a direct matching of an empirical function is applied to the azimuth angle data at a given incident angle, then surface rms height is usually different for different incident angles as shown in Figures 4.26–4.29. This is because the rms height parameter is sensitive to the signal level.

As we shall see in Chapter 5, the SEASAT data and the FASINEX data were acquired at the same frequency and agree with the each other over both the incident and the azimuth angles. Thus, both airborne and satellite data do share the same surface parameters when we change polarization.

4.6 CONCLUDING REMARKS

As a multiscale surface the contributing roughness scale from a sea surface to backscattering is determined by the incident wavelength and the incident angle. In the microwave range between the C- and Ku-bands, only centimeter-size roughness is relevant. For this reason, all orders of the sea spectrum for the effective roughness scale can be represented by an mexp function with length represented in centimeters at these frequencies. This fact allows a substantial simplification in computing backscattering from the sea surface and makes the model calculation practical. Other points of interest in this chapter are described as follows:

1. Contribution to sea surface backscattering comes from two types of terms: one involves the surface correlation function and the other involves the surface skewness function.

2. Surface correlation is a centro-symmetric function. It is not responsible for the difference in backscattering between upwind and downwind, which is due solely to the skewed portion of the sea surface caused by the wind.

3. In matching a set of backscattering data along the azimuthal direction at a specific incident angle and wind speed, it is generally not possible to keep the rms height the same for different incident angles as demonstrated in Figures 4.26 and 4.27. The main difficulty here is to experimentally maintain the correct relative signal level in both azimuthal and incident angle directions simultaneously without a common reference point such as an applicable surface scattering model.

4. In acquiring data along the azimuthal direction at a given incident angle and polarization, there is also the difficulty of maintaining the correct spacing between VV and HH polarizations. As a result, a different surface rms height is needed to fit different polarizations as demonstrated in Figures 4.26 and 4.28. In considering incident angle data, it is found that all incident angle data maintain a spacing between vertical and horizontal polarizations that is consistent with the theoretical backscattering model defined in (4.3) and (4.5).

5. When matching a set of backscattering data with the sea surface scattering model along the incident angle direction at a given wind speed and polarization, surface parameters, σ, L_u, L_c, and r could remain the same for upwind, downwind, and crosswind as demonstrated in Figures 4.38–4.40. It seems that if we calibrate our model first with all acquired data over the incident angles and then use it to define the level of the azimuth angle data at a given incident angle and polarization, we should be able to eliminate the

impact of data fluctuation around the model-predicted level, thus allowing the surface parameters to remain unchanged over different incident angles. Readers should be aware that for most azimuthal data the procedure mentioned in the last statement is not carried out. Hence, normal fluctuations in angular data are to be expected.

6. After a large data set has been acquired in terms of the incident angle, azimuth angle, and polarization at a given wind speed, it is important to do an internal consistency check to make sure that the data levels are consistent in the incident and azimuth angles before using the data in an application.

7. The incident angle data from the sea surface requires the use of the expl correlation function because its backscattering angular curve takes on a bell shape over small incident angles and an exponential shape over large incident angles as shown in Figures 4.23, 4.24, and 4.36.

8. In the event an application does not use the data at normal incidence, it is possible to use a backscattering curve with only a modified exponential shape to estimate the data trend as shown in Figures 4.34 and 4.35.

9. A large skewness effect can cause the signal minimum near the crosswind region to shift toward the downwind side as shown in the horizontally polarized data at an incident angle of 52 degrees in Figure 4 of [Masuko et al., 1986] or Figure 4.29 in this chapter.

References

Amar, F., *Directional Random Sea Surface Generation,* M.S. Thesis, University of Texas at Arlington, 1989.

Chen, K. S., and A. K. Fung, "A Bragg Scattering Model for the Sea Surface," *Ocean 90, Conference Proc.*, 1990, pp. 249–252.

Chen, K. S., A. K. Fung, and D. E. Weissman, "A Backscattering Model for Ocean Surface," *IEEE Trans. Geosci. and Remote Sensing*, Vol. 30, No. 4, 1992, pp. 811–817.

Fung, A. K., and K. S. Chen, "Kirchhoff Model for a Skewed Random Surface," *J. of Electromagnetic Waves and Applications*, Vol. 5, No. 2, 1991, pp. 205–216.

Fung, A. K, and K. K. Lee, "A Semi-Empirical Sea-Spectrum Model for Scattering Coefficient Estimation," *IEEE J. Ocean Eng.*, Vol. OE-7, No. 4, 1982, pp. 166–176.

Fung, A. K., Z. Li, and K. S. Chen, "Backscattering from a Randomly Rough Dielectric Surface," *IEEE Trans. Geosci. and Remote Sensing*, Vol. 30, No. 2, 1992, pp. 356–369.

Fung, A. K., and K. S. Chen, *Microwave Scattering and Emission Models for Users*, Norwood, MA:

Artech House, 2009

Fung, A. K., *Microwave Scattering and Emission Models and Their Applications*, Norwood, MA: Artech House, 1994

Grant, C. R., and B. S. Yaplee, "Backscattering from Water and Land at Centimeter and Millimeter Wavelengths," *Pro IRE*, Vol. 45, 1957, pp. 976–982.

Hasselmann, K., W. Munk, and G. MacDonald, "Bispectra of Ocean Waves," in *Time Series Analysis* (ed. M. Rosenblatt), New York: John Wiley & Sons, 1963, pp. 126–139.

Jones, W. L., L. C. Schroeder, and J. L. Mitchell, "Aircraft Measurements of the Microwave Scattering Signature of the Ocean," *IEEE Trans. Antennas and Propagation*, Vol. 25, No. 2, 1977, pp. 52–61.

Li, F., et al., "Ocean Radar Backscatter Relationship with Near Surface Winds: A Case Study During FASINEX"*J. Phys. Oceanogr.*, Vol. 12, 1989, pp. 342–353.

Longuet-Higgins, M. S., "The Effect of Nonlinearities on Statistical Distribution in the Theory of Sea Waves," *J. Fluid Mech.*, Vol. 17, 1963, pp. 459–480.

Longuet-Higgins, M. S., "On the Skewness of Sea Surface Slopes,"*J. Phys. Ocean*, Vol. 12, 1982, pp. 1283–1291.

MacDonald, F. C., "The Correlation of Radra Sea Clutter on Vertical and Horizontal Polarization with Wave Height and Slope," 1956 IRE Convention Record, Part 1, 1956, pp. 29–32.

Masuda, A., and Y. Kuo, "A Note on the Imaginary Part of Bispectra," *Deep-Sea Research*, Vol. 28A, No. 3, 1981, pp. 213–222.

Masuko, H., et al., "Measurement of Microwave Backscattering Signatures of the Ocean Surface Using X-Band and Ka-Band Airborne Scatterometers," *J. Geophysical Res.*, Vol. 91, No. C11, 1986, pp. 13605–13083.

Moore, R. K., and A. K. Fung, "Radar Determination of Winds at Sea," *Proceedings of the IEEE*, Vol. 67, No. 11, Sept 1979, pp. 1504–1521.

Nghiem, S. V., et al., Ocean Remote Sensing with Airborne Ku-band Scatterometer, In *Proceeding of: OCEANS '93. Engineering in Harmony with Ocean*, Vol. 1, p. J 25.

Pierson, W. J., and L. Moskowitz, "A Proposed Spectral Form of Fully Developed Ideas Based on the Similarity Theory of S.A. Kitaigorodskii," *J. Geophysical Res.*, Vol. 69, No. 24, 1964, pp. 5181–5190.

Schroeder, L. C., et al., "AAFE RADSCAT 13.9-GHz Measurements and Analysis: Wind-speed Signature of the Ocean, " *IEEE J. Oceanic Engineering,* Vol. OE-10, No. 4, Oct. 1985, pp. 346–357.

Srokosz, M. A., and M. S. Longuet-Higgins, "On the Skewness of Sea-Surface Elevation," *J. Fluid Mech.*, Vol. 164, 1980, pp. 487–497.

Weissman, D. E., "Dependence of the Radar Cross Section on Ocean Surface Variables: Comparison of Measurements and Theory Using Data from the Frontal Air-Sea Interaction Experiment, *J. Geophys. Res.*, Vol. 95, No. c3, 1990, pp. 3387–3398.

Wiltse, C. J., S. P. Schlesinger, and C. M. Johnson, "Backscattering Characteristics of the Sea in the Region from 10 to 50 kMc," *Proc. IRE,* Vol. 45, 1957, pp. 220–227.

APPENDIX 4A: Dielectric Constant of Sea Water

4A.1 Introduction

For model calculations we need the dielectric constant of sea water as an input. It is known that sea water has a relatively large dielectric constant. Hence, a small percentage change in the estimate of this quantity has relatively little impact in scattering calculations. Here, we quote the dielectric model for sea water given in Appendix E, p. 2022 of Ulaby et al. [1986].

4A.2 A Dielectric Model of Sea Water

The complex dielectric constant of sea water can be expressed in terms of the operating frequency, f in gigahertz; the sea water temperature, T in centigrade; and salinity, S in parts per thousand through the following three quantities:

1. Ionic conductivity:

$$\sigma_i = S(0.18252 - 1.4619\,10^{-3}S + 2.093\,10^{-5}S^2 - 1.282\,10^{-7}S^3)\exp[-\Delta(A - SB)]$$

where $\Delta = 25 - T$,
$A = 2.033\,10^{-2} + 1.266\,10^{-4}\Delta + 2.464\,10^{-6}\Delta^2$ and
$B = 1.849\,10^{-5} - 2.551\,10^{-7}\Delta + 2.551\,10^{-8}\Delta^2$

2. Static dielectric constant:

$$\varepsilon_s = CD$$

where $C = 87.134 - 0.1949\,T - 0.01276\,T^2 + 0.0002491\,T^3$;
$D = 1 + 1.613\,10^{-5}TS - 3.656\,10^{-3}S + 3.21\,10^{-5}S^2 - 4.232\,10^{-7}S^3$

3. Relaxation time:

$$\tau = \tau_0 E$$

where $\tau_0 = (1.1109\,10^{-10} - 3.824\,10^{-12}T + 6.938\,10^{-14}T^2 - 5.096\,10^{-16}T^3)/(2\pi)$;
$E = 1 + 2.282\,10^{-5}TS - 7.638\,10^{-4}S - 7.76\,10^{-6}S^2 + 1.105\,10^{-8}S^3$

The real part of the dielectric constant is

$$\varepsilon_r = 4.9 + \frac{\varepsilon_s - 4.9}{1 + (2\pi\tau f 10^9)^2}$$

The imaginary part of the dielectric constant is

$$\varepsilon_i = \frac{2\pi\tau f 10^9 (\varepsilon_s - 4.9)}{1 + (2\pi\tau f 10^9)^2} + \frac{18\sigma_i}{f}$$

In the above model S is in parts per thousand on a weight basis, and for the above expression it is restricted to $4 \le S \le 35$. For oceans the average value of S is 32.54 parts per thousand.

Chapter 5

A Geophysical Model Function for Wind Scatterometry

5.1 INTRODUCTION

The concept of inverting the wind-speed response of a radar to determine the speed of the winds at sea using a satellite scatterometer was proposed by [Moore and Pierson, 1966]. Since that time many experiments have been conducted to ascertain the way in which the radar signal responds to variations in the surface of the sea caused by variations in local winds, and the theory of radar return from the sea has been advanced significantly. However, the spectrum of the sea surface is so complex that the use of it in modeling backscattering from the sea surface has been computationally impractical. Our study in Chapters 1 and 2 indicates that radar return responds to surface roughness scales comparable to or smaller than the incident wavelength (i.e., only a small portion of the sea spectrum is relevant to radar backscattering). For incident angles larger than 25 degrees it is generally possible to use a simple exponential spectrum to approximate this small portion of the real spectrum. In this chapter we shall show that the parameters in this simple exponential spectrum can be calibrated based on experimental data. With this simple exponential spectrum, there is no computational problem with the use of a physically based backscattering model.

Wind scatterometry is an existing technique currently being used to measure near-surface winds from space. It is an indirect method requiring the use of a geophysical model function (GMF) relating the measured radar backscattering coefficient to the wind and other environmental parameters. Hence, the accuracy of the inferred wind is dependent on both the accuracy of measuring the backscattering coefficient and the accuracy of estimating winds with the GMF. Currently, many GMFs have been developed [Ricciardulli and Wentz, 2012; Fernandez et al., 2006; Hersbach, 2010, 2002; Wentz and Smith, 1999; Long, 1996] for operational use, and all of them are based on empirical approaches assuming the backscattering coefficient σ^0 to be a function of the azimuth angle ϕ such as given in (5.1)

$$\sigma^0 = A_0 + A_1 \cos\phi + A_2 \cos 2\phi \qquad (5.1)$$

where the coefficients A_n are functions of wind speed, incident angle, and polarization with $\phi = 0$ chosen to be the upwind direction. If so, in the upwind direction, $\sigma_u^0 = A_0 + A_1 + A_2$, in the crosswind direction, $\sigma_c^0 = A_0 - A_2$, and in the downwind direction, $\sigma_d^0 = A_0 - A_1 + A_2$. At a given wind speed, polarization and incident angle, the A_n coefficients can be uniquely determined, because $\sigma_u^0, \sigma_c^0, \sigma_d^0$ are known from measurements. Thus, a lookup table for σ^0 can be generated. What is not known is whether the backscattering coefficient defined this way will vary correctly along other view directions [i.e., whether the assumed empirical form in (5.1) is in agreement with the physical behavior of σ^0 along other view directions]. Indeed, when [Fernandez et al., 2006] compared the behaviors of different GMFs (NSCAT2, KUSCAT, QuikSCAT, CMOD-5, and CSCAT) with their data sets, all these GMFs behaved differently. In general, these GMFs work for a few low wind cases and depart significantly in both level and azimuth angle trend at higher wind speeds. Thus, [Fernandez et al., 2006] found it necessary to further modify the coefficients A_n given in (5.1). Instead of showing a direct comparison of their model with σ^0, they presented data trends versus wind speed for each A_n. Their data trend versus wind speed at each incident angle, frequency, and polarization for A_0 is very clear, but for A_1 and A_2, significant fluctuations exist, especially in the higher wind speed region. In 2012, a different way to modify the empirical function was reported by [Ricciardulli and Wentz, 2012] who chose to use three more cosine terms to handle wind speeds in the range 20–30 m/s:

$$\sigma^0 = A_0 + \sum_{n=1}^{4} A_n \cos n\phi \qquad (5.2)$$

While additional cosine terms can control more view directions, they also introduce nonphysical oscillations and further complicate the empirical model.

The data presented by [Fernandez et al., 2006] indicate that when the wind speed is between 25 and 60 m/s, the following problems occur:

1. σ^0 saturates in level when wind speed reaches 40–50 m/s for both VV and HH polarizations and all incident angles in the range 29–50 degrees at C- and

K_u-bands, except for HH polarization at C-band and an incident angle of 49 degrees. Thus, it is best to use HH polarization at C-band and an incident angle of 49 degrees to detect wind speed.

2. The azimuth angle response of σ^0 around the downwind location tends to flatten and approach the level of the crosswind return at C- and K_u-bands, except for VV polarization at K_u-band and an incident angle of 29 degrees. Thus, it is best to use VV polarization at K_u-band and an incident angle of 29 degrees to detect wind direction.

At lower wind speeds the two problems mentioned above do not exist. In this writing we want to present GMFs based on the IEM backscattering model given in Chapter 4, thus offering another approach to GMF development. We shall illustrate our approach with low wind speeds first for both VV and HH polarizations and then consider the application to high wind speeds using data reported in [Fernandez et al., 2006].

5.2 GMF FOR LOW WIND SPEEDS

This section develops a geophysical model function (GMF) to link $\sigma^0_{pp}(\phi)$ to wind speed, sea surface temperature, and salinity based on the sea surface backscattering model defined by (4.3)–(4.5). The dielectric constant in the scattering model is linked to the sea surface temperature and salinity through the dielectric model given in Appendix 4A. Other surface geometric parameters in the model are related to wind speed based on measurements. Thus, the GMF can be updated whenever a modification is made to the data set or a better dielectric model becomes available. The procedure to develop the GMF remains the same.

From Chapter 4 we know that the surface parameters in the IEM surface scattering model are the surface rms height σ, the correlation length along the upwind-downwind direction L_u, the correlation length along the crosswind direction L_c, the skewness parameter s_0, and the dielectric constant ε. Whenever the incident frequency, surface temperature, and salinity are given, the dielectric constant can be calculated using the model in Appendix 4A. The overall level of the backscattering coefficient is used to determine σ, while the backscattering levels along the upwind and downwind directions are used to determine L_u, and similarly the backscattering level along the crosswind direction is used to determine L_c. The difference in the backscattering coefficients between the upwind and downwind directions is used to determine the skewness parameter s_0.

When the backscattering coefficient measurements along the azimuth direction at a given wind speed are available at a given frequency and polarization, the surface parameters can be determined. Once determined, the values of these surface parameters are applicable only to the given wind speed. When data are available at several wind speeds such as in [Schroeder et al., 1985], then we can fit a curve to each surface parameter, leading to a functional form for each surface parameter in wind speed. These functions of the surface parameters plus the IEM surface backscattering model together form the GMF we want to construct. Since σ affects the level of the backscattering curve, its trend with wind speed can indicate whether the data level at a given wind speed is low or high relative to the overall trend.

5.2.1 Data Behavior at 13.9 GHz and VV Polarization

As an illustration we shall use a set of azimuth angles, vertically polarized data in [Schroeder et al., 1985] consisting of six wind speeds at 4.2, 5.5, 7.5, 12, 15, and 19.4 m/s at an incident angle of 40 degrees. This data set is shown in Figure 5.1, where a 0.3-dB error bar has been added to the plot to give readers an idea of the amount of deviation when we compare model with data.

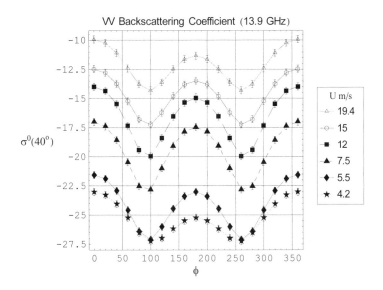

Figure 5.1 Vertically polarized data acquired by [Schroeder et al., 1985] at 13.9 GHz and an incident angle of 40 degrees.

Figure 5.1 shows that $\sigma^0_{vv}(\phi)$ increases with wind speed except at two locations near the crosswind regions for wind speeds from 4.2 to 5.5 m/s. Based on data at other azimuth angles we believe that those four data points at $\phi = 80$, 100, 260, and 280 degrees for the 5.5-m/s wind speed should be higher. They should not overlap with the 4.2-m/s data. Wind direction is indicated by the specific variation of $\sigma^0_{vv}(\phi)$ over the azimuth angle. There is also a clear difference between upwind and downwind because $\sigma^0_{vv}(0)$ is clearly greater than $\sigma^0_{vv}(180)$.

Our next step is to match the IEM model given in (4.3) and (4.5) to these data, thus fixing the surface parameters at each wind speed. To demonstrate that it is possible to pin down these surface parameters, we shall show what changes would take place, should we alter just one parameter at a time. In order to see the change more easily we alter each parameter by about 5–10%, although smaller changes are noticeable.

5.2.2 Selection of Model Parameters

For illustration let us consider the 4.2-m/s data and make a simple change in the surface rms height σ from 0.088 cm to 0.08 and 0.092 cm, when other surface parameters are fixed at $L_u = 19$, $L_c = 31$, and $s_0 = 0.087$. All lengths are in centimeters and the sea surface dielectric constant is taken to be $46.59 - j38.98$ at 13.9 GHz, 20°C, and a salinity of 32.54 parts per thousand. In Figure 5.2 we see that we can fit the data quite well with $\sigma = 0.088$ cm. An increase of σ to 0.092 cm simply raises the entire curve, and a decrease of σ to 0.08 cm lowers the entire curve. This means that σ is positively correlated with the backscattering coefficient, which is proportional to σ^2. A 0.3-dB error bar has been added to the plot to give readers an idea of the amount of deviation between model and data.

Next, we consider keeping σ fixed at 0.088 cm and change the upwind correlation parameter L_u. This is the parameter that controls the level around the upwind and downwind direction with a decreasing effect toward the crosswind direction, where its influence is zero. A smaller value of L_u will cause a larger backscattering at both upwind and downwind locations. Figure 5.3 illustrates this situation. There, the maximum effect is clearly seen at the upwind and downwind directions, and the effect tapers off toward the crosswind direction. A larger value of this parameter has the opposite effect. It is clear that the change at the upwind or downwind locations is large enough to allow a proper selection of this parameter. Again, a 0.3-dB error bar has been added to the plot to give readers an idea of the amount of deviation between model and data.

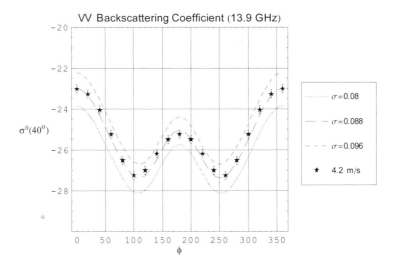

Figure 5.2 An illustration of the effect of changing the surface rms height σ on backscattering. A good match with data at 4.2 m/s wind speed is realized at σ = 0.088 cm.

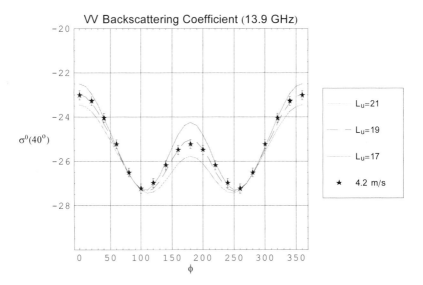

Figure 5.3 An illustration of the effect of changing the surface correlation length L_u on backscattering. A good match with data at 4.2 m/s wind speed is realized at L_u = 19 cm.

The influence of the crosswind correlation length L_c acts in a similar way as L_u (i.e., a smaller value of L_c will lead to a larger value of the backscattering coefficient at the crosswind location). As expected, its influence is maximum at the crosswind location and decreases toward both the upwind and the downwind directions. These changes are gradual and vanish at both the upwind and downwind locations as shown in Figure 5.4. The size of the change at the crosswind direction is large enough to pin down a proper value for L_c as long as there is a clear trend in the data.

In matching our backscattering model to data we have chosen to match the two datapoints on both sides of the downwind location in Figures 5.2–5.4 instead of at the downwind location. This way the model predictions are closer to all other data points in the downwind region all the way out to near the crosswind locations instead of just at the downwind location.

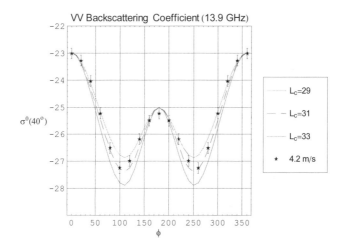

Figure 5.4 Effects in changing the surface correlation length L_c on backscattering. A good match with data at 4.2 m/s wind speed is realized at $L_c = 31$ cm. Note that because the crosswind return is always much lower than upwind, it follows that L_c is always larger than L_u. A 0.3-dB error bar has been added to the plot to give readers an idea of the amount of deviation between model and data.

Finally, we want to show the effect of the skewness parameter. For an anisotropic surface that is not skewed, the backscattering coefficients at azimuth angles of 0 and 180 degrees should be the same. The skewness makes the upwind return higher than the downwind as shown in Figure 5.5.

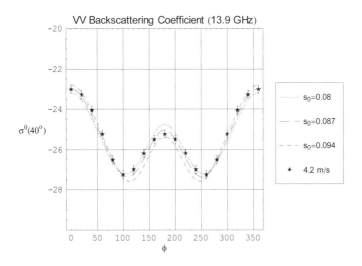

Figure 5.5 Effects of the skewness parameter s_0 on backscattering. A good match with data at 4.2 m/s wind speed is realized at $s_0 = 0.087$ cm. This is the only parameter responsible for the upwind-downwind difference. It also affects the location of the dip in the crosswind direction.

Generally, a larger s_0 causes a larger upwind-downwind difference in Figure 5.5. A larger s_0 value causes the downwind backscattering coefficient to go down and the upwind scattering to go up simultaneously. A larger s_0 also moves the dip near crosswind toward the downwind location. This parameter may change with the incident angle and polarization, but its variation with the azimuth angle is built in and cannot be selected. In this section we have described the function and the effect of each surface parameter. Our next step is to determine all the surface parameters at all wind speeds with the data given in Figure 5.1.

5.2.2.1 Determination of Surface Parameters

To determine model parameters by matching the model given in (4.3) and (4.5) to the data in Figure 5.1, recall that at each wind speed, the value of L_u is selected to match the upwind signal level, L_c is for the crosswind signal level, s_0 is to establish the difference between upwind and downwind, while σ is to adjust the overall signal level across all azimuth angles. After this process is carried out for all six wind speeds, we obtain the matching between the IEM model and the data in Figure 5.1 shown in Figure 5.6.

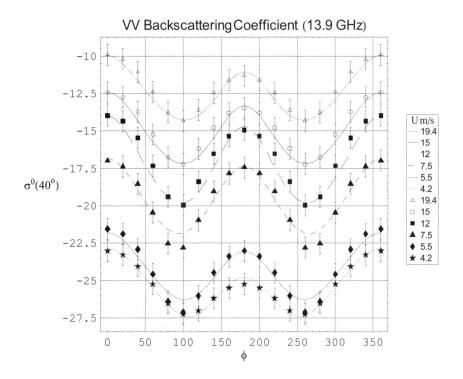

Figure 5.6 A comparison of the IEM surface model with VV measurements by [Schroeder et al., 1985] to determine the surface parameters at various wind speeds. Results are shown in Table 5.1. The azimuth parameter $a = 2$. A 0.3-dB error bar has been added to the plot to give readers an idea of the amount of deviation between model and data.

Note that the data for the 5.5-m/s wind at 80, 100, 260, and 280 azimuth angles dip down to the level of the data at 4.2 m/s. They are also off the trend of data at other angles of the 5.5-m/s set. Hence, we believe they are outliers and do not attempt to include them in matching the 5.5-m/s data (i.e., we use the IEM model to establish the general angular trend over the azimuth angle excluding these four data points). Further examination of the data at 7.5–19.4-m/s wind speeds also shows that data at these four azimuth angles is generally lower than the rest of the data at these wind speeds, although the dip is smaller at wind speeds equal to or higher than 15 m/s. The matching of data in Figure 5.6 leads to the surface parameters listed in Table 5.1. It is seen that the four surface parameters, σ, L_u, L_c, and s_0, vary with wind speed. We can determine a functional form for each of them by fitting a curve to each parameter. Readers are reminded that all GMFs are developed for rain-free surfaces.

Table 5.1 Surface Parameters for VV Data in Figure 5.6

Wind Speed, m/s	Surface Height (cm)	L_u (cm)	L_c (cm)	s_0 (cm)
4.2	0.088	19	31	0.085
5.5	0.096	16	30	0.078
7.5	0.152	12.5	26	0.066
12	0.19	10	22	0.07
15	0.2	8	16	0.08
19.4	0.235	6	12	0.1

5.2.2.2 Surface Parameters as a Function of Wind Speed

In view of Table 5.1 we can fit a polynomial curve to each surface parameter, thus obtaining the surface parameter as a function of wind speed. Of course, *these functions are only valid within the range of wind speeds reported in the measurements.* Results of the functional fits for L_u and L_c are shown in Figure 5.7 and for s_0 and σ in Figure 5.8.

In Figure 5.7 we see that the six points for L_u have a smooth decreasing trend as wind speed increases. By using a fourth-order polynomial fit, all six points are on the curve. The fitted curve drops fast between 4.2 and 12 m/s and slows down between 12 and 17 m/s before it speeds up its decline toward 19.4 m/s.

The six points for L_c in Figure 5.7 also decrease with wind speed and coincide with the fitted fourth-order polynomial curve. The initial behavior of the fitted curve is a slow decline from 4.2 to about 10 m/s. Then, it speeds up its decline to about 18 m/s before it slows down again as it reaches 19.4 m/s. Approximately, its rates of change are the opposite of those for L_u.

The use of the polynomial curve is just one way to fit these points to provide a general trend of the correlation parameter as a function of wind speed. It serves only as an illustration. Readers may have a better way to express these surface parameters in terms of wind speed. Definitely, the results obtained are not unique, but it is likely that the backscattering coefficients calculated based on these curves for L_u and L_c are within measurement error.

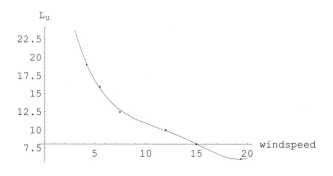

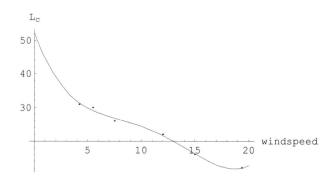

Figure 5.7 Polynomial fits to the values of L_u and L_c at various wind speeds for VV polarization. The correlation parameters determined by measurements are mostly close to the curves. Thus, these curves are expected to be useful representations of how L_u and L_c vary with wind speed within the range of wind speeds considered.

The functional forms for L_u and L_c are given below:

$$L_u = 23.97 - 0.4159u - 0.2808u^2 + 0.02642u^3 - 0.0006858u^4 \tag{5.3}$$

$$L_c = 52.137 - 8.76427u + 1.2109u^2 - 0.07897u^3 + 0.00177u^4 \tag{5.4}$$

The fourth-order polynomial we used is a reasonable choice because it preserves the major trend versus wind speed similar to a second-order polynomial and allows some fluctuations in data points. If an oscillatory shape appears in the curve, it is an indication that the data fluctuations are excessive and that there could be a problem with the values established for the model parameter.

In Figure 5.8 we show a fourth-order polynomial fit to the surface parameters s_0 and σ.

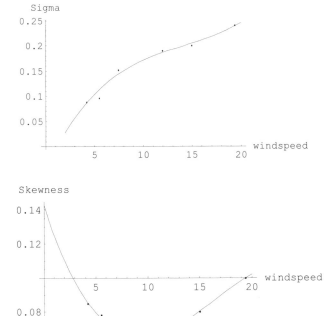

Figure 5.8 Polynomial fits to the values of s_0 and σ at various wind speeds for VV polarization. The skewness and rms height values determined by measurements are close to the curves, except at 5.5 and 7.5 m/s wind speeds. The established trends for the rms height and skewness parameter suggest that the level of the 7.5-m/s data should be lower and the level of the 5.5-m/s data should be higher. In fact, at 80, 100, 160, and 280 degrees in azimuth, data at these locations coincide with those of the 4.2-m/s data.

The fit for the surface rms height is off the fitted curve at wind speeds of 5.5 and 7.5 m/s. The deviation suggests that at 5.5 m/s σ is low, and it is high at 7.5 m/s. This curve is based on all six points of σ and is an indication of the likely trend for σ. When we examine the backscattering data in Figure 5.6 we see a large gap between the 5.5- and 7.5-m/s backscattering curves. This is the cause as to why the 7.5-m/s data may be too high and the 5.5-m/s data too low. Further evidence that the 5.5-m/s data may be low is confirmed by the fact that its data at 260 and 280 degrees in azimuth are at the same level as the 4.2-m/s data. As we mentioned earlier, the rms height surface parameter is positively correlated with the backscattering coefficient. When we try to establish an overall trend for all six values of the rms height, a deviation from the trend serves to indicate that the reported levels at 7.5 m/s and 5.5 m/s are off the trend. Hence, this process we have taken in developing the GMF also helps to identify fluctuations in the measured data.

The equations for the surface parameters s_0 and σ are given as follows:

$$s_0 = 0.14267 - 0.018848u + 0.001363u^2 - 0.0000239u^3 + 0.00177u^4 \quad (5.5)$$

$$\sigma = -0.04351 + 0.040097u - 0.00244u^2 + 0.5798 \times 10^{-4}u^3 + 1.728 \times 10^{-7}u^4 \quad (5.6)$$

5.2.3 GMF for 13.9 GHz and VV Polarization at 40° Incident Angle

With equations for all the surface geometric parameters known, the surface scattering model given by (4.3) and (4.5) becomes the desired GMF. This GMF is clearly data-dependent and responds to the overall data trends of the four surface parameters as a function of wind speed. Theoretically, VV and HH polarizations should share the same parameter behaviors in their GMF as indicated by the incident angle data. In practice, this is not possible for the azimuth angle data. For this reason we shall consider the HH polarization in Section 5.2.4. Obviously, if we use (5.3)–(5.6) to determine the surface parameters and compute the backscattering at the same wind speeds as we did in Figure 5.6, we shall not obtain the same result because we are using the general trend variation of the surface parameters instead of those used for the matching at each wind speed. To see the differences we show our computation using this GMF in Figure 5.9.

In Figure 5.9 we see that using our GMF provides good agreements for all wind speeds except at 5.5 m/s and 7.5 m/s. For these wind speeds there is a very good agreement on angular trends similar to those in Figure 5.6 because the surface parameters for L_u, L_c, and s_0 are close to those in Figure 5.6. On the other hand, the rms surface heights at these two low wind speeds are different from those in Figure 5.6. As we mentioned before, the general trend for the rms height parameter indicates that the 7.5-m/s data level is high, while the 5.5-m/s data level is low. However, the level difference to be adjusted on the average is less than 1 dB. According to [Schroeder et al., 1985] the size of this difference is within measurement error.

The assumption used in our construction of the GMF is that every parameter in our backscattering model has a trend with wind speed. This trend is established by all available data. Measured data will fluctuate about the trends along both the incident and the azimuth angle. To obtain self-consistent data sets would require establishing trends for both the incident and the azimuth angles, so that a proper relative level can be assigned. In Chapter 4 we examined incident angle data with two different trends over small and large incident angles. For wind vector sensing only the trend over large incident angles is relevant.

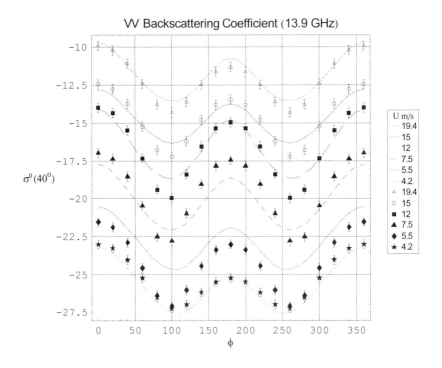

Figure 5.9 A comparison of the VV GMF [IEM surface model in which surface parameters are computed from (5.3)–(5.6)] with VV measurements by [Schroeder et al., 1985]. Numbers in the plot legend are in meters per second; lines are computed from our GMF and symbols are representing reported data. The disagreement at 5.5 and 7.5 m/s suggests that the levels of these two data sets are off the general trend established by other data sets. A 0.3-dB error bar has been added to the plot to give readers an idea of the amount of deviation between model and data.

5.2.4 Data Behavior at 13.9 GHz and HH Polarization

[Schroeder et al., 1985] have provided another data set at the same wind speeds for HH polarization as they did for VV. Thus, we can apply the same process to this set as we did in Section 5.2.3. Before we start we want to call attention to the possible problem that at every wind speed the data points at 80°, 100°, 260°, and 280° azimuth angles are low relative to the rest of the data at the same wind speed especially at 4.2 m/s as shown in Figure 5.10. This problem is more obvious with the HH data than we saw with the VV. The other problem we found with the VV set where the 7.5-m/s data was too close to the 12-m/s data also applies here. In fact, the separation between the data of these two wind speeds is between 1 and 2 dB. Most likely the data level at 7.5 m/s is higher than it should be. As we shall see later in this section, when we consider how the surface rms height varies with wind speed, the general trend will indicate that the rms height value of the 7.5-m/s data set is higher than the level indicated by the general trend.

5.2.4.1 Determination of Surface Parameters

Figure 5.10 shows a comparison of the IEM surface scattering model with this HH data set. The set of four surface parameters, σ, L_u, L_c, and s_0, at each wind speed is determined independent of other wind speeds and is carried out one at a time. With the exception of the four datapoints at 80°, 100°, 260°, and 280° in azimuth, very good agreements are obtained at each wind speed. Note that any attempt to include those four datapoints will cause the curve to be off from many more datapoints. Hence, we have decided to exclude those four points. This situation is most apparent when we look at the matching of the data at 15 or 19.4 m/s, where the model-predicted curves touch the data at all azimuth angles except those four. Should we shift the curve around the crosswind region to include, say, 80° and 100° data, then we would miss 40° and 60° data to the left and 120° and 140° data to the right of these two angles. Similar remarks apply to the data at the other two angles, 260° and 280°. Data at lower wind speeds in HH polarization also have a similar problem. In fact, the largest drop-off from the data trend occurs at 80° and 280° in the 4.2-m/s data. The spread in data indicated in [Schroeder et al., 1985] (their Figure 6, for example) is more than one decibel. Figure 5.10 uses a much smaller error bar so that it is easier to see the difference in levels and angular trends at different wind speeds. It is quite apparent that the level of the 7.5-m/s data is very close to the 12-m/s data and is widely separated from the 5.5-m/s data. In both the VV and HH data sets we see a very clear well-defined angular trend for each wind speed. This is the reason why wind directions can be estimated. While there are data fluctuations in all measurements, we believe that when enough wind speed measurements are available, it is possible to establish a reliable trend versus wind speed so that the impact of data fluctuation can be reduced to a minimum.

Surface parameters chosen to realize the matching shown in Figure 5.10 are given in Table 5.2. Except for the 4.2-m/s data set (which could be due to a hysteresis in small wave generation [Donelan and Plant, 2009]), all correlation lengths parameters for HH are either the same or within one point of the corresponding parameters we obtained earlier for VV. The situation is quite similar to the data acquired by [Masuko et al., 1986] where the same correlation length parameters were used for both VV and HH polarizations as shown in Chapter 4. Of course, the wind speed trends of the surface parameters here are expected to be similar to but different from those for VV polarization due to differences in the 4.2-m/s data set and other model parameters.

Table 5.2 Surface Parameters for HH Based on Figure 5.10

Wind Speed (m/s)	Surface Height (cm)	L_u (cm)	L_c (cm)	s_0 (cm)
4.2	0.112	16.5	36	0.075
5.5	0.135	16	29	0.071
7.5	0.195	12.5	25	0.069
12	0.21	10	22	0.087
15	0.245	8	15.5	0.1
19.4	0.29	6	11.5	0.13

In both [Masuko et al., 1986] and [Schroeder et al., 1985] reported data, we do not see a strong connection between VV and HH polarizations like what we saw with the FASINEX [Li et al., 1989] data (i.e., very little sharing exists in the surface parameters between these two polarizations). It is not known at this time why the relation between the polarizations only exists for some azimuth angle data such as the upwind, downwind, and crosswind data in FASINEX [Li et al., 1989] and Seasat-A satellite scatterometer (SASS) data to be shown later in this chapter. Physically, there should be a connection between the polarizations, and this is the reason why L_u and L_c come out the same or very close for both polarizations at all other wind speeds except at 4.2 m/s. At very high wind speeds, this connection should be lost, because the sea surface is no longer just a surface but has significant spray over it. There will be enough volume scattering present to change the properties of the backscattered signal.

Strictly speaking, once a physical model based GMF is established at one incident angle, polarization, and frequency over a specified wind speed range, it should work at other incident angles and polarization within the same range of wind speeds and at the same frequency. This fact was established in Chapter 4 for all incident angle data. Due to the nature of the azimuth angle data currently available, there is some uncertainty in the specified incident angle (i.e., the data acquired at different wind speeds is not truly at the same incident angle). Instead some averaging scheme has been applied and even the averaged incident angles at different wind speeds are really not the same. For example, the average incident angles at wind speeds of 3.2, 9.3, and 14.5 m/s for all azimuth angles are 52.3°, 52.7°, and 51.7° for vertical polarization and 52.2°, 52.2°, and 50.8° for horizontal polarization in [Masuko et al., 1986]. As a result, the GMF for vertical polarization does not share the same surface parameters with horizontal polarization.

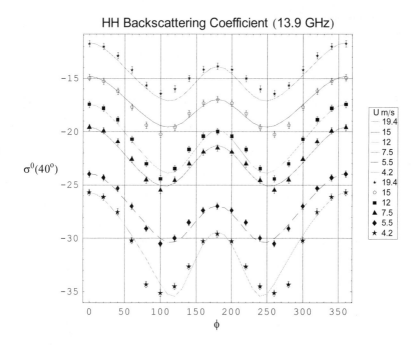

Figure 5.10 A comparison between the IEM surface backscattering model with a horizontally polarized data set collected by [Schroeder et al., 1985] at an incident angle of 40 degrees. A 0.3-dB error bar has been added to the plot to give readers an idea of the amount of deviation between model and data.

5.2.4.2 Surface Parameters as a Function of Wind Speed

In view of Table 5.2 we can generate the functional forms for the surface parameters with the values shown in the table by fitting a polynomial to the six values of each surface parameter. We begin with L_u and L_c, and results are shown in Figure 5.11. We use a third-order polynomial for L_u. The matching is quite good at all wind speeds except at 5.5 and 7.5 m/s, where the L_u value at 7.5 m/s needs to be increased or the data level lowered and conversely for the L_u at 5.5 m/s. The need to lower the data level at 7.5 m/s is quite obvious when we examine the data levels in Figure 5.10. The need to raise the data level at 5.5 m/s is less obvious. For L_c there is some oscillatory behavior in its values versus wind speeds. Hence, we apply a fourth-order polynomial to it, and the fit is very good at all wind speeds.

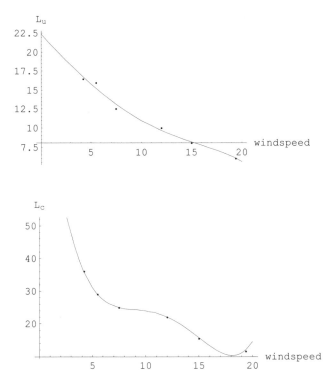

Figure 5.11 Polynomial fits to the values of L_u and L_c at various wind speeds for HH polarization. The correlation parameters determined by measurements are quite close to the curves except for L_u at 5.5 and 7.5 m/s. Thus, these curves are expected to be a useful representation of how L_u and L_c vary with wind speed.

The functional forms for L_u and L_c are given as follows:

$$L_u = 22.371 - 1.3494u - 0.01138u^2 + 0.004659u^3 - 0.0001408u^4 \qquad (5.7)$$

$$L_c = 110.504 - 31.986u + 4.3847u^2 - 0.25913u^3 + 0.005393u^4 \qquad (5.8)$$

Equations (5.7) and (5.8) give a representation of the correlation lengths along upwind and crosswind directions at the wind speeds reported in measurements. They also provide estimates of these correlations lengths at other wind speeds within the range 4.2–19.4 m/s.

In Figure 5.12 we show polynomial fits to the surface parameters s_0 and σ. The fit for s_0 is fairly close to the actual values used in matching the IEM model to the measurements, but for the surface rms height it is clear that the points for 5.5 and 7.5 m/s are off the general trend curve.

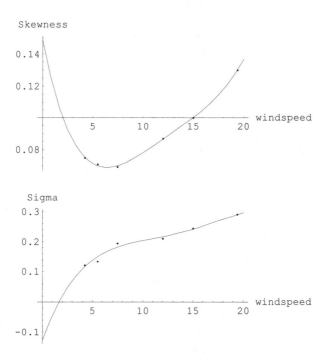

Figure 5.12 Polynomial fits to the values of s_0 and σ at various wind speeds for HH polarization. The skewness values determined by measurements are quite close to the curve, but not the rms height values, particularly at 5.5- and 7.5-m/s wind speeds.

Based on the overall trend for all the rms height values the level of the 7.5-m/s data should be lower and that for 5.5-m/s data should be higher. Once again, the process we have taken to develop the GMF also helps to identify possible problems in the level of the measured data.

The equations for the surface parameters s_0 and σ are given as follows:

$$s_0 = 0.149\text{-}0.03183u\text{+}0.004267u^2 - 2.239\times10^{-4}u^3 + 4.427\times10^{-6}u^4 \qquad (5.9)$$

$$\sigma = -0.127366 + 0.0913896u - 0.00989u^2 + 0.000493u^3 - 8.7074\times10^{-6}u^4 \quad (5.10)$$

5.2.5 GMF for 13.9 GHz and HH Polarization at 40° Incident Angle

With equations for all the surface geometric parameters known as a function of wind speed, the surface scattering model given by (4.3) and (4.5) becomes the desired GMF. This GMF is clearly data-dependent, and it responds to the overall data trends of all the surface parameters as functions of wind speed. Hence, the use of this GMF will produce similar but not the same type of matching shown in Figure 5.10. Based upon the fit shown in Figure 5.12 for the surface rms height, we expect a close matching for the three high wind speeds and a fairly good matching at 4.2 m/s only. Our predicted curve will be low at 7.5 m/s and high at 5.5 m/s. Such a result is shown in Figure 5.13, which has been generated by (5.7)–(5.10) together with the IEM surface scattering model.

5.3 GMF FOR HIGH WIND SPEEDS

At high wind speeds there will be such factors as sprays, breaking waves, and white caps. These are the causes of volume scattering as opposed to surface scattering. Usually, volume scattering is more isotropic but much weaker relative to surface scattering over small incident angles around 30 degrees or less. Furthermore, they occupy a smaller region within the illuminated area. Thus, for some frequency, polarization, and incident angle combinations, certain surface features may still be visible despite the presence of volume scattering. The presence of breaking waves and sprays is also an indication that the increase in surface roughness with wind speed has reached some maximum, which could translate to a saturation effect in backscattering. For the purpose of wind speed and wind direction sensing, we are interested in a clear change in the level of backscattering as wind speed increases. We are also interested in the angular shape of the backscattering curve along the azimuth direction. The former is for wind speed sensing, and the latter is for wind direction sensing.

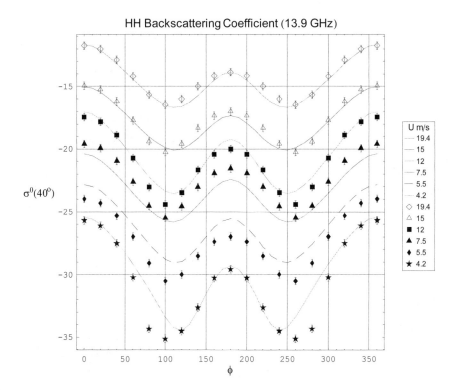

Figure 5.13 A comparison of the GMF with HH measurements by [Schroeder et al., 1985]. Numbers in plot legend are in meters per second; lines are computed from our GMF and symbols are reported data. As expected the wind speed trend set up by all data indicates that the backscattered signals at 5.5 and 7.5 m/s are not on the trend. A 0.3-dB error bar has been added to the plot to give readers an idea of the amount of deviation between model and data.

A very complete data set at 5.3 GHz and another one at 13.5 GHz over high wind speeds in the range 25–60 m/s was reported by [Fernandez et al., 2006]. The available incident angles are around 30 and 50 degrees. Note that wind speeds over 35 m/s are considered hurricane-force winds. We shall begin by examining features of data at 5.3 GHz and 13.5 GHz, before we embark on developing GMFs for different data sets.

5.3.1 Data Behavior at 5.3 and 13.5 GHz

At 5.3 GHz backscattering measurements versus the azimuth angle at 29° and 50° incident angles for vertical polarization and 31° and 49° incident angles for horizontal polarizations are available from [Fernandez et al., 2006]. At a 29° incidence and the range of wind speeds, 25–35 m/s, VV measurements change about 1 dB in amplitude along the upwind direction, and the same is true of HH polarization at the 31° incidence. Only the VV polarization is able to preserve a variation pattern versus the azimuth angle through 40° incidence. The HH polarization loses its proper angular shape when the incident angle exceeds 35°. Hence, these incident angles cannot provide useful information due to saturation and loss of pattern along the azimuth direction. We shall not consider them further. The VV and HH measurements available at incident angles of 50° and 49°, respectively, are more useful in that they show both a larger increase with wind speeds and an expected variation pattern over the azimuth angle. We consider first the vertically polarized data shown in Figure 5.14.

Upon examining the VV data we notice that between 25 and 35 m/s in wind speed, on average there is a more than 0.5-dB change in the level of backscattering every 5 m/s around the upwind direction. Between 35 and 40 m/s in wind speed, the average change in the backscattering level is now less than 0.5 dB. The level difference between 40 and 45 m/s is on average less than 0.25 dB, indicating that the backscattering signal is saturating, but the expected variations along the azimuth direction are still visible. Beyond 45 m/s the backscattering coefficient shows saturation at -8 dB and loses the expected variation versus the azimuth angle (more results are available in [Fernandez et al., 2006]). Hence, no further information can be gathered from collecting more data at higher wind speeds with this polarization, angle, and frequency.

For horizontally polarized backscattering near the upwind direction the increase in the backscattering coefficient over the 25–45-m/s wind speed range is from about -13.5 dB to near -10 dB, a total close to 3.5 dB as compared to 2 dB for vertical polarization. Around the upwind direction, backscattering continues to increase to -9 dB as wind speed increases from 45 to 60 m/s (Figure 5.15). Around the crosswind direction the backscattering signal level is lower, but its range of increase from 25 to 45 m/s is more than 4 dB as compared to 3.5 dB near the upwind direction. However, HH polarization is losing its angular shape around the downwind direction for wind speeds at and beyond 40 m/s. In conclusion, at an incident angle near 50 degrees and 5.3 GHz, both polarizations cannot retain a useful azimuth pattern around the downwind direction for wind direction sensing. For wind speed sensing there is the hope of using the HH polarization near the upwind or crosswind direction.

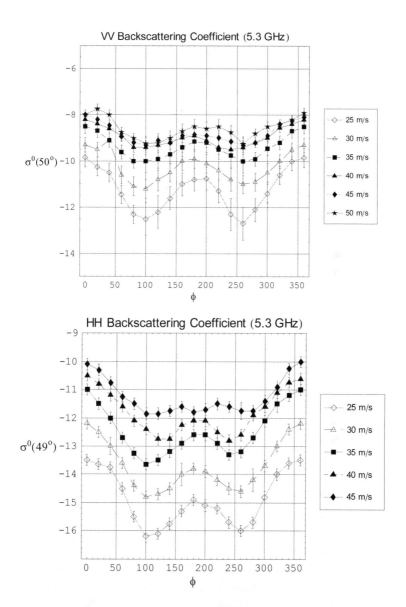

Figure 5.14 High wind speed data reported for VV and HH at 5.3 GHz. For VV polarization there is an indication of saturation in the backscattering level at 45 m/s, but expected variations in the azimuth angle are retained. For HH polarization, the level increase around the upwind direction with wind speed is still intact, but it is losing its variation around the downwind direction at 45 m/s.

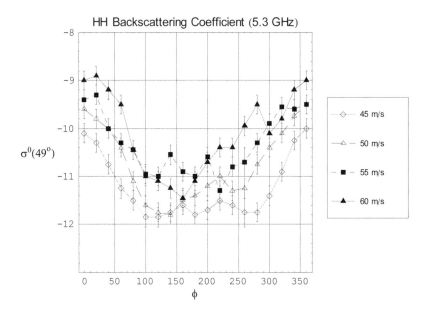

Figure 5.15 High wind speed data reported for HH polarization at 5.3 GHz. The level increase around the upwind direction with wind speed appears to continue to 60 m/s, but it is losing its variation around the downwind direction at 45 m/s and beyond.

In [Fernandez et al., 2006], the authors report data at 13.5 GHz and incident angles of 29 and 48 degrees in VV and HH polarizations over the wind speed range 25–60 m/s. At this frequency saturation in signal level occurs near 35 m/s or less for both polarizations and all incident angles. Hence, no useful information about wind speed can be retrieved from them. However, the VV polarization with incident angle of 29 degrees is able to keep its azimuth angular shape over this wind speed range. This result is shown in Figure 5.16, where we show backscattering data from 25 to 45 m/s in intervals of 5-m/s wind speed, and then we add the backscattering data at 60 m/s. It is seen that the levels of all wind speeds fall within 1 dB of one another. Thus, we see no benefit to add 50- and 55-m/s data into Figure 5.16. The key point here is that even at 60 m/s the azimuth angular pattern is kept over all possible wind directions.

In conclusion, under high wind conditions the data reported by [Fernandez et al., 2006] suggest that we can use 5.3 GHz, an incident angle of 49 degrees, and HH polarization for wind speed sensing around the upwind or the crosswind directions. For wind direction sensing, the combination of 13.5 GHz, 29 degree incident angle, and VV polarization offers the best possibility. For wind speeds below 45 m/s, the data at 5.3 GHz, 49 degree incident angle, and VV polarization can also provide wind speed information.

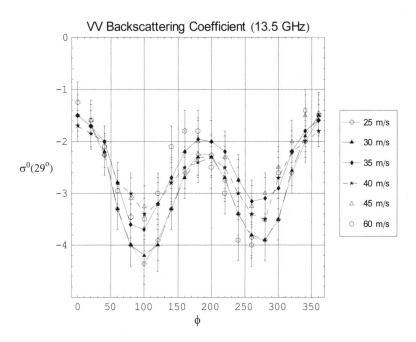

Figure 5.16 Vertically polarized data at 13.5 GHz and 29 degree incident angle showing saturation in high wind conditions but retaining a clear angular pattern along the azimuth direction. Note that the spread in level over all wind speeds is within 1 dB over all azimuth angles.

5.3.1.1 Determination of Surface Parameters

We are now ready to apply the IEM model to the data presented in Figure 5.15 for 5.3 GHz, HH polarization, and 49 degree incident angle to determine the surface parameters at each wind speed. The matching is shown in Figure 5.17. As before, the eight curves fitting the eight sets of data in Figure 5.17 are done one at a time for each wind speed. Each set of four surface parameters is determined independently of other sets and is fixed only by the data at one wind speed. The objective is to fit as many data points as we can in each set, which is generally possible for lower wind speeds except there is a lack of symmetry in the data with respect to 180 degrees. At high wind speeds above 45 m/s, more points will depart from the azimuth angular pattern established at lower wind speeds. Knowing that beyond 45 m/s in wind speed we do lose our angular pattern around the downwind region, we shall focus our attention on getting as good a match as possible around the upwind region.

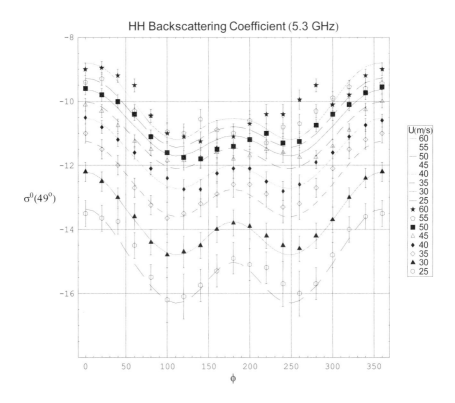

Figure 5.17 Application of the IEM surface model at 5.3 GHz and 49 degree incident angle to determine surface parameters σ, L_u, L_c, s_0. Parameters obtained are listed in Table 5.3. The azimuth parameter $a = 2$. Note that the data level continues to rise in HH backscattering around the upwind region up to 60 m/s in wind speed.

The resulting parameter values based on Figure 5.17 are listed in Table 5.3.

Table 5.3 Surface Parameters for HH, 5.3 GHz, and High Wind Speeds

Wind Speed (m/s)	Rms Height (cm)	L_u (cm)	L_c (cm)	s_0 (cm)
25	0.673	7.3	12	0.25
30	0.7	6.3	9.3	0.27
35	0.74	5	8.2	0.28
40	0.75	4.5	6.8	0.3
45	0.755	3.8	5.5	0.31
50	0.76	3.2	5.3	0.32
55	0.775	2.8	5.1	0.33
60	0.79	2.4	5.0	0.36

5.3.1.2 Surface Parameters as a Function of Wind Speed

To construct a GMF we need to relate all the surface parameters to wind speed. Again, this can be achieved by fitting a polynomial to the eight points obtained for each surface parameter shown in Table 5.3. The fits to L_u and L_c are given in Figure 5.18.

The resulting equations representing the wind speed trends of these parameters are

$$L_u = 16.2324 - 0.451304u + 0.00322348u^2 + 0.3485 \times 10^{-4}u^3 - 4.54545(10^{-7})u^4$$

$$(5.11)$$

$$L_c = 41.0786 - 2.072345u + 0.0491364u^2 - 0.0005919u^3 + 3.0303(10^{-6})u^4$$

$$(5.12)$$

With (5.11) and (5.12) the L_u points at 30 and 35 m/s are clearly off the curve and so are L_c points at 30, 35, and 45 m/s. As we shall see when we recompute backscattering coefficients based on (5.11) and (5.12), the changes in these parameters simply allow different portions of the data to fit better. Consequently, the resulting GMF appears to be a good representation of radar backscattering versus wind speed.

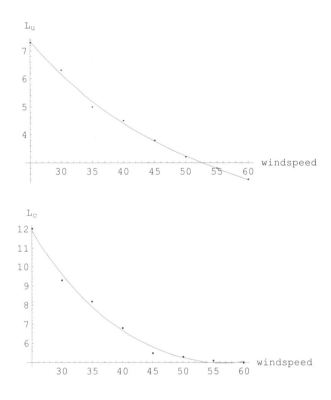

Figure 5.18 Polynomial fits to the values of L_u and L_c over wind speeds 25 to 60 m/s for HH polarization. Some correlation parameters determined by measurements are not close to the curves. However, the scatter in the data at each wind speed is such that the matching with this GMF still provides a very good fit to all wind speeds where there is a clear angular trend.

Next, we show the fits to the surface parameters σ and s_0 in Figure 5.19. Here again some points are clearly off the curves, indicating that when we use our polynomial equations to provide the value of the surface parameters, they will be different from those we used for matching the data. However, as we indicated above, the variations in the data set are such that these polynomial equations do provide predictions in line with the data set.

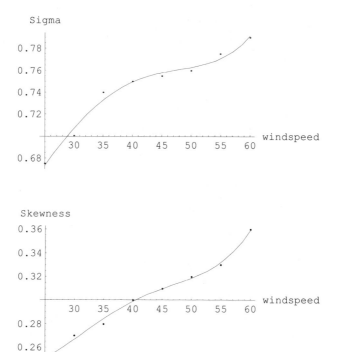

Figure 5.19 Polynomial fits to the values of s_0 and σ over wind speeds 25–60 m/s for HH polarization. Some of the skewness and the rms height values are not very close to their curves, but the scatter in the data at each wind speed is such that the matching with this GMF still provides a very good fit to all wind speeds where there is a clear angular trend.

The polynomial equations for σ and s_0 are given as follows:

$$\sigma = 0.632489 - 0.014655u + 0.00119147u^2 - 0.00002629u^3 + 1.874242(10^{-7})u^4$$

$$(5.13)$$

$$s_0 = 0.62645 - 0.0486328u + 0.00214242u^2 - 0.3798 \times 10^{-4}u^3 + 2.42424(10^{-7})u^4$$

$$(5.14)$$

5.3.2 GMF for 5.3 GHz and HH Polarization at 49° Incident Angle

With all the surface parameters expressed as functions of wind speed at 5.3 GHz, HH polarization, and 49 degrees incidence, the IEM model using these parameters becomes a GMF. We are now ready to compare this GMF with the measurements as shown in Figure 5.20.

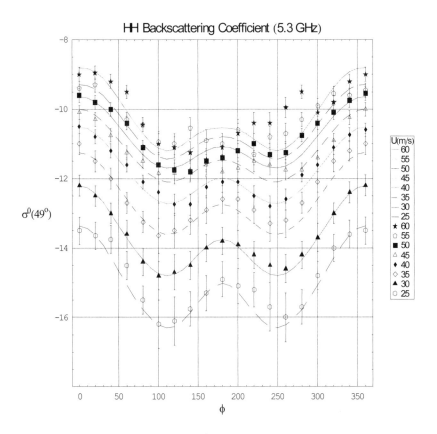

Figure 5.20 A comparison of the GMF-derived backscattering with the high wind speed data reported for HH polarization at 5.3 GHz and 49 degree incident angle. The level of backscattering has been adjusted to various amounts to come out with a wind speed trend defined by the surface parameters. The azimuth parameter $a = 2$.

Compared with Figure 5.17 we see that the level at 30 m/s has been raised in Figure 5.20, which turns out to be a better match. The level for 35 m/s has been lowered in Figure 5.20 and that is not as good as the matching in Figure 5.17. However, these and all other level changes at other wind speeds are less than 0.25 dB. It is a small adjustment to how the backscattering coefficients change with wind speed.

5.3.3 GMF for 13.5 GHz and VV Polarization at 29° Incident Angle

The data presented in Figure 5.16 for vertical polarization indicates that for all wind speeds in the range 25–60 m/s, the backscattering coefficients have saturated, and almost all the spread in data at all azimuth angles falls within 1 dB. Despite the saturation problem, at this frequency and incident angle, we have a clear angular variation along the azimuth direction so that it should be possible to retrieve wind direction from these data.

By choosing $\sigma = 0.295$, $L_u = 1.27$, $L_c = 3.3$, and $s_0 = 0.2$ at 13.5 GHz and 29 degrees incidence, the IEM model predicted values are within 0.5 dB of the data in the wind speed range 25–60 m/s over most of the azimuth angles. Thus, the desired GMF for this case is only one simple angular curve. To illustrate this point we show a comparison of the model-predicted values with the data at 25, 30, 35, 45, and 60 m/s. To make it easier to see, we show only three wind speeds in Figure 5.21(a) (25, 30, 60 m/s) and three others (35, 45, 60 m/s) in Figure 5.21(b).

5.4 COMMENTS ON THE RELATION BETWEEN VV AND HH POLAR-IZATION

In our consideration of backscattering data over the sea surface, we have encountered data that indicates the existence of a strict relation between VV and HH as in the FASINEX experiment and data acquired by [Jones et al., 1977] given in Chapter 4 and a much looser relation in all the azimuth angle data that we have reported in this chapter and Chapter 4. Theoretically, there should be a relation between the two polarizations, but azimuth angle data focuses on azimuth variation and wind speed changes for each polarization independently. Furthermore, the reported incident angle is some average quantity obtained through some kind of an average [Masuko et. al., 1986]. Hence, we cannot expect the rms surface height to be the same due to fluctuations in the incident angle, but L_u and L_c do remain the same for both polarizations at each wind speed. We demonstrated this in Chapter 4, and with the exception of the 4.2 m/s wind speed data, it is also true for the data from Schroder et al. to within measurement error.

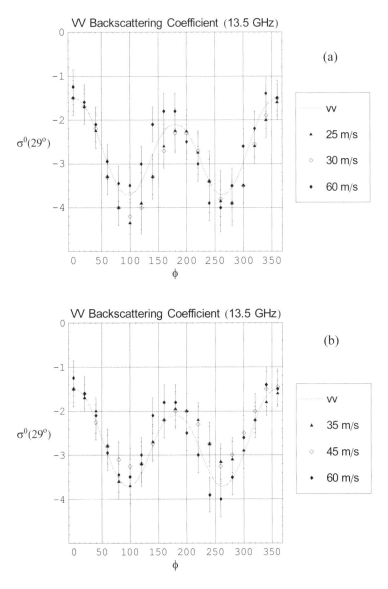

Figure 5.21 A comparison of the IEM surface backscattering model at 13.5 GHz and 29 degree incident angle with vertically polarized data at wind speeds of (a) 25, 30, and 60 m/s and (b) 35, 45, and 60 m/s. The azimuth parameter $a = 2$.

In this section we want to demonstrate that L_u and L_c remain the same for vertical and horizontal polarizations at wind speeds below hurricane-force wind, (i.e., below 35 m/s at 5.3 GHz). In particular, we want to demonstrate that at wind speeds 25 and 30 m/s vertical and horizontal polarizations can share the same correlation parameters. We have already found the correlation parameters for horizontal polarization in Table 5.3. By choosing the surface rms height and the skewness parameter we obtain the model parameters to fit the vertical backscattering data as shown in Table 5.4. The comparison for the 25-m/s case is shown in Figure 5.22. An excellent agreement is obtained at upwind, downwind, and crosswind locations. Hence, the choice of L_u and L_c is justified.

Table 5.4 Surface Parameters for HH, 5.3 GHz, and High Wind Speeds

Wind Speed (m/s)	Surface Height (cm)	L_u (cm)	L_c (cm)	s_0 (cm)
25	0.485	7.3	12	0.25
30	0.49	6.3	9.3	0.24

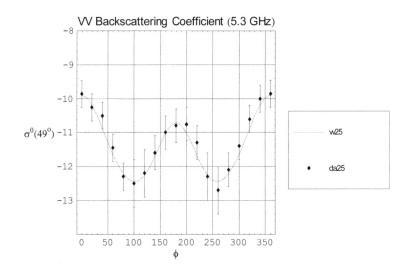

Figure 5.22 A comparison with 5.3-GHz VV polarized data at 25 m/s using the same surface parameters, L_u and L_c, as in HH polarization.

Using the surface parameters in Table 5.4, a comparison with the vertically polarized backscattering data at wind speed, 30 m/s, is shown in Figure 5.23. Here again, very good agreement is realized at upwind, downwind, and crosswind locations, where an accord between model and data is dependent on the correlation parameters.

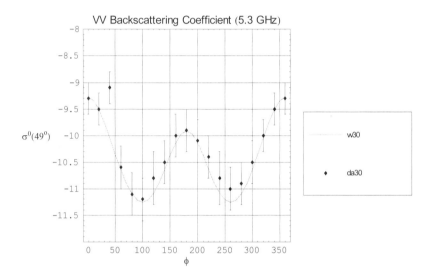

Figure 5.23 A comparison with 5.3-GHz VV polarized data at 30 m/s using the same surface parameters, L_u and L_c, as in HH polarization.

At this point we have demonstrated with the data reported by [Fernandez et al., 2006], [Masuko et al., 1986], and [Schroeder et al., 1985] that in the wind speed region below hurricane-force wind, there is a connection between VV and HH polarizations in the correlation parameters.

5.5 COMPARISONS WITH EMPIRICAL GMF PREDICTIONS

Before comparing the properties of some empirical GMFs versus GMFs based on the physical backscattering model (IEM) presented in Chapter 4, let us summarize some known characteristics of sea surface backscattering based on published data in [Grant and Yaplee, 1957], [Jones et al., 1977], [Moore and Fung, 1979],

[Schroeder et al., 1985], [Masuko et al., 1986], and [Li et al., 1989]. These are the properties that could differentiate backscattering from the sea surface versus the land surface and would be useful for assessing empirical or physical models.

5.5.1 A Summary of Sea Backscattering Characteristics

The following two characteristics are associated with the backscattering coefficient versus the incident angle data from a sea surface:

1. The backscattering versus the incident angle curve takes on a bell shape near normal incidence followed by an exponential angular shape. Evidence of these characteristics can be found in Figures 4.23–4.25 based on [Grant and Yaplee, 1957] and [Jones et al., 1977] data or Figure 7 and Figure 17 in [Moore and Fung, 1979].

2. At a given wind speed and incident frequency there is a fixed relationship between vertically and horizontally polarized backscattering coefficients so that the same model parameters apply to both polarizations with the possible exception of the skewness parameter. Illustrations of these characteristics are available in Figures 4.34–4.36 and Figures 4.38–4.40 based upon [Jones et al., 1977] and [Li et al., 1989] data.

For convenience of reference we have replotted a combined [Li et al., 1989] and [Jones et al., 1977] data in Figure 5.24 to support the last two statements.

Next, we summarize three characteristics associated with the backscattering coefficient versus the azimuth angle data from a sea surface:

1. Backscattering in the upwind direction is always larger than the downwind and much larger than the crosswind. Illustrations are given in Figures 5.25 and 5.26 based on [Masuko et al., 1986] data. These properties are also found in [Jones et al., 1977] and [Schroeder et al., 1985].

2. The upwind-downwind difference in backscattering is usually larger for horizontal polarization than vertical polarization, and the backscattering azimuthal angular pattern is symmetric with respect to the downwind direction as shown in Figures 5.25 and 5.26. Note that the upwind-downwind difference is a higher order effect due to surface skewness. Hence, its trend is not obvious when there is a significant fluctuation in data.

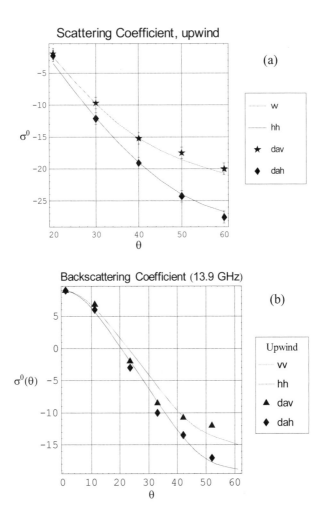

Figure 5.24 An illustration of sea surface backscattering with (a) upwind measurements from FASINEX [Li et al., 1989] at 14.6 GHz. Model parameters chosen are $\sigma = 0.22$, $L_u = 2.8$, $L_c = 6.2$, $r = 1.8$, $s_0 = 0.048$ cm, and $\varepsilon_r = 44.9 - j39$ for both polarizations and all incident angles and (b) measurements reported by [Jones et al., 1977] at 13.9 GHz with model parameters, $\sigma = 0.23$, $L_u = 0.4$, $L_c = 0.4$, $r = 6.5$, $s_0 = 0.02$ cm, and $\varepsilon_r = 46 - j39$ for both polarizations and all incident angles. Note that the difference in the choice of model parameters reflects the difference in the properties of the surface correlation functions. In (a) we have a more exponential type of surface correlation, while in (b) the correlation function is more of a Gaussian type.

3. For wind speeds less than 10 m/s, the upwind-downwind difference can be significantly larger for horizontal polarization than vertical polarization. The large upwind-downwind difference causes the locations of minimum backscattering to move closer toward the downwind direction as shown in Figures 5.26 and 5.27. This movement of the locations of backscatter minima is also a higher order effect. Its presence could be masked by data fluctuation.

For convenience of reference we have plotted the data from [Masuko et al., 1986] to support the last three statements in Figures 5.25 and 5.26.

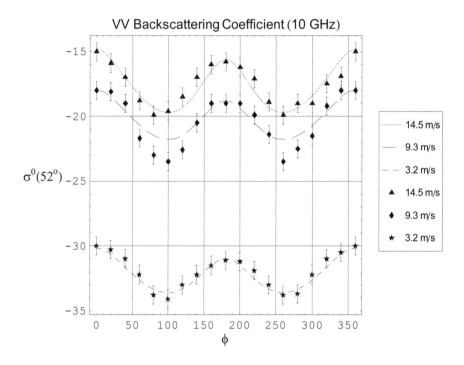

Figure 5.25 An illustration of the expected symmetrical backscattering signal distribution with respect to the downwind direction ($\phi = 180^0$) in vertical polarization at 10 GHz over three wind speeds. Symbols are the actual data from [Masuko et al., 1986] and lines are model predictions. Note that the upwind-downwind difference is around 1 dB and is smaller at higher wind speeds. The locations of minimum backscattered signal do not seem to change at all three wind speeds. The azimuth parameter $a = 2$.

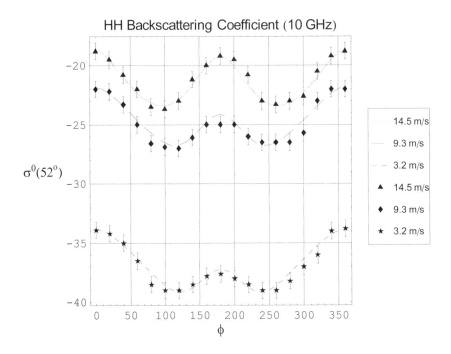

Figure 5.26 An illustration of the expected symmetrical backscattering signal distribution with respect to the downwind direction ($\phi = 180^0$) in horizontal polarization at 10 GHz over three wind speeds. Symbols are the actual data from [Masuko et al., 1986] and lines are model predictions. Note that the upwind-downwind difference is more than 3 dB at 3.2 m/s and is about 2 dB at 9.3 m/s. These large differences indicate a strong influence of the skewness effect on backscattering. This influence causes the signal minima to move closer to the downwind direction especially at lower wind speeds. The azimuth parameter $a = 2$.

In Figures 5.25 and 5.26 we have provided data at 10 GHz and modeling curves to show that the backscattered signal versus the azimuth angle from a windblown sea surface has the general characteristics we summarized. In real life, sea surface statistics cannot be perfectly stationary, and departure from predicted scattering coefficient values at some azimuth angles is to be expected. We have selected the 52-degree data from [Masuko et al., 1986] in Figures 5.25 and 5.26, because the angular trends are better defined at this angle for both vertical and horizontal polarizations. To show that these characteristics are not restricted to 10 GHz, we show additional data from [Masuko et al., 1986] at 34.43 GHz in Figure

5.27. In addition to data, Masuko et al. provided expected angular shapes in solid lines. In Figure 5.27, we have replaced those lines with model-predicted lines.

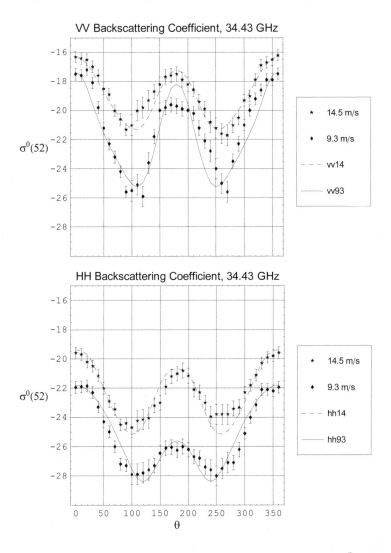

Figure 5.27 The expected symmetry with respect to the downwind direction ($\phi = 180^0$) in vertical and horizontal polarizations at 34.43 GHz is clear. Symbols are the actual data from [Masuko et al., 1986] and lines are model predictions. The azimuth parameter $a = 2$.

In Figure 5.27 we can see that there is symmetry in the signal distributions with respect to the downwind locations in both vertical and horizontal polarizations and the two wind speeds. Although data fluctuations in the azimuth angle are present, they occur at different azimuth angles for different polarizations and at different wind speeds. It is also clear that the upwind-downwind difference is larger for horizontal than vertical polarization, and there is a shift in the minima locations at 9.3 m/s as compared to the 14.5-m/s wind speed in horizontal polarization. Such a shift is not present in vertical polarization because it is not affected as much by the skewness effect.

5.5.2   Comparisons with the SASS-2 Model Function

Empirical GMFs are developed based on specific but very large-sized data sets. They are tied to a specific frequency and in some cases also the incident angle. They cover a wide range of wind speeds and all azimuth angles. In [Wentz et al., 1984], three months of Seasat-A satellite scatterometer (SASS) measurements at 14.6 GHz were used to derive a relation between the backscattering coefficient σ^0 and wind speed U in meters per second over the ocean based on the statistics of the SASS observations. The scattering coefficient is assumed to take the form,

$$\sigma^0 = A_0 + A_1 \cos\phi + A_2 \cos 2\phi \tag{5.15}$$

where $A_0 = a_0 U^{\alpha_0}$, $A_1 = (a_1 + \alpha_1 \log U)A_0$, and $A_2 = (a_2 + \alpha_2 \log U)A_0$.

For each incident angle θ the values of the coefficients $10(\alpha_0 + \log a_0)$, $a_1 + \alpha_1$, $a_2 + \alpha_2$, and α_0, α_1 and α_2 are tabulated for each polarization and selected incident angles. When the tables for these parameters are given for vertical and horizontal polarizations, the only restriction on the use of this empirical model is the incident frequency, which is 14.6 GHz. In other words, the empirical model is good only at 14.6 GHz and the tabulated incident angles. To illustrate, a sample table is given in Table 5.5 for vertical polarization. With the information in Table 5.5, it is possible to calculate all the coefficients needed in (5.15) so that we can determine the backscattering coefficient for each incident angle listed in Table 5.5. The formula for σ^0 accepts all possible values of the azimuth angle ϕ and wind speed. Of course, the range of acceptable wind speeds is restricted to those available in the data used to establish the empirical model. Note that for each incident angle the coefficients listed in Table 5.5 are different. Thus, we have a separate σ^0 model for each incident angle and polarization, but we can input wind speed and the azimuth angle. We may view an empirical model as a convenient replacement for the data set used to establish the model. Every empirical model is also restricted by its assumed mathematical expression, which may or may not be able to fully account for the physical phenomenon it is supposed to represent.

Table 5.5 Parameters for Vertical Polarization

θ	$10(\alpha_0 + \log a_0)$	$a_1 + \alpha_1$	$a_2 + \alpha_2$	α_0	α_1	α_2
0	10.5	0.00	0.00	-0.58	0.00	0.00
10	6.3	0.00	0.08	-0.04	0.00	0.05
20	-2.0	0.00	0.27	0.82	0.00	0.13
30	-9.6	0.05	0.42	1.55	-0.04	0.11
40	-14.7	0.09	0.51	1.77	-0.08	-0.08
50	-17.6	0.14	0.54	1.68	-0.12	-0.28
60	-20.3	0.18	0.54	1.51	-0.16	-0.48

To illustrate horizontal polarization, a sample is given in Table 5.6.

Table 5.6 Parameters for Horizontal Polarization

θ	$10(\alpha_0 + \log a_0)$	$a_1 + \alpha_1$	$a_2 + \alpha_2$	α_0	α_1	α_2
0	10.5	0.00	0.00	-0.58	0.00	0.00
10	6.3	0.00	0.08	-0.04	0.00	0.05
20	-2.2	0.01	0.26	0.82	-0.01	0.13
30	-10.7	0.13	0.39	1.64	-0.16	0.13
40	-17.9	0.25	0.45	2.13	-0.32	0.04
50	-22.8	0.38	0.46	2.24	-0.49	-0.29
60	-27.2	0.51	0.46	2.26	-0.65	-0.69

With the above information we can make comparisons of this empirical model with the FASINEX data because the measurements were made at the same frequency, 14.6 GHz. We have already made comparisons of this data set with our model defined by (4.3) and (4.5). They are illustrated in Figures 5.28–5.30 for the upwind, downwind, and crosswind cases.

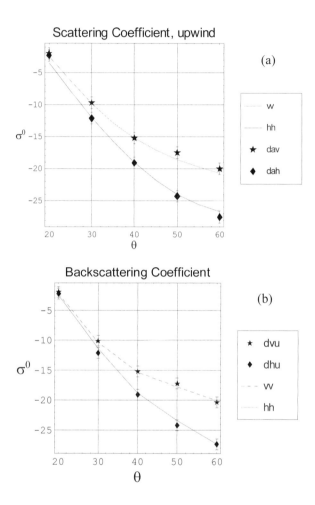

Figure 5.28 (a) A comparison of the IEM model with FASINEX data under upwind condition. (b) A comparison of the SASS-2 model with FASINEX data under upwind condition. Both models seem to work well in level and angular trends. Some differences are (1) there is no separation between VV and HH polarization at 20 degrees for SASS-2 model, and (2) the separation between polarizations predicted by the SASS-2 model at 30 degrees is also smaller than the data. However, these differences are small and within measurement error.

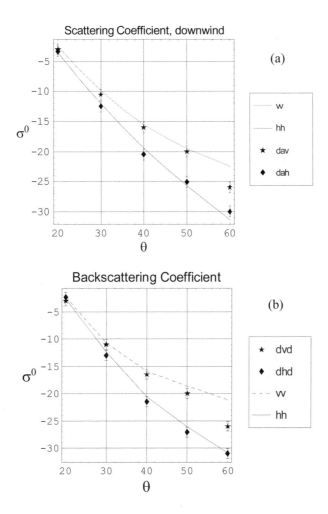

Figure 5.29 (a) A comparison of the IEM model with FASINEX data under downwind condition. (b) A comparison of the SASS-2 model with FASINEX data under downwind condition. Both models seem to work well in level and angular trends. Some differences are (1) there is no separation between VV and HH polarization at 20 degrees for SASS-2 model, and (2) the separation predicted by the IEM and SASS-2 models at 60 degrees appears wider than data. However, the VV data point at 60 degrees should be in error because it is off the angular trend of other data. Furthermore, the SASS-2 model is itself representing the trend of a very large volume of data.

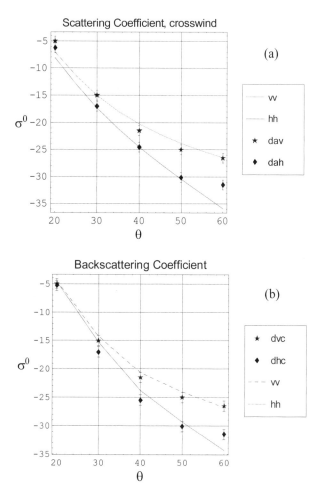

Figure 5.30 (a) A comparison of the IEM model with FASINEX data under the crosswind condition. (b) A comparison of the SASS-2 model with FASINEX data under the crosswind condition. Both models seem to work well in level and angular trends. Some differences are (1) there is no separation between VV and HH polarization at 20 degrees for SASS-2 model, and (2) the HH signal level predicted by the IEM and SASS-2 model at 60 degrees is low. However, this datapoint is off the trend of other datapoints. Also, the SASS-2 model is itself representing the trend of a very large volume of data.

The comparisons in Figures 5.28–5.30 for the upwind, downwind, and crosswind cases indicate that both the IEM model and the SASS-2 model agree with the incident angle data acquired at the FASINEX experiment [Li et al., 1989], Weissman [1990] in level and angular trends. In particular, the IEM model uses the same model parameters for both vertical and horizontal polarizations provided in Figures 4.38–4.40, showing that physically there is a definite link between the two polarizations. This kind of information is not available from empirical models. The fact that there is good agreement between the models and data along the upwind, crosswind, and downwind directions means that the data behavior in the azimuth direction is also in agreement with the models.

Next, we want to compare the IEM model directly with the SASS-2 model with both plotted versus the azimuth angle. The SASS-2 model will be presented in discrete points at an interval of 10 degrees, while the IEM model is represented in solid lines. Frequency is fixed at 14.6 GHz and we select wind speeds to be the same as given in Table 5.1. A comparison for vertical polarization is shown in Figure 5.31 where excellent agreement is seen at every wind speed. Note that the lobe around the downwind direction is generally wider than the one around the crosswind.

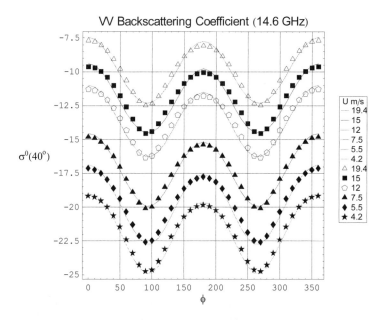

Figure 5.31 A comparison of the SASS-2 model with the IEM model in vertical polarization at 14.6 GHz over six wind speeds. Symbols are the computed backscattering based on the SASS-2 model. Solid lines are predictions from the IEM model.

The signal minima from the SASS-2 model are located exactly at ϕ = 90 and 270 degrees. In real data there will be some shifting depending upon the amount of skewness. However, whenever the effect of skewness is small, the changes in the location of the signal minima will also be small.

When we repeat a similar comparison with horizontal polarization, we obtain the result in Figure 5.32. In making the comparison we match each wind speed independently of what we have learned from vertical polarization. As mentioned in Chapter 4, the relation between vertical and horizontal polarization is generally not preserved in the azimuth angle data. The indicated incident angle is actually an average over several incident angles. This is another reason why the lobe with respect to the downwind location is always wider than the lobe corresponding to a = 2, but the difference is likely to be within measurement error. Overall, an excellent agreement between the IEM model and the SASS-2 model is obtained in Figure 5.32.

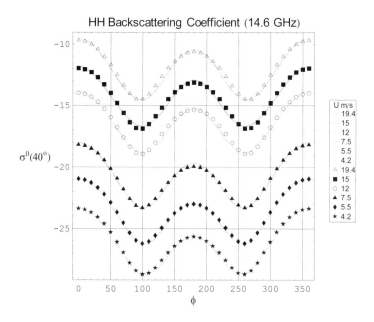

Figure 5.32 A comparison of the SASS-2 model with the IEM model in horizontal polarization at 14.6 GHz over six wind speeds. Symbols are the computed backscattering based on the SASS-2 model. Solid lines are predictions from the IEM model.

The SASS-2 model has the signal minima locations fixed at ϕ = 90 and 270 degrees. This fix is artificial and inconsistent with data behavior where the minima would shift toward the downwind direction in proportion to the effect of skewness as seen in Figures 5.26 and 5.27. We can see this shift in the IEM model in Figure 5.27 also. Hence, there is an expected difference between the SASS-2 and the IEM model. However, this difference is not large because surface skewness is a higher order effect. Based upon the matching in Figures 5.31 and 5.32, we can develop GMFs using the IEM model, which will work the same as SASS-2 except that they will not contain nonphysical properties.

To develop the GMFs for vertical and horizontal polarization at 14.6 GHz, we need to relate the four model parameters L_u, L_c, σ, and s_0 to wind speed. Since we are dealing with large incident angles, we have chosen mexp to be our correlation function with z = 0.005 cm in Figures 5.31 and 5.32.

5.5.2.1 GMF for Vertical Polarization at 14.6 GHz

Model parameters used to realize the matching for vertical polarization in Figure 5.31 are tabulated in Table 5.7.

Table 5.7 Surface Parameters for VV Based on Figure 5.31

Wind Speed (m/s)	Surface Height (cm)	L_u (cm)	L_c (cm)	s_0 (cm)	a
4.2	0.117	13	33	0.06	3.5
5.5	0.135	10.8	29	0.065	3.5
7.5	0.16	8.8	23.5	0.067	3.5
12	0.216	6.7	19	0.07	3.5
15	0.24	5.5	16	0.07	3.5
19.4	0.28	4.5	13	0.07	3.5

Following the same procedure as described in Section 5.2, we can apply polynomial functions to the parameters in Table 5.7 to establish the following relations for the vertically polarized backscattering parameters as a function of wind speed u, yielding

$$L_u = 28.7736 - 5.996u + 0.66756u^2 - 0.0348u^3 + 0.00067u^4 \qquad (5.16)$$

$$L_c = 64.2688 - 11.4095u + 1.18142u^2 - 0.0584029u^3 + 0.001072u^4 \qquad (5.17)$$

$$s_0 = 0.031077 + 0.011088u - 0.001214u^2 + 0.5959 \times 10^{-4}u^3 - 1.09 \times 10^{-6}u^4 \qquad (5.18)$$

$$\sigma = 0.10976 - 0.01027u + 0.003967u^2 - 0.0002697u^3 + 5.97 \times 10^{-6}u^4 \qquad (5.19)$$

The combination of the IEM model defined in (4.3) and (4.5) for the sea surface and (5.16)–(5.19) constitutes the GMF for this case. Its comparison with the original outputs from the SASS-2 model at the same wind speeds is shown in Figure 5.33.

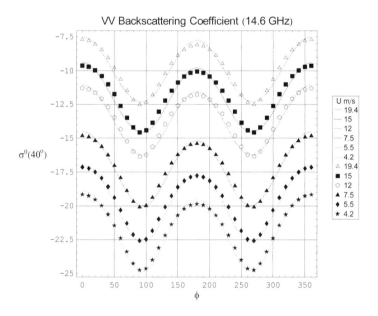

Figure 5.33 A comparison of the developed GMF with the SASS-2 model outputs (in symbols) for vertical polarization at 14.6 GHz over six wind speeds. The larger azimuth parameter ($a = 3.5$) used here appears to correlate with the large amount of data that SASS-2 model represents.

It is clear that the agreement between the GMF and the SASS outputs is excellent in Figure 5.33. We know that the wind dependence shown in (5.16)–

(5.19) is based on the data at a 40 degree incident angle. Although the IEM model itself can work at other incident angles, the use of the 40-degree data restricts the validity of this GMF model to within 5 degrees of the intended 40 degrees.

The excellent agreement shown in Figure 5.33 indicates that the way we develop the GMF is valid and that the GMF can approximate the SASS-2 model without fixing the signal minima artificially at 90 and 270 degrees in azimuth.

5.5.2.2 GMF for Horizontal Polarization at 14.6 GHz

We can apply the same procedure to develop the GMF for horizontal polarization at a 40 degree incident angle by first tabulating the IEM model parameters at a set of discrete wind speeds shown in Table 5.8. Then, we use a polynomial function to fit these wind speeds for each model parameter. The results are given in (5.20)–(5.23). The GMF for horizontal polarization over the wind speeds considered is given by the IEM model plus (5.20)–(5.23) for the model parameters.

Table 5.8 Surface Parameters for HH Based on Figure 5.32

Wind speed (m/s)	Surface Height (cm)	L_u (cm)	L_c (cm)	s_0 (cm)	a
4.2	0.135	14.5	29	0.063	3
5.5	0.155	11.5	25	0.068	3.5
7.5	0.18	8.3	20	0.075	3.5
12	0.25	7	17	0.09	3.5
15	0.268	5	13	0.1	3.5
19.4	0.302	3.8	11	0.116	3.5

The polynomial fit for the IEM model parameters in Table 5.8 for horizontal polarization yields the following relations,

$$L_u = 45.199 - 12.3765u + 1.5407u^2 - 0.08479u^3 + 0.00168u^4 \tag{5.20}$$

$$L_c = 71.4463 - 17.1131u + 2.1504u^2 - 0.121818u^3 + 0.00248248u^4 \tag{5.21}$$

$$s_0 = 0.0443879 + 0.00507861u - 0.000181752u^2$$

$$+ 7.1981 \times 10^{-6}u^{3} - 7.81257 \times 10^{-8}u^{4} \tag{5.22}$$

$$\sigma = 0.18663 - 0.0402785u + 0.00898168u^{2} - 0.00058372u^{3}$$

$$+ 0.1255 \times 10^{-4}u^{4} \tag{5.23}$$

To see how this GMF performs, we use (5.20)–(5.23) in the IEM model to compute horizontally polarized backscattering at a 40 degree incident angle and the six wind speeds in Table 5.8. Results are compared with the original outputs from the SASS-2 model at the same wind speeds in Figure 5.34. An excellent agreement is obtained over all azimuth angles. The SASS-2 model represents a large amount of data, which seems to be the cause for a broader lobe around the upwind-downwind directions due to data fluctuations. As a result the azimuth parameter is around 3.5.

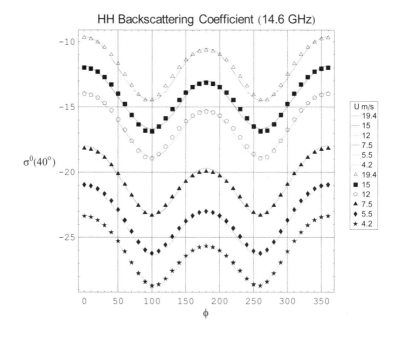

Figure 5.34 A comparison of the developed GMF with the SASS-2 model outputs (in symbols) for horizontal polarization at 14.6 GHz over six wind speeds.

We have made comparisons of the IEM model with the SASS-2 model in terms of the incident and azimuth angle behaviors for vertical and horizontal polarizations. The SASS-2 model represents three months of SASS measurements. Hence, we can say that there is a very good agreement between the IEM model and the Seasat data. We are not able to use the same correlation or the same azimuth parameter for both vertical and horizontal polarizations for the azimuth angle data at the same wind speed. A possible reason could be that the SASS-2 model represents a regressed form of the original data. Furthermore, the assumed mathematical expression of the model automatically filters out all data that fail to fit the chosen expression.

5.5.3 Comparisons with QuikSCAT GMF

The NASA Quick Scatterometer (QuikSCAT) is an Earth observation satellite carrying the Sea Winds 13.4-GHz scatterometer. Its primary mission is to measure the surface wind speed and direction at 10 meters above the sea surface over the ice-free global oceans. Its geophysical data record spans from July 1999 to November 2009. The existing GMF for QuikSCAT is an empirically defined model function based on collocations of QuikSCAT backscattering measurements and numerical weather prediction now casts. It only measures at an incident angle of 46 degrees with horizontal polarization and 54 degrees with vertical polarization.

5.5.3.1 GMF for Vertical Polarization at 13.4 GHz

We want to show that the IEM model can generate a model function comparable to the existing empirical model function, which is based on an enormous amount of backscattering measurements. We begin by first determining the IEM model parameters by matching the outputs from the empirical model function provided by David G. Long (personal communication, December, 2014) at wind speeds from 2 to 16 m/s for vertical polarization. This is shown in Figure 5.35. The agreement between the IEM model and the empirical QuikSCAT GMF is excellent over all six wind speeds. Note that the width of the lobe around the upwind-downwind directions is wider here than the data reported by [Masuko et al., 1986] and [Schroeder et al., 1985]. It seems that this happens whenever we are dealing with empirical GMFs that represent a lot of data. This means that the azimuth parameter a should be larger than 2 at all wind speeds here. Actual values used are given in Table 5.9. The azimuth parameter is not a function of wind speed and is fixed only by the data. As we can see in Table 5.9 different wind speeds may have the same azimuth parameter.

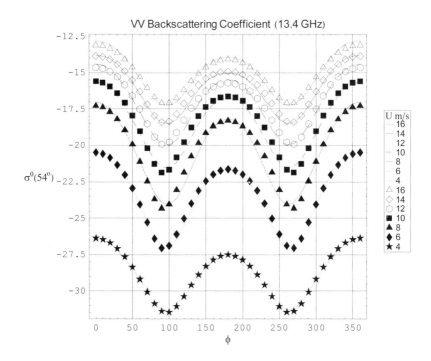

Figure 5.35 A comparison of the IEM model with the QuikSCAT model function outputs for vertical polarization at 13.4 GHz over seven wind speeds. Symbols are the computed backscattering based on the QuikSCAT model function. Solid lines are predictions from the IEM model.

The matching in Figure 5.35 leads to the set of model parameters summarized in Table 5.9. Intuitively, the correlation parameters, L_u and L_c, decrease with wind speed and the surface rms height increases with the wind speed. The skewness parameter s_0 may be increasing as we see in Table 5.9, but it is a higher order effect and is a small quantity difficult to determine experimentally. However, each parameter has a clear meaning and a definite function to perform in surface backscattering. In addition, the azimuth parameter a appears in Table 5.9 because the width of the lobe around the downwind direction is broader than can be represented by $a = 2$.

Table 5.9 Surface Parameters for VV Based on Figure 5.35

Wind Speed (m/s)	Surface Height (cm)	L_u (cm)	L_c (cm)	s_0 (cm)	a
4	0.09	21	36	0.06	2.5
6	0.15	15.5	35	0.06	3.5
8	0.2	13	34	0.061	3.5
10	0.22	11.5	28	0.062	3.5
12	0.25	11	26	0.063	3.5
14	0.26	10.5	22	0.067	3.5
16	0.27	9	19	0.069	3.5

When these surface parameters are linked to the wind speed through a polynomial function, we obtain the following relations for the model parameters:

$$L_u = 43.642857 - 8.249819u + 0.749053u^2 - 0.0268308u^3 + 0.00023674u^4 \quad (5.24)$$

$$L_c = 20.5 + 7.86598u - 1.26515u^2 + 0.070707u^3 - 0.00142045u^4 \quad (5.25)$$

$$s_0 = 0.0527 + 0.00387u - 0.00072348u^2 + 0.56818 \times 10^{-4}u^3 - 1.42045 \times 10^{-6}u^4$$

$$(5.26)$$

$$\sigma = -0.126428 + 0.074262u - 0.0060227u^2 + 0.0002588u^3 - 4.734848 \times 10^{-6}u^4$$

$$(5.27)$$

Although we only show the parameters linked to the fourth power in wind speed, higher powers for better accuracy at the matching points are possible if desired. These relations together with the IEM model form the desired geophysical model function. Usually, there is no need to further refine the model function when it is less than 1 dB off the data to be matched. To show that this is the case with the current model function based on (5.24)–(5.27), we have computed backscattering with the IEM model using (5.24)–(5.27) in Figure 5.36. The discrete symbols are outputs from the QuikSCAT model function provided by David G. Long (personal communication, December, 2014), and the lines are computed backscattering coefficients from the IEM model. The agreement at every wind speed shown is better than one quarter of 1 dB.

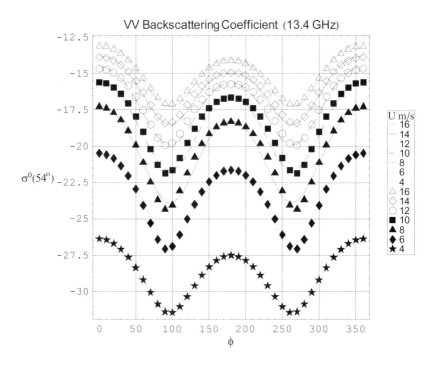

Figure 5.36 A comparison of the GMF based on the IEM model and (5.24)–(5.27), with the Quik-SCAT model function outputs for vertical polarization at 13.4 GHz over seven wind speeds. Symbols are the computed backscattering based on the QuikSCAT model function. Solid lines are predictions from the IEM-based GMF. Very close agreements are realized at all wind speeds shown.

5.5.3.2 GMF for Horizontal Polarization at 13.4 GHz

We want to demonstrate that the same approach works for horizontal polarization. As mentioned previously, for azimuth data, the same correlation function and model parameters that work for vertical polarization do not work for horizontal polarization, especially in the signal level. Most likely, this has to do with the way data have been processed. Hence, we treat the two polarizations independently. For horizontal polarization the available incident angle is 46 degrees. We select the same set of wind speeds as in vertical polarizations to compare the empirical model function outputs with the IEM model to determine the model parameters at the chosen wind speeds. Results are shown in Figure 5.37. Excellent agreements are realized at each wind speed in both the signal level and the angular shape of the backscattering function versus the azimuth angle.

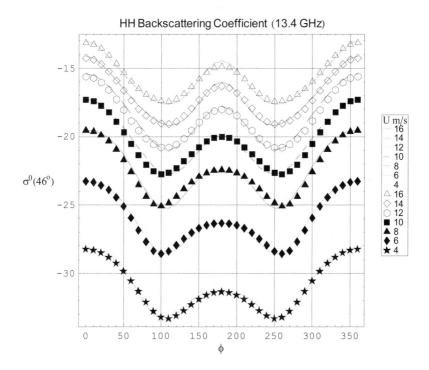

Figure 5.37 A comparison of the IEM model with the QuikSCAT model function outputs for horizontal polarization at 13.4 GHz over seven wind speeds. Symbols are the computed backscattering based on the QuikSCAT model function. Solid lines are predictions from the IEM model. This comparison is used to determine the model parameters at each wind speed.

The signal levels along the upwind-downwind directions are determined mainly by the correlation parameter L_u and are modified somewhat by the skewness parameter s_0, which sets up the upwind-downwind difference. The signal level at crosswind is determined by the correlation parameter L_c. The overall signal level is affected by the surface rms height σ. The width of the lobe centered around the downwind or upwind direction is controlled by the azimuth parameter a. The larger the a, the wider is the lobe. So far we have found that a is near 2 for a single set of measurements. When a large volume of data is being analyzed to produce an empirical model function, the lobe tends to be wider so that a is between 2 and 4. Knowing the properties of these parameters we arrive at the comparisons shown in Figure 5.37. The model parameters used in Figure 5.37 are given in Table 5.10.

Table 5.10 Surface Parameters for VV Based on Figure 5.35

Wind Speed (m/s)	Surface Height (cm)	L_u (cm)	L_c (cm)	s_0 (cm)	a
4	0.13	20	33	0.053	2.0
6	0.175	14	26	0.063	3.0
8	0.22	11	23	0.074	3.5
10	0.265	10	21	0.085	2.5
12	0.3	9	20	0.09	2.5
14	0.326	8.4	17.5	0.102	2.0
16	0.35	7.7	16.6	0.11	2.0

To develop a GMF we need to relate backscattering to wind speed. This can be done by expressing the first four parameters as a function of wind speed. One way to do this is to use a polynomial function to fit the parameters in Table 5.10. This process leads to the following expressions:

$$L_u = 51.21428 - 12.44906u + 1.44195u^2 - 0.075978u^3 + 0.0014914u^4 \quad (5.28)$$

$$L_c = 75.75 - 18.1305u + 2.38324u^2 - 0.142961u^3 + 0.00314867u^4 \quad (5.29)$$

$$s_0 = 0.037857 + 0.0015074u + 0.000804924u^2 - 0.688131 \times 10^{-4}u^3$$
$$+ 1.89394 \times 10^{-6}u^4 \quad (5.30)$$

$$\sigma = 0.103214 - 0.0116113u + 0.00620928u^2 - 0.00044539u^3$$

$$+ 0.101799 \times 10^{-4} u^4 \tag{5.31}$$

The IEM model defined by (4.3) and (4.5) plus (5.28)–(5.31) constitutes the GMF model for the horizontally polarized case, and it is valid over the wind speed range considered. To verify its validity we shall use (5.28)–(5.31) to compute the backscattering at the same set of wind speeds to see whether they provide a similar agreement to that obtained in Figure 5.37. The results are shown in Figure 5.38.

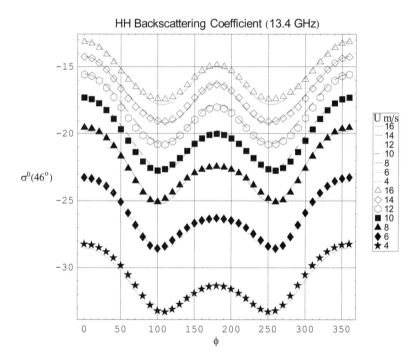

Figure 5.38 A comparison of the GMF based on the IEM model and (5.28)–(5.31), with the QuikSCAT model function outputs for horizontal polarization at 13.4 GHz over seven wind speeds. Symbols are the computed backscattering based on the QuikSCAT model function. Solid lines are predictions from the IEM-based GMF. Very close agreements are realized at all wind speeds shown.

Comparing the predictions by the IEM model in Figures 5.37 and 5.38 we see a maximum difference of about 0.25 dB between the two. Since the IEM backscattering model for the sea surface can match all basic sea surface scattering characteristics summarized in Section 5.5.1, it should be able to match any empirical GMF. We have not seen an empirical model that shows a consistent shift in signal minima around the crosswind directions due to changes in the amount of skewness. We believe this could be due to averaging a large amount of data. Some data that does show the correct shift is being averaged together with data that does not. Another common feature of empirical models is that they have broader lobes around the upwind-downwind directions. It is possible that this is due to the way a large amount of data is averaged or regressed in some way.

5.5.4 Comparisons with NSCAT GMF

The previous two GMFs we considered are at frequencies different from airborne circle flight measurements at 13.9 GHz acquired by [Jones et al., 1977] and [Schroeder et al., 1985] so that a direct comparison of signal level or angular shapes cannot be made. NSCAT is the NASA scatterometer operating at 13.99 GHz. It was launched in August 1996 aboard the Advanced Earth Observing Satellite (ADEOS) to measure the surface wind vector over the global oceans. It has acquired about nine and a half months of data. Its GMF outputs at a 40 degree incident angle can be compared with airborne measurements given by [Schroeder et al., 1985] in Figures 5.1 and 5.10. Before we make these comparisons we shall first show that it is possible to develop a GMF with the IEM model using the outputs of the NSCAT empirical GMF provided David G. Long (private communication, December 2014).

5.5.4.1 GMF for Vertical Polarization at 13.99 GHz

The procedure to develop a GMF based on outputs from an empirical model function has been carried out several times in the previous sections. Hence, we shall focus here mainly on the results of each step. The first step is to determine the IEM model parameters at six wind speeds 5 m/s apart between 5 and 30 m/s. However, because the gap in backscattering between 5 and 10 m/s is too large, we add another wind speed, 7 m/s, to consider a total of seven wind speeds. By applying the IEM model to the outputs of the empirical model function one wind speed at a time, we establish the model parameters for each wind speed. The matching for the seven wind speeds is shown in Figure 5.39, while the model parameters are summarized in Table 5.11.

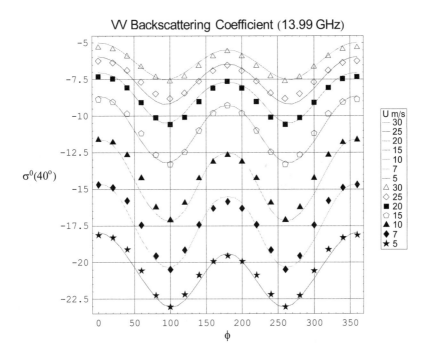

Figure 5.39 A comparison of the IEM model with the NSCAT model function outputs for vertical polarization at 13.99 GHz over seven wind speeds. Symbols are the computed backscattering based on the NSCAT model function. Solid lines are predictions from the IEM model. Very close agreements are realized at all wind speeds shown.

The matching in Figure 5.39 is realized with the model parameters shown in Table 5.11. The use of these parameters allows an agreement between the IEM model predictions and the empirical model function outputs to lie within 0.25 dB of each other. At 7- and 10-m/s wind speeds we have to use an azimuth width up to $a = 5$, which is exceptional among all the cases we have studied. The large variation in a for these cases, from a low of 2.5 to a high of 5 in the azimuth angle, indicates a large spread in data for these two wind speeds. We believe that the actual width at these wind speeds should not be this wide, because similar cases at 13.9 GHz reported by [Schroeder et al., 1986] remain around $a = 2$. This result also indicates that the azimuth parameter does not depend on wind speed, because data taken under the same wind speed, incident angle, polarization, and frequency requires different values of a.

Table 5.11 Surface Parameters for VV Based on Figure 5.39

Wind Speed (m/s)	Surface Height (cm)	L_u (cm)	L_c (cm)	s_0 (cm)	a
5	0.085	6	15	0.12	3
7	0.105	4	12.7	0.11	5
10	0.13	3	9.5	0.12	5
15	0.17	2.4	6.5	0.11	3.8
20	0.195	2.1	4.5	0.116	3.5
25	0.2	1.6	3.5	0.115	3.0
30	0.23	1.6	3	0.115	2.5

The second step to develop a GMF with the IEM model is to link the model parameters in Table 5.11 to wind speed. This can be done by fitting a polynomial function to each model parameter, yielding:

$$L_u = 15.5315 - 2.92823u + 0.24194u^2 - 0.0086884u^3 + 0.00011206u^4 \quad (5.32)$$

$$L_c = 23.7394 - 2.15335u + 0.0928216u^2 - 0.0020333u^3 + 0.1879 \times 10^{-4}u^4 \quad (5.33)$$

$$s_0 = 0.126732 - 0.00242778u + 0.000144363u^2 - 2.95925 \times 10^{-6}u^3$$

$$+ 1.3644 \times 10^{-8}u^4 \quad (5.34)$$

$$\sigma = 0.0770549 + 0.00554223u + 0.00193539u^2 - 1.0003 \times 10^{-4}u^3$$

$$+ 1.5776 \times 10^{-6}u^4 \quad (5.35)$$

The IEM model together with (5.32)–(5.35) form the desired GMF that can work like the NSCAT model function for vertical polarization over the wind speed range considered. To verify this last statement we compute the backscattering coefficients using (5.32)–(5.35) for the same wind speeds to compare with the NSCAT model function outputs in Figure 5.40.

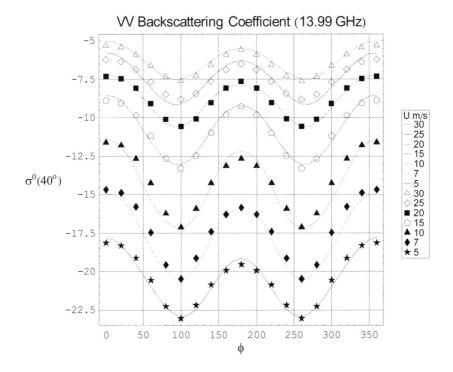

Figure 5.40 A comparison of the GMF based on the IEM model and (5.32)–(5.35), with the NSCAT model function outputs for vertical polarization at 13.99 GHz over seven wind speeds. Symbols are the computed backscattering based on the NSCAT model function. Solid lines are predictions from the IEM-based GMF. Very close agreements are realized at all wind speeds shown.

In Figure 5.40 we see a very good agreement between the developed GMF and the outputs from the empirical model function. This further validates the capability of our sea scatter model defined in (4.3) and (4.5). To complete our study we shall develop the GMF for horizontal polarization in Section 5.5.4.2.

5.5.4.2 GMF for Horizontal Polarization at 13.99 GHz

The empirical GMF for horizontally polarized backscattering measurements acquired by the NSCAT instrument is also available. Hence, it can be used to calculate backscattering from the sea surface at the same set of wind speeds as in vertical polarization. This set of backscattering coefficients was provided to the author by David G. Long (private communication, December, 2014). The application of the IEM model to match the outputs of this GMF is shown in Figure 5.41. Again, we see that there is an excellent agreement between the IEM model and the outputs of the empirical model function at every wind speed.

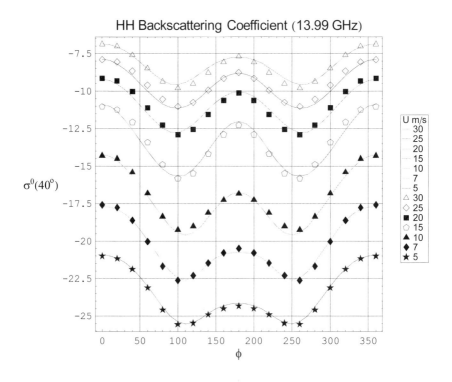

Figure 5.41 A comparison of the IEM model with the NSCAT model function outputs for horizontal polarization at 13.4 GHz over seven wind speeds. Symbols are the computed backscattering based on the NSCAT model function. Solid lines are predictions from the IEM model. This comparison is used to determine the model parameters at each wind speed.

Note that the upwind-downwind difference is clearly larger at lower wind speeds. This means that the skewness effect is stronger at lower wind speeds. Hence, the locations of signal minimum should be closer to the downwind location according to the IEM model prediction, which is the characteristic of sea scatter we summarized in Section 5.5.1. At higher wind speeds the upwind-downwind difference is smaller and the locations of signal minimum move farther away from the downwind location. This characteristic of sea scatter is not in this empirical model function. However, since it is a higher order effect, this difference does not appear as a difference between the IEM model and the empirical model function. The model parameters used in the IEM model to realize the matching in Figure 5.41 are summarized in Table 5.12.

Table 5.12 Surface Parameters for HH Based on Figure 5.41

Wind Speed (m/s)	Surface Height (cm)	L_u (cm)	L_c (cm)	s_0 (cm)	a
5	0.085	6	15	0.12	3.0
7	0.105	4	12.7	0.11	3.5
10	0.13	3	9.5	0.12	3.0
15	0.17	2.4	6.5	0.11	3.0
20	0.195	2.1	4.5	0.116	3.5
25	0.2	1.6	3.5	0.115	3.0
30	0.23	1.6	3	0.115	2.5

To develop a model function we need to link the parameters in Table 5.12 to wind speed. One way is to use polynomial functions leading to the following relations,

$$L_u = 13.366 - 2.079222u + 0.150799u^2 - 0.00499425u^3 + 0.6163 \times 10^{-4}u^4 \quad (5.36)$$

$$L_c = 20.02678 - 2.61234u + 0.205756u^2 - 0.00773278u^3 + 0.00010612u^4 \quad (5.37)$$

$$s_0 = 0.444802 - 0.18572u + 0.0377883u^2 - 0.00364038u^3 + 0.00017943u^4$$

$$- 4.37149 \times 10^{-6'}u^5 + 4.17602 \times 10^{-8}u^6 \quad (5.38)$$

$$\sigma = 0.0910512 - 0.00265804u + 0.0019708u^2 - 1.03315 \times 10^{-4}u^3$$

$$+ \ 1.64707 \times 10^{-6})u^4 \tag{5.39}$$

With (5.36)–(5.39) we can form a GMF with the IEM model. When we recompute the backscattering coefficients with (5.36)–(5.39) and the IEM model, we obtain the matching in Figure 5.42, where the overall agreement between the IEM-based model function and the empirical model function is excellent.

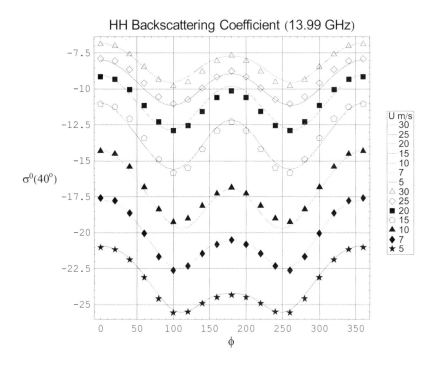

Figure 5.42 A comparison of the GMF based on the IEM model and (5.36)–(5.39), with the NSCAT model function outputs for horizontal polarization at 13.99 GHz over seven wind speeds. Symbols are the computed backscattering based on the NSCAT model function. Solid lines are predictions from the IEM-based GMF. Very close agreements are realized at all wind speeds shown.

Actually, there is a subtle difference in that the locations of signal minima are in agreement at wind speeds above 15 m/s but not at lower wind speeds. The clearest case is at 10 m/s, where the IEM model-based GMF shows signal minima at 110 and 240 degrees in the azimuth angle, while the empirical model function shows them at 100 and 260 degrees at all wind speeds, indicating that the locations of signal minima are fixed and do not change with surface skewness or wind speeds. Clearly, this is artificial and not in agreement with measurements. However, the difference in the computed signal levels is small and falls within measurement error, but signal minima locations can cause error in wind direction determination. This problem is also reflected in the need to fit s_0 with a higher order polynomial, indicating that there is an excessive amount of fluctuations in the values of s_0. We have noticed that whenever we need a polynomial higher than the fourth order to fit a model parameter versus wind speed, it is an indication that the parameter values are oscillating and do not have a meaningful trend.

5.5.4.3 Comparison of NSCAT with Airborne Data

The operating frequency in NSCAT is about the same as used by [Schroeder et al., 1985], which is 13.9 GHz. We can select a 40 degree incident angle in NSCAT to make comparisons. Note that the wind speed reported by [Schroeder et al., 1985] is at an altitude of 19.5m, while NSCAT uses 10m. We know that the wind speed is larger at higher altitude. Thus, we can compare the 7.5-m/s data in [Schroeder et al., 1985] with the 7-m/s data in NSCAT. This comparison shows that the upwind and crosswind backscattering signal levels in NSCAT are about -14.7 and -20.5 dB in vertical polarization versus -17 and -22.5 dB in [Schroeder et al., 1985]. For horizontal polarization the corresponding comparison is -17.6 and -22.5 dB in NSCAT versus -19.7 and -25.5 dB in [Schroeder et al., 1985]. For both polarizations the NSCAT data are higher by about 2 dB or more. Another illustration of the uncertainty in absolute signal level is to carry out a similar comparison between the 10-m/s data in NSCAT and the 12-m/s data in [Schroeder et al., 1985]. For vertical polarization we have -11.5 and -17 dB in NSCAT versus -14 and -18.5 dB, and for horizontal polarization we have -14.3 and -19.4, in NSCAT versus -17.5 and -24 dB. Again, the NSCAT data have higher signal levels, especially in horizontal polarization, where the upwind and crosswind signal levels are more than 3 dB higher. As we have seen before, the current azimuth angle data does not preserve relative signal levels in polarization, and empirical model functions have artificial signal minima locations.

5.6 CONCLUDING REMARKS

This chapter has demonstrated that it is possible to use an existing surface scattering model to serve as a GMF because the surface parameters in the model can be defined by available data as a function of wind speed. This approach is made possible by the investigation in Chapters 1 and 2 that allows us to use a simple exponential-like function to represent the correlation function of the sea surface. This representation is crucial to make the computation of the backscattering coefficient simple and practical. For data at large angles of incidence further simplification to use the mexp is made possible for analyzing azimuthal angle data.

Examples showing the steps to construct a GMF with a physical surface scattering model and a set of data are given, and the function of each surface parameter in the model is explained. We determine that, unlike the incident angle data, the existing azimuth data showing wind speed and azimuth angle dependence does not allow VV and HH polarizations to share the same set of surface parameters at a given incident angle and wind speed, except for the correlation parameters, L_u and L_c, in some cases for wind speeds below the hurricane-force wind and above 4.2 m/s.

The approach to developing GMFs with the backscattering model in Chapter 4 is also applicable to outputs from empirical GMFs, because they represent large volumes of data. The excellent agreement between the developed GMFs and the empirical GMFs considered in this chapter indicates that the approach offers an alternative to empirical GMF development.

References

Bentamy, A., et al., "Compatibility of C- and Ku-band Scatterometer Winds: ERS-2 and QuikSCAT," *J. Marine Systems*, Vol. 117-1182, 2013, pp. 72–80.

Donelan, M. A., and W. J. Plant, "A Threshold for Wind-Wave Growth," DOI:10.1029/2008JC005238, *J. Geophys. Research*, Vol. 114, Issue C7, July 2009.

Fernandez, D. E., et al., "Dual-Polarized C- and Ku-band Ocean Backscatter Response to Hurricane-Force Winds, " *J. Geophys. Res.*, 111, C08013, 2006, pp. 1–17.

Grant, C. R., and B. S. Yaplee, "Backscattering from Water and Land at Centimeter and Millimeter Wavelengths," *Proc. IRE*, Vol. 45, 1957, pp. 976–982.

Hersbach, H., "CMOD: An Improved Geophysical Model Function for ERS C-band Scatterometry" Technical memorandum, European Centre for Medium-Range Weather Forecasts, Shinfield Park, Reading, RG2 9AX, England (http://www.ecmwf.int/publications/), September 2002.

Hersbach, H., "Comparison of C-Band Scatterometer CMOD5.N Equivalent Neutral Winds with ECMWF," *J. Atm. Ocean. Techn.*, 27, 2010, pp. 721–736.

Jones, W. L., L. C. Schroeder, and J. L. Mitchell, "Aircraft Measurements of the Microwave Scattering Signature of the Ocean," *IEEE Trans. Antennas and Propagation*, Vol. 25, No. 2, 1977, pp. 52–61.

Li, F., et al., "Ocean Radar Backscatter Relationship with Near-Surface Winds: A Case Study During FASINEX," *J. Phys. Oceanogr.*, Vol. 12, 1989, pp. 342–353.

Long, D. G., "Current Progress in Ku-Band Model Functions," Microwave Earth Remote Sensing (MERS) Laboratory Report 96-002, A Report by the NSCAT Science Working Team Subcommittee on Geophysical Model Functions, Dept. of Electrical and Computer Engineering, Brigham Young University, Provo, Utah, 1996.

Masuko, H., et al., "Measurement of Microwave Backscattering Signatures of the Ocean Surface Using X-Band and Ka-Band Airborne Scatterometers," *J. Geophysical Res.*, Vol. 91, No. C11, 1986, pp. 13605–13083.

Moore, R. K., and A. K. Fung, "Radar Determination of Winds at Sea," *Proceedings of the IEEE*, Vol. 67, No. 11, September 1979, pp. 1504–1521.

Moore, R. K., and W. J. Pierson, Jr., "Measuring Sea State and Estimating Surface Winds from a Polar Orbiting Satellite," *Proc. Inter. Symp. Electromagnetic Sensing of the Earth from Satellites*, Miami Beach, FL, November 1966, pp. R1–R28.

Plant, W. J., "A Two-Scale Model of Short Wind-Generated Waves and Scatterometry," *J. Geophys. Res.*, Vol. 91, 1986, pp. 10735–10749.

Ricciardulli, L., and F. Wentz, "Development of Consistent Geophysical Model Functions for Different Scatterometer Missions: Ku and C-Band," Remote Sensing Systems, Santa Rosa, California. Presented at the 2012 NASA International Ocean Vector Wind Science Team meeting, Utrecht, Netherlands, June 2012.

Schroeder, L. C., et al., "AAFE RADSCAT 13.9-GHz Measurements and Analysis: Wind-speed Signature of the Ocean," *IEEE J. Oceanic Engineering*, Vol. OE-10, No. 4, October 1985, pp. 346–357.

Weissman, D. E., "Dependence of the Radar Cross Section on Ocean Surface Variables: Comparison of Measurements and Theory Using Data from the Frontal Air-Sea Interaction Experiment," *J. Geophys. Res.*, Vol. 95, No. C3, 1990, pp. 3387–3398.

Wentz, F. J., and D. K. Smith, "A Model Function for the Ocean Normalized Radar Cross Section at 14 GHz Derived from NSCAT Observations," *J. Geophys. Res.*, Vol. 104, No. C5, 1999, pp. 11499–11514.

About the Author

Adrian K. Fung earned a Ph.D. from the University of Kansas, Lawrence. He was the director of the Wave Scattering Research Center and Jenkins Garrett professor of electrical engineering and a member of the Academy of Distinguished Scholars at the University of Texas at Arlington. Dr. Fung is a life fellow of the Institute of Electrical and Electronic Engineers and a member of U.S. Commission F of the International Scientific Radio Union. He was awarded the Halliburton Excellence in Research Award (1987), the Distinguished Research Award from the University of Texas at Arlington (1989), and the Distinguished Achievement Award from the IEEE Geoscience and Remote Sensing Society (1989). Dr. Fung is the author of *Microwave Scattering and Emission Models and Their Applications* (Artech House, 1994). He is a coauthor of Artech House's three-volume graduate textbook, *Microwave Remote Sensing* (1981–1986), and *Microwave Scattering and Emission Models for Users* (2009) and is a contributor to the *Manual of Remote Sensing* and the *Encyclopedia of Electrical Engineering*. He has served as an associate editor of *Radio Science* and the *IEEE Journal of Oceanic Engineering,* and he was an editor of the *Journal of Electromagnetic Waves and Applications*. He has published over 150 journal articles, and his research interests include electromagnetic wave scattering and emission from irregular surfaces and random media, radar image simulation, numerical simulation of electromagnetic scattering, and inversion and classification techniques.

Index

The Artech House Remote Sensing Series

Fawwaz T. Ulaby, Series Editor

Understanding Synthetic Aperture Radar Images, Chris Oliver and Shaun Quegan

Wavelets for Sensing Technologies, Andrew K. Chan and Cheng Peng

For further information on these and other Artech House titles, including previously considered out-of-print books now available through our In-Print-Forever® (IPF®) program, contact:

Artech House	Artech House
685 Canton Street	16 Sussex Street
Norwood, MA 02062	London SW1V 4RW UK
Phone: 781-769-9750	Phone: +44 (0)20-7596-8750
Fax: 781-769-6334	Fax: +44 (0)20-7630-0166
e-mail: artech@artechhouse.com	e-mail: artech-uk@artechhouse.com

Find us on the World Wide Web at:
www.artechhouse.com